Prentice-Hall Foundations of Modern Organic Chemistry Series

KENNETH L. RINEHART, JR., Editor

Volumes published or in preparation

N. L. ALLINGER and J. ALLINGER	**STRUCTURES OF ORGANIC MOLECULES**
TRAHANOVSKY	**FUNCTIONAL GROUPS IN ORGANIC COMPOUNDS**
STEWART	**THE INVESTIGATION OF ORGANIC REACTIONS**
SAUNDERS	**IONIC ALIPHATIC REACTIONS**
GUTSCHE	**THE CHEMISTRY OF CARBONYL COMPOUNDS**
PRYOR	**INTRODUCTION TO FREE RADICAL CHEMISTRY**
STOCK	**AROMATIC SUBSTITUTION REACTIONS**
RINEHART	**OXIDATION AND REDUCTION OF ORGANIC COMPOUNDS**
DePUY	**MOLECULAR REACTIONS AND PHOTOCHEMISTRY**
IRELAND	**ORGANIC SYNTHESIS**
DYER	**APPLICATIONS OF ABSORPTION SPECTROSCOPY OF ORGANIC COMPOUNDS**
BATES and SCHAEFER	**RESEARCH IN ORGANIC CHEMISTRY**
TAYLOR	**HETEROCYCLIC COMPOUNDS**
HILL	**COMPOUNDS OF NATURE**
BARKER	**ORGANIC CHEMISTRY OF BIOLOGICAL COMPOUNDS**
STILLE	**INDUSTRIAL ORGANIC CHEMISTRY**
RINEHART and SIM	**X-RAY CRYSTALLOGRAPHY AND MASS SPECTROMETRY OF ORGANIC COMPOUNDS**
BATTISTE	**NON-BENZENOID AROMATIC COMPOUNDS**

APPLICATIONS OF ABSORPTION SPECTROSCOPY OF ORGANIC COMPOUNDS

John R. Dyer

Georgia Institute of Technology

PRENTICE-HALL, INC., ENGLEWOOD CLIFFS, N.J.

Current printing (last digit):
12 11 10 9 8 7 6 5

Library of Congress Catalog Card Number 65-15701
Printed in the United States of America
C-03880(p)
C-03881(c)

PRENTICE-HALL INTERNATIONAL, INC., London
PRENTICE-HALL OF AUSTRALIA, PTY, LTD., Sydney
PRENTICE-HALL OF CANADA, LTD., Toronto
PRENTICE-HALL OF INDIA (PRIVATE) LTD., New Delhi
PRENTICE-HALL OF JAPAN, INC., Tokyo

Foreword

Organic chemistry today is a rapidly changing subject whose almost frenetic activity is attested by the countless research papers appearing in established and new journals and by the proliferation of monographs and reviews on all aspects of the field. This expansion of knowledge poses pedagogical problems; it is difficult for a single organic chemist to be cognizant of developments over the whole field and probably no one or pair of chemists can honestly claim expertise or even competence in all the important areas of the subject.

Yet the same rapid expansion of knowledge—in theoretical organic chemistry, in stereochemistry, in reaction mechanisms, in complex organic structures, in the application of physical methods—provides a remarkable opportunity for the teacher of organic chemistry to present the subject as it really is, an active field of research in which new answers are currently being sought and found.

To take advantage of recent developments in organic chemistry and to provide an authoritative treatment of the subject at an undergraduate level, the *Foundations of Modern Organic Chemistry Series* has been established. The series consists of a number of short, authoritative books, each written at an elementary level but in depth by an organic chemistry teacher active in research and familiar with the subject of the volume. Most of the authors have published research papers in the fields on which they are writing. The books will present the topics according to current knowledge of the field, and individual volumes will be revised as often as necessary to take account of subsequent developments.

The basic organization of the series is according to reaction type, rather than along the more classical lines of compound class. The first ten volumes in the series constitute a core of the material covered in nearly every one-year organic chemistry course. Of these ten, the first three are a general introduction to organic chemistry and provide a background for the next six, which deal with specific types of reactions and may be covered in any order. Each of the reaction types is presented from an elementary viewpoint, but in a depth not possible in conventional textbooks. The teacher can decide how much of a volume to cover. The tenth examines the problem of organic synthesis, employing and tying together the reactions previously studied.

The remaining volumes provide for the enormous flexibility of the series. These cover topics which are important to students of organic chemistry and are sometimes treated in the first organic course, sometimes in an intermediate course. Some teachers will wish to cover a number of these books in the one-year course; others will wish to assign some of them as outside reading; a complete intermediate organic course could be based on the eight "topics" texts taken together.

The series approach to undergraduate organic chemistry offers then the considerable advantage of an authoritative treatment by teachers active in research, of frequent revision of the most active areas, of a treatment in depth of the most fundamental material, and of nearly complete flexibility in choice of topics to be covered. Individually the volumes of the Foundations of Modern Organic Chemistry provide introductions in depth to basic areas of organic chemistry; together they comprise a contemporary survey of organic chemistry at an undergraduate level.

KENNETH L. RINEHART, JR.
University of Illinois

Preface

The productive pursuit of organic chemical research imposes upon the chemist a formidable task: he must be proficient in the interpretation of the data obtained from all of the instruments at his disposal.

Ultraviolet, infrared, and nuclear magnetic resonance spectroscopy are among the more important techniques that the organic chemist now uses routinely to gain information about a particular substance. This short book is intended to serve as an *introduction* to the use of these extremely valuable spectroscopic methods. Space limitations prohibit a detailed discussion of the instrumentation and an exact development of the theoretical aspects of these spectroscopic methods of analysis. A full understanding of the electronics of complex instruments and of the theoretical foundations of the phenomena is unnecessary for an accurate interpretation of spectral results. Many excellent texts are available that describe in detail the instrumental aspects of these methods. The theoretical aspects of these spectroscopic methods are described in this book only insofar as is necessary to provide that understanding required for the correct interpretation of the results obtained.

This book contains much useful spectral data in tables, charts, and figures. Interpretation of spectra is emphasized. In most cases, the organic chemist should be able to interpret a spectrum using these compilations of data without having to search through more detailed texts in the areas. The book contains photographic reductions of many infrared and nuclear magnetic resonance spectra, so the reader who is not familiar with these techniques can see how the spectra actually appear. Problems, the solutions of which require the use of the spectral data presented, are included at the end of each chapter. In addition to the subject index, there is a separate index that contains a list of all compounds for which specific spectral data are given in the text.

This book is intended to be useful to organic chemists at all levels. For graduate students and organic research chemists who are not spectroscopists, the book can be a valuable reference for the interpretation of most spectra. At the undergraduate level, the book can be used as a text to supplement a course in the identification of organic compounds or as a text for a part of a course in physical methods of organic analysis.

It is with pleasure that I thank those students and faculty of the Georgia Institute of Technology who read and commented on portions of the manuscript. I also wish to thank Walter S. Fleming (who calculated many of the nuclear magnetic resonance spectra), Howard M. Deutsch, and especially William E. McGonigal, whose generous help at every stage greatly eased the task of the preparation of the manuscript.

The author will gratefully receive comments pertaining to the content of this book, especially those dealing with errors of typography, omission, or commission, so that a revision, if necessary, can be of more general use.

For instructional purposes, faculty may obtain a list of the answers to the problems in this book by writing the publisher.

John R. Dyer
Atlanta, Georgia

Contents

1

INTRODUCTION 1

ULTRAVIOLET SPECTROSCOPY 4

2.1 Mechanics of Measurement 4
2.2 Electronic Excitation 5
2.3 Simple Chromophoric Groups 8
2.4 Conjugated Systems 11
2.5 Systems of Extended Conjugation 15
2.6 Aromatic Systems 17
2.7 Stereochemistry 19
2.8 Problems 20
Selected References 21

INFRARED SPECTROSCOPY 22

3.1 Molecular Vibration 22
3.2 Mechanics of Measurement 24
3.3 Applications of Infrared Spectroscopy 29
3.4 Absorptions of Common Functional Groups 32
3.5 Problems 53
Selected References 57

NUCLEAR MAGNETIC RESONANCE SPECTROSCOPY 58

4.1 Magnetic Properties of Nuclei 58
4.2 Theory of Nuclear Resonance 60
4.3 The Chemical Shift 62
4.4 Spin-Spin Interactions 66
4.5 Chemical Exchange 69
4.6 Mechanics of Measurement 71
4.7 Shielding Mechanisms 74
4.8 Correlations: Hydrogen Bound to Carbon 83
4.9 Correlations: Hydrogen Bound to Other Nuclei 89
4.10 Complex Spin-Spin Interactions 97
4.11 Hindered Rotation 113
4.12 Stereochemistry 114
4.13 Nuclear Magnetic Double Resonance 122
4.14 Resonance of Other Nuclei 123
4.15 Problems 125
Selected References 132

SUPPLEMENTAL PROBLEMS 133

APPENDIX: Wavelength—Wave Number Conversion Table 137

COMPOUND INDEX 141

SUBJECT INDEX 144

Applications of Absorption Spectroscopy of Organic Compounds

1 Introduction

The field of spectroscopy is divided into emission and absorption spectroscopy. An emission spectrum is obtained by spectroscopic analysis of some light source, such as a flame or an electric arc. This phenomenon is primarily caused by the excitation of *atoms* by thermal or electrical means; absorbed energy causes electrons in a ground state to be promoted to a state of higher energy. The lifetime of electrons in this metastable state is short, and they return to some lower excited state or to the ground state; the absorbed energy is released as light. Fluorescent lights and colors obtained by heating salts of certain elements in a flame are common examples of emission spectra. In some cases the excited states may have appreciable lifetimes such that emission of light continues after excitation has ceased; such a phenomenon is called *phosphorescence*.

An absorption spectrum is obtained by placing the substance between the spectrometer and some source of energy that provides electromagnetic radiation in the frequency range being studied. The spectrometer analyzes the transmitted energy relative to the incident energy for a given frequency. Again, the high-energy states are usually short-lived. The major fate of absorbed energy in the infrared region is heat; thus, the temperature of the substance (or solution) increases while the spectrum is being determined. The major fate of absorbed energy in the ultraviolet region is re-emission of light. Occasionally, the absorbed energy may cause photochemically induced reactions.

The use of early spectrometers involved the laborious procedure of determining the intensity of transmitted energy for a large number of set frequencies. Within the past twenty years instrumentation has so improved that a variety of recording instruments is available. The frequency is continually changed and the transmitted energy automatically analyzed; a record which represents the intensity of transmitted or absorbed energy versus frequency is obtained. These instruments provide a record of the complete spectrum in thirty minutes or less.

Although other units of measurement are used, the common unit of measurement of wavelength in the ultraviolet and visible regions is the millimicron ($m\mu$, 10^{-7} cm); in the infrared region the common units are the micron (μ, 10^{-4} cm) and the wave number (cm^{-1}), the number of waves per centimeter. The regions of greatest interest to the organic chemist are 200–400 $m\mu$ (ultraviolet), 400–800 $m\mu$ (visible), and 2–16 μ (infrared).

Although the mechanism of absorption of energy is different in the ultraviolet, infrared, and nuclear magnetic resonance regions, the fundamental process *is* the absorption of a certain amount of energy. The energy required for the transition from a state of lower energy to a state of higher energy is directly related to the frequency of electromagnetic radiation that causes the transition; the energy absorbed is given by $E = h\nu$, where h is the universal Planck's constant, 6.624×10^{-27} erg sec, and ν is the frequency of incident light (in cycles per second, cps). The frequency and wavelength of light are related by $\nu = c/\lambda$, where c is the velocity of light, 2.998×10^{10} cm/sec (in vacuum). The wave number is also used in the description of spectra. The relationship is $K = 1/\lambda$, where K is the wave number in cm^{-1} (reciprocal centimeters or Kaysers), and λ is the wavelength in centimeters. The basic relationships of energy in calories per mole to frequency and wavelength are given by the expressions $E = Nh\nu = Nhc/\lambda$, where N is Avogadro's number and E is the energy absorbed in ergs. The energy in electron volts is given by ev $= 1/8{,}066\lambda$, where the wavelength λ is measured in centimeters; one electron volt $=$ 23.060 Kcal/mole. Relationships between these quantities are given in Fig. 1-1.

For a given excitation process, a molecule absorbs only one discrete amount of energy, and hence absorbs radiation of only one frequency. If this were the case with all molecules of a substance, one would observe a series of absorption *lines*. However, a group of molecules exists in a number of different vibrational and rotational states, each state differing from another by a relatively small amount of energy. Thus, a group of molecules absorbs energy over a small range and gives rise to an absorption band or peak.

Interpretations of molecular spectra by the organic chemist are based largely on empirical correlations with extensive compilations of data; consequently, a given absorption can usually be attributed with reasonable assurance to a particular group or arrangement of atoms within the molecule. When the organic chemist investigates the structure of an unknown compound, he uses all of the modern physical methods at his disposal, as well as the more traditional, classical methods. At the present time, the various spectral methods are among the more commonly used physical methods. Absorption of ultraviolet and visible light is chiefly caused by electronic excitation; the spectrum provides limited information about the structure of the molecule. Absorption in the infrared region is due to molecular vibrations of one kind or another; the spectrum is generally very complicated and contains many absorption peaks, relatively few of which can be interpreted with a high degree of assurance. On the other hand, the proton magnetic resonance spectrum of a compound, owing to nuclear spin transitions, can usually be completely interpreted, and it provides information about the number, nature, and environment of all of the protons in the molecule.

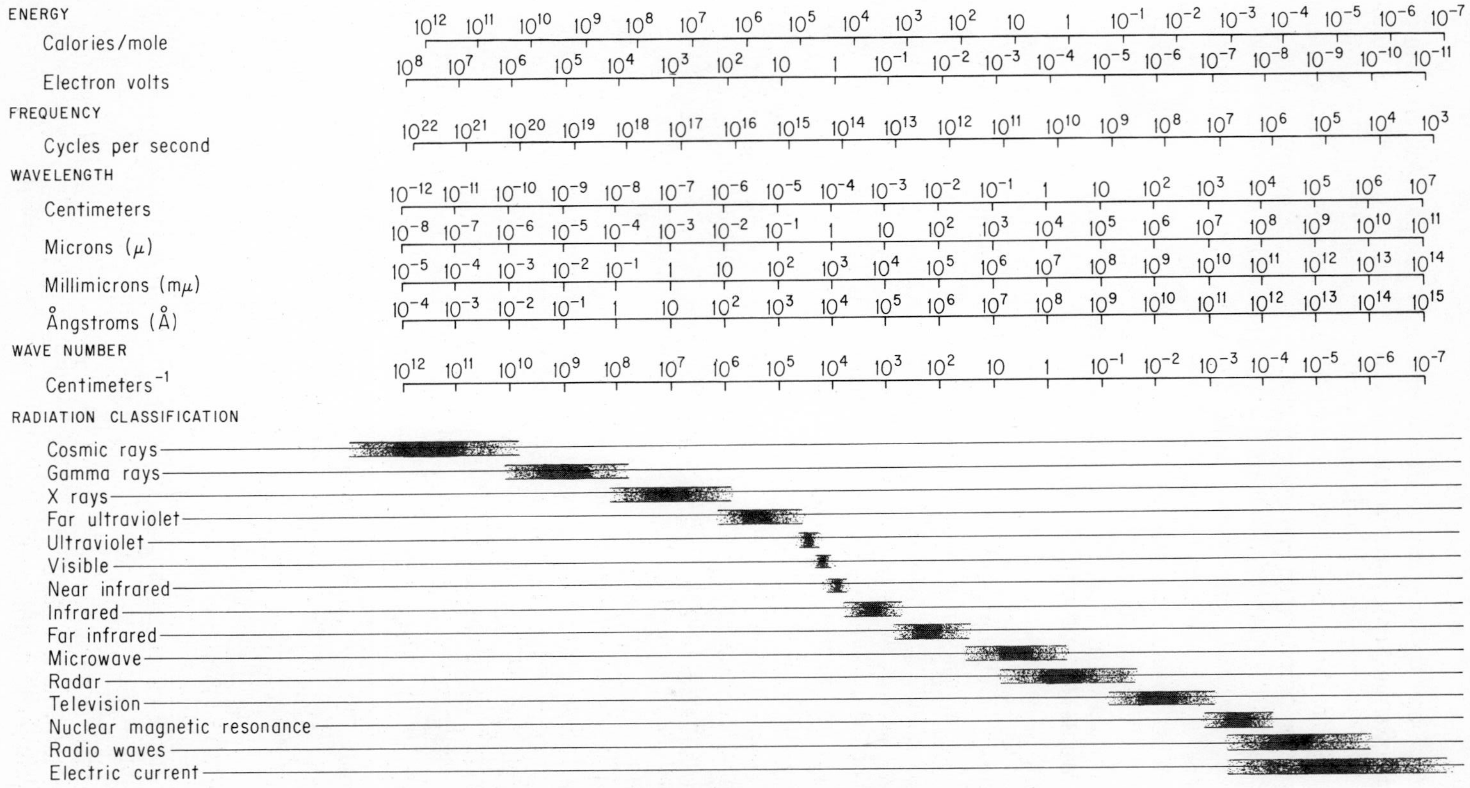

ENERGY

Calories/mole: 10^{12} 10^{11} 10^{10} 10^{9} 10^{8} 10^{7} 10^{6} 10^{5} 10^{4} 10^{3} 10^{2} 10 1 10^{-1} 10^{-2} 10^{-3} 10^{-4} 10^{-5} 10^{-6} 10^{-7}

Electron volts: 10^{8} 10^{7} 10^{6} 10^{5} 10^{4} 10^{3} 10^{2} 10 1 10^{-1} 10^{-2} 10^{-3} 10^{-4} 10^{-5} 10^{-6} 10^{-7} 10^{-8} 10^{-9} 10^{-10} 10^{-11}

FREQUENCY

Cycles per second: 10^{22} 10^{21} 10^{20} 10^{19} 10^{18} 10^{17} 10^{16} 10^{15} 10^{14} 10^{13} 10^{12} 10^{11} 10^{10} 10^{9} 10^{8} 10^{7} 10^{6} 10^{5} 10^{4} 10^{3}

WAVELENGTH

Centimeters: 10^{-12} 10^{-11} 10^{-10} 10^{-9} 10^{-8} 10^{-7} 10^{-6} 10^{-5} 10^{-4} 10^{-3} 10^{-2} 10^{-1} 1 10 10^{2} 10^{3} 10^{4} 10^{5} 10^{6} 10^{7}

Microns (μ): 10^{-8} 10^{-7} 10^{-6} 10^{-5} 10^{-4} 10^{-3} 10^{-2} 10^{-1} 1 10 10^{2} 10^{3} 10^{4} 10^{5} 10^{6} 10^{7} 10^{8} 10^{9} 10^{10} 10^{11}

Millimicrons (mμ): 10^{-5} 10^{-4} 10^{-3} 10^{-2} 10^{-1} 1 10 10^{2} 10^{3} 10^{4} 10^{5} 10^{6} 10^{7} 10^{8} 10^{9} 10^{10} 10^{11} 10^{12} 10^{13} 10^{14}

Ångstroms (Å): 10^{-4} 10^{-3} 10^{-2} 10^{-1} 1 10 10^{2} 10^{3} 10^{4} 10^{5} 10^{6} 10^{7} 10^{8} 10^{9} 10^{10} 10^{11} 10^{12} 10^{13} 10^{14} 10^{15}

WAVE NUMBER

Centimeters^{-1}: 10^{12} 10^{11} 10^{10} 10^{9} 10^{8} 10^{7} 10^{6} 10^{5} 10^{4} 10^{3} 10^{2} 10 1 10^{-1} 10^{-2} 10^{-3} 10^{-4} 10^{-5} 10^{-6} 10^{-7}

RADIATION CLASSIFICATION

Cosmic rays
Gamma rays
X rays
Far ultraviolet
Ultraviolet
Visible
Near infrared
Infrared
Far infrared
Microwave
Radar
Television
Nuclear magnetic resonance
Radio waves
Electric current

Fig. 1-1 The electromagnetic spectrum.

2 Ultraviolet Spectroscopy

2.1 MECHANICS OF MEASUREMENT

In order to obtain useful information from the ultraviolet or visible spectrum of a compound, the wavelength of maximum absorption (λ_{max}) and the intensity of absorption must be measured accurately. The compound should be dissolved in some suitable solvent that does not itself absorb light in the region under investigation. The most commonly used solvent for ultraviolet spectral determinations is 95% ethyl alcohol. Water and hexane are also commonly used. The positions of the absorption peaks of a compound may be shifted somewhat if different solvents are used. The λ_{max} for nonpolar compounds is generally the same in alcohol and hexane; the λ_{max} for polar compounds is usually shifted.

The solution must be placed in some suitable container that is transparent to light in the region being studied. Although ordinary glass is satisfactory for work in the visible region, glass absorbs ultraviolet light strongly; hence, quartz cells must be used. The most commonly used cells have 1.0 cm path length. Modern spectrophotometers provide a plot of the intensity of transmitted or absorbed light versus wavelength. The most suitable source of light in the ultraviolet region (180–400 mμ) is the hydrogen-discharge lamp. A tungsten-filament lamp is usually used for the visible region (400–800 mμ) of the spectrum. Most spectrophotometers are double-beam instruments. The primary source of light is split into two beams, one of which passes through a cell containing the sample solution and the other of which passes through a cell containing the reference solvent. The spectrophotometer electronically subtracts the absorption of the solvent in the reference beam from the absorption of the solution in the sample beam. Thus, effects owing to absorption of light by the solvent are minimized.

The ordinary visible-ultraviolet spectrophotometer provides acceptable spectra over the range 220–800 mμ. Better instruments have mechanical improvements that extend the short-wavelength range to about 185 mμ. The major limitation in this short-wavelength range is the presence of air in the instrument. Oxygen absorbs strongly at about 200 mμ and below; frequently the range of the instrument can be extended by flushing the instrument with nitrogen, which absorbs strongly at about 150 mμ and below. The technique of using an evacuated spectrophotometer enables the range below 200 mμ to be studied. This region is frequently called the *vacuum ultraviolet region.*

Most recording spectrophotometers record wavelength versus absorbance. The absorbance A or "optical density" is given by

$$A = \log \frac{I_0}{I}$$

where I_0 is the intensity of incident light and I is the intensity of transmitted light. The range of absorbance commonly recorded is 0–2.0. The calculation of the intensity of an absorption band involves the use of Lambert's and Beer's laws. Lambert's law states that the intensity of transmitted light passing through a homogeneous medium decreases geometrically as the thickness of the layer increases arithmetically. Beer's law states that each molecule of solute absorbs the same fraction of light incident upon it, regardless of concentration, in a nonabsorbing medium. Beer's law does not hold over the entire concentration range, but in very dilute solutions, as is usually the case in ultraviolet spectroscopy, the deviations are small. These laws can be formulated by the relationship

$$\varepsilon = \frac{A}{cl}$$

where ε is the molar extinction coefficient, c is the molar concentration, and l is the path length in centimeters. Experimental results are usually reported in terms of the molar extinction coefficient ε or its logarithm $\log \varepsilon$. When the molecular weight of a substance is unknown, the intensity of absorption is conveniently expressed as the $E^{1\%}_{1\,\mathrm{cm}}$ (or $A^{1\%}_{1\,\mathrm{cm}}$) value, the absorbance of a 1% solution of the substance in a 1.0 cm cell. This value is easily related to the molar extinction coefficient by the expression

$$10\,\varepsilon = E^{1\%}_{1\,\mathrm{cm}} \times \text{mol. wt.}$$

2.2 ELECTRONIC EXCITATION

The absorption of light energy by organic compounds in the visible and ultraviolet region involves promotion of electrons in σ, π, and n-orbitals† from the ground state to higher-energy states. These higher-energy states are described by molecular orbitals that are vacant in the ground or unexcited state and are commonly called *antibonding orbitals.* The antibonding orbital associated with the σ bond is called the σ^* (sigma star) orbital and that associated with the π bond is called the π^* (pi star)

† Many molecules contain electrons that are not directly involved in bonding; these are called nonbonding or n electrons and are mainly located in atomic orbitals of oxygen, sulfur, nitrogen, and the halogens.

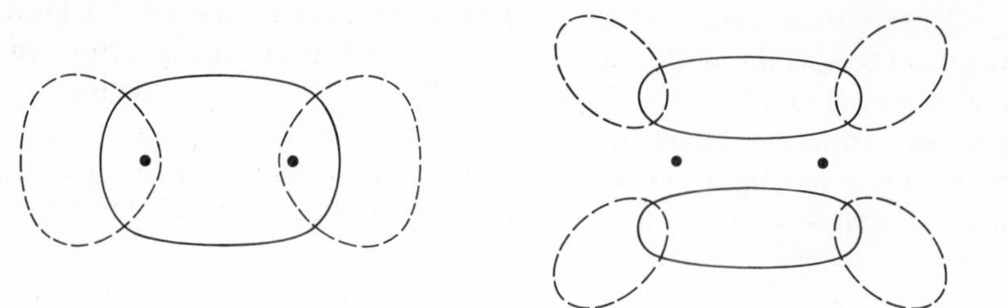

Fig. 2-1 Left, σ and σ^* orbitals; right, π and π^* orbitals.

orbital. As the *n* electrons do not form bonds, there are no antibonding orbitals associated with them. The generalized shapes of σ, σ^*, π, and π^* orbitals are shown in Fig. 2-1, where solid lines refer to σ and π bonding orbitals and dashed lines refer to σ^* and π^* antibonding orbitals; the dots represent atomic centers. The presence of an electron in an antibonding orbital clearly indicates that the molecule is in a high-energy state. The electron density between the atomic nuclei is *less* than that at the same distance from the nucleus in an isolated atom. In the excited state some, but not all, of the electrons in a molecule occupy antibonding orbitals; were it not for the fact that bonding orbitals in lower-energy states have sufficient bonding character to insure stability, dissociation would occur.

The electronic transitions ($\rightarrow$) that are involved in the ultraviolet and visible regions are of the following types: $\sigma \rightarrow \sigma^*$, $n \rightarrow \sigma^*$, $n \rightarrow \pi^*$, and $\pi \rightarrow \pi^*$. The energy required for the $\sigma \rightarrow \sigma^*$ transition is very high; consequently, compounds in which all valence shell electrons are involved in single-bond formation, such as saturated hydrocarbons, do not show absorption in the ordinary ultraviolet region. An exception is cyclopropane, which shows λ_{max} about 190 mμ. (Propane shows λ_{max} about 135 mμ.)

Compounds that contain nonbonding electrons on oxygen, nitrogen, sulfur, or halogen atoms are capable of showing absorptions, owing to $n \rightarrow \sigma^*$ transitions. These transitions are of lower energy than $\sigma \rightarrow \sigma^*$ transitions; consequently, molecules containing nonbonding electrons usually exhibit absorption in the ordinary ultraviolet region. Examples of $n \rightarrow \sigma^*$ transitions are shown by methyl alcohol, λ_{max}^{vapor} 183 mμ, ε 150, trimethylamine, λ_{max}^{vapor} 227 mμ, ε 900, methyl chloride, λ_{max}^{vapor} 173 mμ, $\varepsilon \sim 100$, and methyl iodide, λ_{max}^{hexane} 258 mμ, ε 378. The spectrum of trimethylamine determined in aqueous acid shows no absorption due to a $n \rightarrow \sigma^*$ transition, because the protonated amine contains no nonbonding electrons. Whether an organic compound contains a particular spectral pattern above 210 mμ or not, it will quite generally show some absorption that increases in intensity toward shorter wavelength in this region. This absorption is due in part to $n \rightarrow \sigma^*$ transitions near 200 mμ if the molecule contains oxygen, nitrogen, sulfur, or halogen atoms. This absorption is generally called *end absorption*.

Transitions to antibonding π^* orbitals are associated only with unsaturated centers in the molecule; these are of still lower energy requirement and occur at longer wavelengths, usually well within the region of the ordinary ultraviolet spectrophotometer. For example, saturated aldehydes and ketones exhibit an absorption of low intensity around 285 mμ, which is attributed to an $n \rightarrow \pi^*$ transition, and an absorption of high intensity around 180 mμ, which is attributed to a $\pi \rightarrow \pi^*$ transition. The $\pi \rightarrow \pi^*$ transitions are of intermediate energy; absorptions owing to these transitions are usually between those owing to $n \rightarrow \pi^*$ and $n \rightarrow \sigma^*$ transitions. Figure 2-2 shows the general relative electronic excitation energies for these transitions. The high-energy transitions ($\sigma \rightarrow \sigma^*$) occur at shorter wavelength and the low-energy transitions ($n \rightarrow \pi^*$) occur at longer wavelength.

Identical functional groups in different molecules will not necessarily absorb at exactly the same wavelength. The energy change for a particular transition dictates the position of absorption of a given group. Transitions in identical functional groups in different molecules will not necessarily have *exactly* the same energy requirement because of different structural environments.

The magnitude of the molar extinction coefficient for a particular absorption is directly proportional to the *probability* of the particular electronic transition; the more probable a given transition, the larger the extinction coefficient.

The exact electronic structures of the high-energy states of molecules that have absorbed ultraviolet or visible light are not well understood. Some appear to have greater or less polar character than the ground-state structure; some appear to be biradicals; other activated structures are possible. In any event, electronic transitions result in a redistribution of electrons within the molecule. The structures of the excited states of carbonyl compounds such as aldehydes and ketones have perhaps been

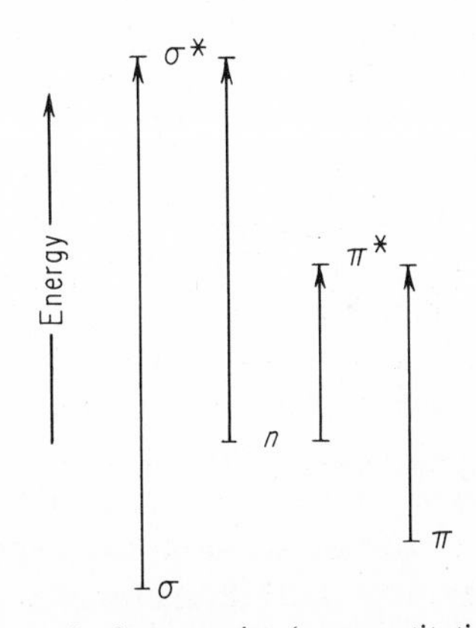

Fig. 2-2 Schematic electronic excitation energies (no quantitative aspects are intended).

studied most extensively. In the ground state the structure of the carbonyl group $\left(\rangle C{=}O\right)$ contains an important contribution from the polar form $\rangle C^{\pm}{-}O^{-}$ $\left(\rangle \overset{\delta+}{C}\overset{\cdots}{=}O^{\delta-}\right)$. The position of an absorption that involves nonbonding electrons ($n \rightarrow \pi^*$ and $n \rightarrow \sigma^*$) is particularly sensitive to the polarity of the solvent used in the determination. If the group is more polar in the ground state than in the excited state, the nonbonding electrons in the ground state are stabilized (*relative* to the excited state) by hydrogen bonding or electrostatic interaction with a polar solvent; the absorption is shifted to shorter wavelength (higher energy) with increasing solvent polarity. Conversely, if the group is more polar in the excited state, the nonbonding electrons of the excited state are stabilized (*relative* to the ground state) by interaction with a polar solvent; the absorption is shifted to longer wavelength (lower energy) with increasing solvent polarity. Polar solvents generally shift the $n \rightarrow \pi^*$ and $n \rightarrow \sigma^*$ bands to shorter wavelength and the $\pi \rightarrow \pi^*$ band to longer wavelength. The magnitude of the shift in the latter case is not usually as large as that in the former.

The α,β-unsaturated ketone mesityl oxide (4-methyl-3-penten-2-one) shows λ_{max} 230 mμ, ε 12,600 and λ_{max} 329 mμ, ε 41 in hexane and λ_{max} 243 mμ, ε 10,000 and λ_{max} 305 mμ, ε 60 in water. These data indicate that the long wavelength $n \rightarrow \pi^*$ absorption is shifted 24 mμ to shorter wavelength (higher energy) in the more polar solvent; thus the excited state would appear to be less polar than the ground state. The excited state of the $n \rightarrow \pi^*$ transition of ketones seems to have major contributions from structures such as

$\rangle C{=}O$ and $\rangle C^{-}{-}O^{+}$ $\left(\rangle \overset{\delta-}{C}\overset{\cdots}{=}O^{\delta+}\right)$ rather than $\rangle C^{\pm}{-}O^{-}$ as in the ground state.

The shift to longer wavelength (lower energy) observed in the $\pi \rightarrow \pi^*$ transitions of α,β-unsaturated ketones (13 mμ for mesityl oxide) with increasing solvent polarity indicates that the excited state in this transition is more polar than the ground state. For this transition the data have been interpreted as the promotion of an ethylenic π electron to a carbonyl π^* orbital. Because intramolecular effects such as these involve the transfer of charge from one atom to another, they are frequently called *charge-transfer* spectra.

2.3 SIMPLE CHROMOPHORIC GROUPS

Saturated hydrocarbons and compounds containing only saturated alkyl groups, alcohol groups, and ether groups are transparent (that is, they show no absorption) in the region 200–1000 mμ. Such compounds are useful as solvents for spectral determinations throughout this region.

An isolated functional group not in conjugation with any other group is said to be a *chromophore* if it exhibits absorption of a characteristic nature in the ultraviolet or visible region. If a series of compounds has the same functional group and no complicating factors are present, all of the compounds will generally absorb at very nearly the same wavelength and will have nearly the same molar extinction coefficient. Thus, it is readily seen that the spectrum of a compound, when correlated with data from the literature for known compounds, can be a very valuable aid in determining the functional groups present in the molecule. A tabulation of some isolated chromophoric groups is given in Table 2-1.

Table 2-1
CHARACTERISTICS OF SIMPLE CHROMOPHORIC GROUPS†

Chromophore	Example	λ_{max}, $m\mu$	ε_{max}	Solvent
>C=C<	Ethylene	171	15,530	Vapor
	1-Octene	177	12,600	Heptane
—C≡C—	2-Octyne	178	10,000	Heptane
		196	*ca* 2,100	Heptane
		223	160	Heptane
>C=O	Acetaldehyde	160	20,000	Vapor
		180	10,000	Vapor
		290	17	Hexane
	Acetone	166	16,000	Vapor
		189	900	Hexane
		279	15	Hexane
$—CO_2H$	Acetic acid	208	32	Ethanol
—COCl	Acetyl chloride	220	100	Hexane
$—CONH_2$	Acetamide	178	9,500	Hexane
		220	63	Water
$—CO_2R$	Ethyl acetate	211	57	Ethanol
$—NO_2$	Nitromethane	201	5,000	Methanol
		274	17	Methanol
$—ONO_2$	Butyl nitrate	270	17	Ethanol
—ONO	Butyl nitrite	220	14,500	Hexane
		356	87	Hexane
—NO	Nitrosobutane	300	100	Ether
		665	20	Ether
>C=N	*neo*-Pentylidene *n*-butylamine	235	100	Ethanol
—C≡N	Acetonitrile	167	weak	Vapor
$—N_3$	Azidoacetic ester	285	20	Ethanol
$=N_2$	Diazomethane	*ca* 410	3	Vapor
	Diazoacetic ester	249	10,050	Ethanol
		378	16	Ethanol
—N=N—	Azomethane	338	4	Ethanol

† Data in the tables and in the text were selected mostly from Vols. I, II, and IV of *Organic Electronic Spectral Data.* [See Chapter 2 Selected References listings for complete reference data.]

Absorptions caused by $\sigma \rightarrow \sigma^*$ transitions are of such high energy that they occur only in the vacuum ultraviolet region and are of little use to the qualitative interpretation of spectra. The absorption of olefinic double bonds in the 160–180 mμ region is caused by $\pi \rightarrow \pi^*$ transitions. The absorption of aldehyde and ketone carbonyl groups in the 150–160 mμ region is caused by $n \rightarrow \sigma^*$ transitions; that in the 180–190 mμ region is caused by $\pi \rightarrow \pi^*$ transitions, and that in the 275–295 mμ region is caused by $n \rightarrow \pi^*$ transitions. Although all compounds have characteristic spectral patterns below 200 mμ, this region is not usually examined because of its relative inaccessibility. For qualitative interpretation of spectra, only the region above 200 mμ is of real value; in Table 2-1 and in the following tables only useful correlations are given.

Among the simple chromophoric groups, the absorption resulting from the $n \rightarrow \pi^*$ transitions of the carbonyl group of aldehydes and ketones is among the most easily recognized. Although the peak is ordinarily of low intensity, its position in the range 275–295 mμ is readily determined. The position and intensity of the simple ketone absorption varies somewhat with ring size and the presence of large bulky groups. A steric effect is shown by *t*-butyl methyl ketone, which absorbs at 10 mμ longer wavelength than acetone and has a slightly larger extinction coefficient. This indicates that slightly less energy is required for the transition, and the transition is slightly more probable.

The various derivatives of carbonyl compounds show well-defined ultraviolet absorption. Perhaps the most convenient of these are the 2,4-dinitrophenylhydrazones, which are easily prepared and purified. The 2,4-dinitrophenylhydrazones of simple saturated aldehydes show λ_{max} at 358 $\pm$ 2 mμ in alcohol solution (formaldehyde, λ_{max} 348 mμ, is an exception), and the derivatives of saturated ketones show λ_{max} at 364 $\pm$ 2 mμ in alcohol solution. The extinction coefficient for this chromophore is about 22,000; absorption extends well into the visible range, which accounts for the yellow-to-orange color of these compounds.

Placement of a halogen, amino, hydroxyl, or alkoxyl group on the carbonyl group results (see Table 2-1) in a very significant displacement of the absorption resulting from the $n \rightarrow \pi^*$ transition to shorter wavelengths. The result is that the absorptions of simple carboxylic acids and derivatives are frequently difficult to determine.

Some other chromophoric groups that contain nitrogen and/or oxygen in multiply bonded linkages show an absorption pattern similar to the carbonyl chromophore—that is, a band of low intensity at longer wavelength and a band of high intensity at shorter wavelength. Compounds that contain the nitroso group are monomeric in solution and are an intense blue in color, owing to absorption near 665 mμ.

Auxochromes are groups that do not in themselves show selective absorption above 200 mμ but which, when attached to a given chromophoric system, usually cause a shift in the absorption to longer wavelength and an increased intensity of the absorption peak. Common auxochromic groups are hydroxyl, amino, sulfhydryl (and their derivatives), and some of the halogens. These groups all contain nonbonding electrons; transitions involving these n electrons are responsible for these effects. For example, the absorption band at longest wavelength of *trans-p*-ethoxyazobenzene is shifted 65 mμ to longer wavelength and is about twice as intense as that of the corresponding band of *trans*-azobenzene. Benzene shows λ_{max} 255 mμ, ε 230, and aniline shows λ_{max} 280 mμ, ε 1430. (Interestingly, the anilinium ion, which has no nonbonding electrons, shows λ_{max} 254 mμ, ε 160.)

2.4 CONJUGATED SYSTEMS

If two or more chromophoric groups are present in a molecule and they are separated by two or more single bonds, the effect on the spectrum is usually additive; there is little electronic interaction between isolated chromophoric groups. However, if two chromophoric groups are separated by only one single bond (a conjugated system), a large effect on the spectrum results, because the π electron system is spread over at least four atomic centers. When two chromophoric groups are conjugated, the high-intensity ($\pi \rightarrow \pi^*$ transitions) absorption band is generally shifted 15–45 mμ to longer wavelength with respect to the simple unconjugated chromophore. Examples of various conjugated chromophoric groups are given in Table 2-2. The low-intensity ($n \rightarrow \pi^*$ transition) band of certain chromophoric groups is also shifted about 30 mμ to longer wavelength; sometimes this band cannot be observed, as it is obscured by the peak with large extinction.

The ultraviolet spectra of α,β-unsaturated ketones, α,β-unsaturated aldehydes, and conjugated dienes lend themselves to an excellent numerical correlation depending on the number of alkyl, alkoxyl, or acetoxyl substituent groups attached to the ethylenic linkages present. The rules are relatively simple for systems containing the α,β-unsaturated ketone chromophore **1.** In order to estimate the absorption of an α,β-unsaturated ketone, a base value of 215 mμ is assumed. For an α substituent, 10 mμ are added; for each β substituent, 12 mμ are added. For each ring (six-membered or less) to which the carbon-carbon double bond is *exo*cyclic, 5 mμ are added. If the carbon-carbon double bond and the carbonyl group are contained in a five-membered ring (cyclopentenones), 10 mμ are *subtracted* from the calculated value and if only the carbon-carbon double bond is in a five-membered ring, 5 mμ are *added.* In addition, 35 mμ are added for an enolic α- or β-hydroxyl group, 15 mμ for an

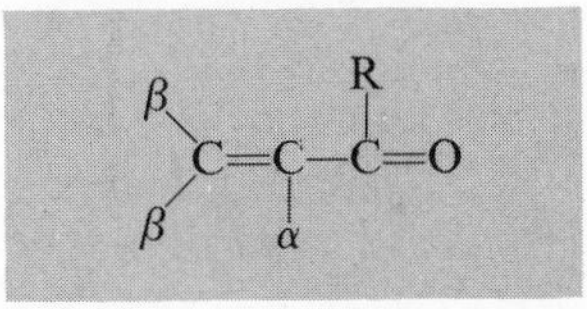

$$(\beta)(\beta)C{=}C(\alpha){-}C(R){=}O$$

1

Table 2-2

CHARACTERISTICS OF SIMPLE CONJUGATED CHROMOPHORIC GROUPS

Chromophore	Example	λ_{max}, mμ	ε_{max}	Solvent
>C=C—C=C<	Butadiene	217	20,900	Hexane
>C=C—C≡C—	Vinylacetylene	219	7,600	Hexane
		228	7,800	Hexane
>C=C—C=O	Crotonaldehyde	218	18,000	Ethanol
		320	30	Ethanol
	3-Penten-2-one	224	9,750	Ethanol
		314	38	Ethanol
—C≡C—C=O	1-Hexyn-3-one	214	4,500	Ethanol
		308	20	Ethanol
>C=C—CO_2H	*cis*-Crotonic acid	206	13,500	Ethanol
		242	250	Ethanol
—C≡C—CO_2H	*n*-Butylpropiolic acid	*ca* 210	6,000	Ethanol
>C=C—C=N—	*N*-*n*-Butylcrotonaldimine	219	25,000	Hexane
>C=C—C≡N	Methacrylonitrile	215	680	Ethanol
>C=C—NO_2	1-Nitro-1-propene	229	9,400	Ethanol
		235	9,800	Ethanol
O=C—C=O	Glyoxal	195	35	Hexane
		280	3	Hexane
		463	4	Hexane
$HO_2C—CO_2H$	Oxalic acid	*ca* 185	4,000	Water
		250	63	Water

Table 2-3

COMPARISON OF OBSERVED AND "ESTIMATED" ABSORPTIONS OF SOME α,β-UNSATURATED KETONES IN ALCOHOL SOLUTION

Compound	"Estimated" λ_{max}, mμ	Observed λ_{max}, mμ	ε_{max}
Methyl vinyl ketone	215	213, 320	7,100, 27
2-Methyl-1-buten-3-one	225	220	6,300
3-Penten-2-one	227	224, 314	9,750, 38
Mesityl oxide	239	237, 310	11,700, 57
3-Methyl-3-penten-2-one	237	236	4,600
2-Cyclopentenone	217	218, 311	9,500, 26
2-Cyclohexenone	227	225	10,300
1-Acetylcyclopentene	242	239	12,000
1-Acetylcyclohexene	237	233, 308	12,500, 50
2-Cyclohexylidenecyclohexanone	259	256	6,500
2,3-Dimethyl-2-penten-4-one	249	246	5,300

α-chloro group, and 23 mμ for an α-bromo group. The correlation of estimated values and experimental results has generally been within several millimicrons. Table 2-3 compares some estimated values and experimental results.

A similar empirical correlation exists for α,β-unsaturated aldehydes; the positions of absorption are generally about 5 mμ less than the corresponding α,β-unsaturated ketone. Ultraviolet spectra for several aldehydes and ketones are shown in Fig. 2-3.

Absorption values commonly given for α,β-unsaturated ketones and

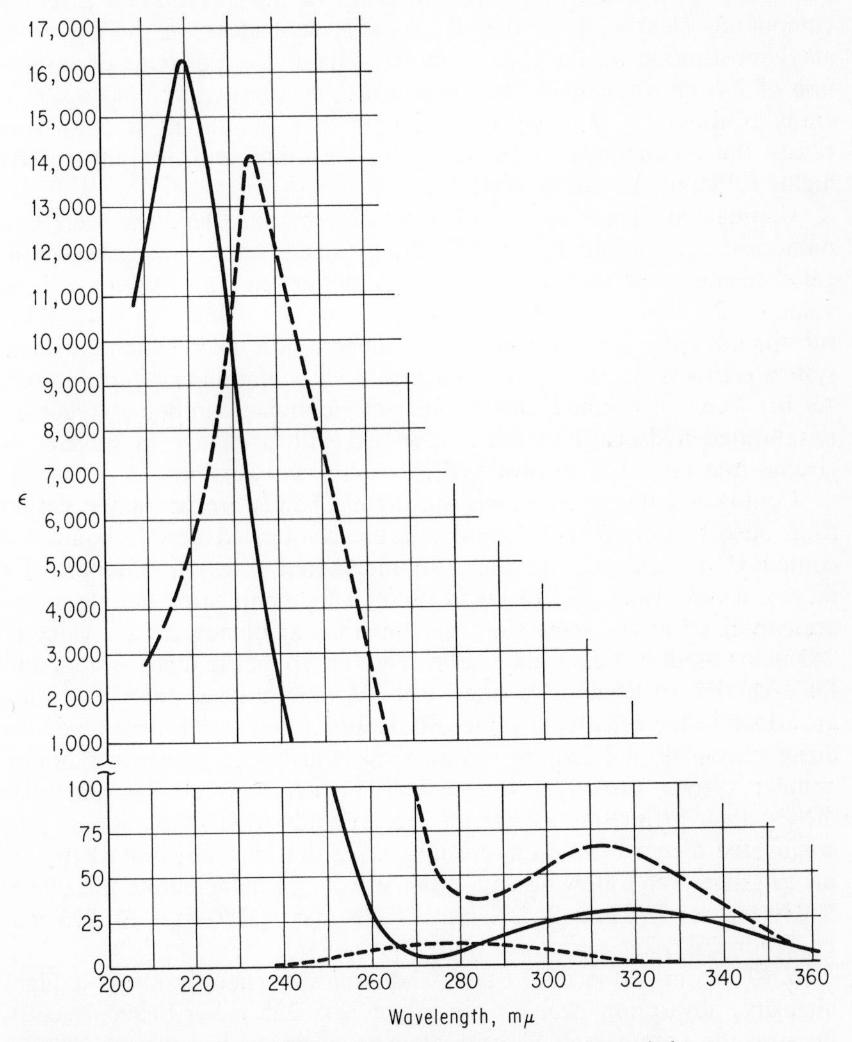

Fig. 2-3 Ultraviolet spectra of acetone in isooctane (------), mesityl oxide in methanol (— — —), and crotonaldehyde in ethanol (———).

aldehydes are for 95% ethyl alcohol solutions. To obtain the position of this band in ethanol when another solvent is used, the following numerical corrections to the observed λ_{max} are made: water, -8 mμ; methanol, 0 mμ; chloroform, $+1$ mμ; dioxane, $+5$ mμ; ether, $+7$ mμ; hexane, $+11$ mμ. This is necessary to correct for the degree of hydrogen bonding of the excited state of the $\pi \rightarrow \pi^*$ transition relative to that of the ground state, depending on the polarity of the solvent used.

The spectral properties of 2,4-dinitrophenylhydrazones of saturated carbonyl compounds have already been mentioned. The position of absorption of 2,4-dinitrophenylhydrazones of α,β-unsaturated carbonyl compounds clearly shows that the λ_{max} is dependent on the degree of alkyl substitution on the chromophoric system. The positions of absorption of 2,4-dinitrophenylhydrazones of α,β-unsaturated ketones are generally at about 150 mμ longer wavelength than the parent ketones. This causes the compounds to be orange-red in color and, for particularly highly substituted systems, scarlet.

Conjugated dienes having alkyl substituents also lend themselves to numerical correlation. For acyclic conjugated dienes and cyclic conjugated dienes contained in nonfused six-membered ring systems, a base value of 217 mμ (butadiene) is used; 5 mμ are added for each alkyl substituent, 5 mμ for each ring (six-membered or less) to which the diene system is *exo*cyclic, and 17 mμ for a substituent chlorine or bromine atom. As has been mentioned, absorptions of nonpolar compounds such as unsaturated hydrocarbons are not shifted with a change in solvent; in general, the same λ_{max} is observed in alcohol and hexane.

Conjugated dienes in which the double bonds are contained within rings absorb somewhat differently. If the conjugated double bonds are contained in separate, but fused six-membered rings (a heteroannular diene), a base value of 214 mμ is used; if the conjugated double bonds are contained in the same ring (a homoannular diene), a base value of 253 mμ is used. For each alkyl substituent group on the diene system and for each ring to which a carbon-carbon double bond is *exo*cyclic, 5 mμ are added to the calculated value. Alkoxyl or acetoxyl substituents on the diene system do not require a numerical adjustment. In general, homoannular dienes absorb at longer wavelengths than do heteroannular dienes; their extinction coefficients are generally less. Simple monocyclic conjugated dienes form an interesting series that depends remarkably on the ring size. The following data (ring size, λ_{max}) demonstrate this effect: 5, 239 mμ; 6, 257 mμ; 7, 248 mμ; 8, 228 mμ; 9, 220 mμ; 10, 223 mμ; 11, 225 mμ; 12, 232 mμ.

α,β-Unsaturated acids, esters, and amides generally show a high-intensity absorption peak in the region 205–225 mμ (ε 10,000–20,000). Because the absorptions of some of these compounds are near 200 mμ, the spectra will frequently show no maximum and only intense end absorption unless determined on a good instrument in good operating

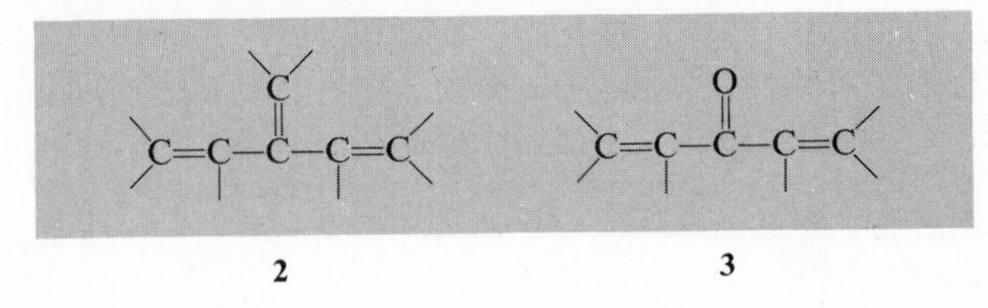

2 3

condition. A numerical correlation for α,β-unsaturated acids and esters uses a base value of 197 mμ; 10 mμ are added for each alkyl substituent present. In addition, 5 mμ are added for an *exo*cyclic double bond or for an *endo*cyclic double bond present in a five- or seven-membered ring compound. The numerical correlation for α,β-unsaturated acids and esters does not appear to correspond as closely with experimental values as the conjugated systems previously mentioned.

Cross-conjugated systems are those which contain a "branched" conjugated system. Examples are the triene **2** and the dienone **3.** Two overlapping α,β-unsaturated chromophoric groups may be said to be present; each may give rise to transitions expected to have a reasonably large extinction coefficient. Both systems generally give rise to absorption, but because of the band nature of spectra, only that system having absorption at longer wavelength and higher intensity is usually observed. In cross-conjugated systems, the position of absorption observed appears to be due to the most highly substituted simple conjugated system present. An example is the steroidal dienone **4.**

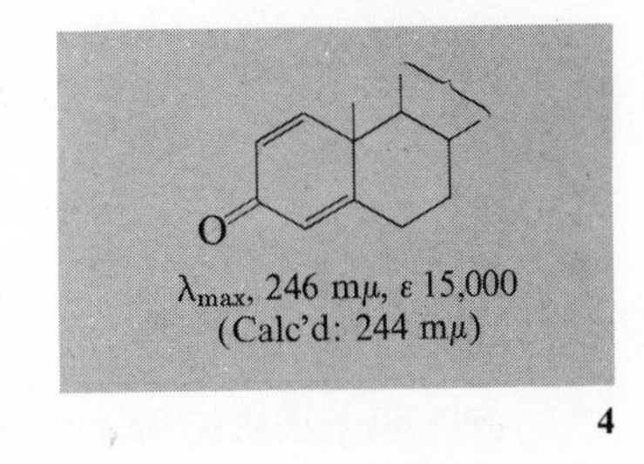

4

2.5 SYSTEMS OF EXTENDED CONJUGATION

As might be anticipated from the change in spectral characteristics when a simple chromophore is compared to one in conjugation with another chromophore, the addition of still another chromophoric group or more in conjugation results in a shift of the position of absorption by the system to longer wavelengths. The extinction coefficient generally increases in a stepwise manner, depending on the number of additional conjugated chromophoric groups present. The lengthened π electron system results in greater delocalization of the π electrons; the energy required for the $\pi \rightarrow \pi^*$ transitions is less, and the probability of these transitions is higher. An example of this effect is shown by the series of polyene aldehydes (Table 2-4) in alcohol solution.

The numerical correlations for α,β-unsaturated ketones and dienes have been extended to include systems of extended conjugation. The same base values are used for conjugated acyclic, heteroannular, and

Table 2-4

ULTRAVIOLET ABSORPTION OF SOME POLYENE ALDEHYDES, $CH_3—(CH=CH)_n—CHO$

$n =$	λ_{max}, mμ	ε_{max}
1	217	15,650
2	270	27,000
3	312	40,000
4	343	40,000
5	370	57,000
6	393	65,000
7	415	63,000

homoannular dienes of extended conjugation as in the simple series. As these compounds are relatively nonpolar, no solvent corrections are needed when different solvents are used. For each double bond extending the conjugated unit, 30 mμ are added, and 5 mμ are added for each alkyl substituent and every ring to which a carbon-carbon double bond is *exo*cyclic; alkoxyl and acetoxyl groups require no added increment. The base value for a conjugated unsaturated ketone of extended conjugation is 245 mμ (a dienone), and the following increments are added: 10 mμ for an α substituent, 12 mμ for a β substituent, 18 mμ for each γ, δ, or other substituent, 30 mμ for each double bond extending conjugation, 5 mμ for each ring to which the carbon-carbon double bonds are *exo*cyclic, and 39 mμ for a homoannular diene component. As has been mentioned, solvent corrections are required when a solvent other than ethyl alcohol is used.

Similar spectral characteristics are shown by all systems of extended conjugation; frequently it is possible to determine the length of the conjugated system from the spectrum obtained. Studies of systems of extended conjugation were originally initiated by consideration of the spectra of many of the carotenoid pigments such as *trans*-β-carotene, a pigment widely distributed in plants (purple prismatic crystals from benzene-methanol), which shows λ_{max} at 452 mμ and 478 mμ (ε 139,000 and 122,000, respectively).

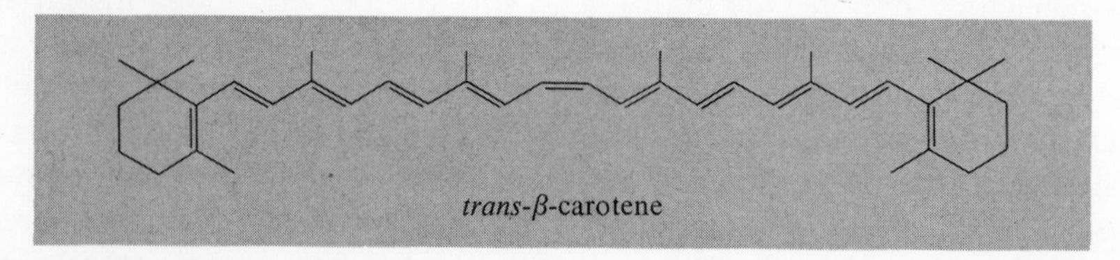

trans-β-carotene

Polyacetylenes are characterized by a series of bands at short wavelength of extremely high intensity and a series of bands at longer wavelength of medium intensity. For example, 2,4,6,8-decatetrayne shows:

λ_{max}:	205	215	226	234	286	306	328	354 mμ
ε_{max}:	24,000	91,000	200,000	280,000	145	178	178	105

Compounds containing a series of conjugated chromophoric groups will appear colored to the eye if they absorb at all above 400 mμ. As ultraviolet absorption peaks are frequently broad, the absorption of a peak with λ_{max} *ca* 350 mμ will generally extend into the visible region. If the compound appears colored, it will contain not less than four and usually five or more conjugated chromophoric and auxochromic groups. The only common exceptions to this rule are azo- and diazo-compounds, glyoxal, α-diketones, iodoform, and monomeric nitroso compounds.

2.6 AROMATIC SYSTEMS

Benzene absorbs strongly at 184 mμ (ε 47,000) and at 202 mμ (ε 7,000) and has a series of bands in the region between 230 and 270 mμ of relatively low intensity, λ_{max} 255 mμ, ε_{max} 230 (in cyclohexane). The series of fine-structure bands in the 230–270 mμ region of the spectrum of benzene (Fig. 2-4) and those of most aromatic hydrocarbons are associated with vibrational effects on the $\pi \rightarrow \pi^*$ transitions. These fine-structure bands are particularly susceptible to solvent effects (see Fig. 2-4) and are diminished or frequently destroyed in alcohol solution.

When benzene is substituted with a single functional group, the fine-structure bands generally appear to be diminished in complexity. The intensity of this absorption is increased, and there is generally a shift to

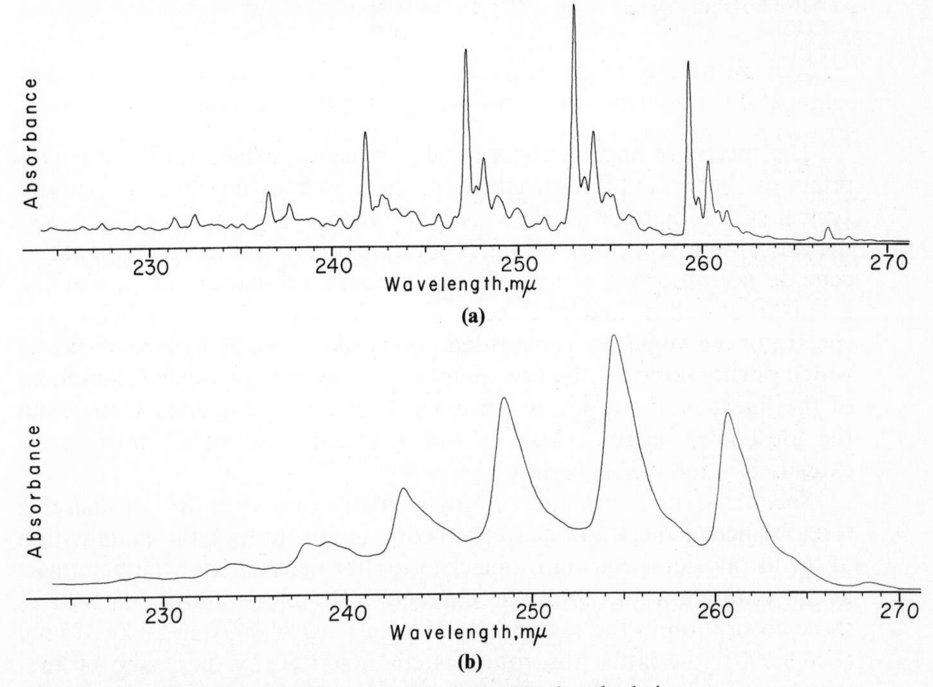

Fig. 2-4 Ultraviolet spectrum of benzene: (**a**) vapor, (**b**) ethanol solution.

longer wavelength. Substitution by halogen or alkyl groups causes only a slight shift with a small increase in extinction coefficient, but substitution by groups carrying nonbonding or π electrons such as $—OH$, $—NH_2$, or $—CHO$ causes a very pronounced shift and a greatly intensified absorption. Table 2-5 summarizes data for some simple compounds.

Table 2-5

ULTRAVIOLET ABSORPTION OF SOME MONOSUBSTITUTED BENZENES (IN WATER)

C_6H_5X X =	Primary band λ_{max}, mμ	ε_{max}	Secondary band λ_{max}, mμ	ε_{max}
—H	203.5	7,400	254	204
$—NH_3^+$	203	7,500	254	169
$—CH_3$	206.5	7,000	261	225
—I	207	7,000	257	700
—Cl	209.5	7,400	263.5	190
—Br	210	7,900	261	192
—OH	210.5	6,200	270	1,450
$—OCH_3$	217	6,400	269	1,480
$—SO_2NH_2$	217.5	9,700	264.5	740
—CN	224	13,000	271	1,000
$—CO_2^-$	224	8,700	268	560
$—CO_2H$	230	11,600	273	970
$—NH_2$	230	8,600	280	1,430
$—O^-$	235	9,400	287	2,600
$—NHCOCH_3$	238	10,500	...	...
$—COCH_3$	245.5	9,800	...	...
—CHO	249.5	11,400	...	...
$—NO_2$	268.5	7,800	...	...

The spectra of linearly constituted polynuclear aromatic hydrocarbons retain the benzenoid fine-structure bands as well as the other absorptions typical of the benzene nucleus. As the number of fused rings increases, the absorption is shifted to longer wavelength. Naphthalene and anthracene do not absorb in the visible region, but naphthacene (λ_{max} 480 mμ, ε 11,000) is yellow and pentacene (λ_{max} 580 mμ, ε 12,600) is blue. The spectra of the angularly constituted polycyclic aromatic hydrocarbons, of which phenanthrene is the first member, are more complicated than those of the linear isomers. All, however, have intense absorption throughout the ultraviolet region, which, if sufficient aromatic nuclei are present, extends into the visible region.

Spectra of nonbenzenoid aromatic hydrocarbons show considerable resemblance to spectra of benzenoid compounds. In fact, the examination of the ultraviolet spectrum is one criterion for determining whether a particular compound has aromatic character. Tropolone and its derivatives show absorption in the region 220–250 mμ (ε *ca* 30,000) and 340–375 mμ (ε *ca* 8,000); the latter absorption is characterized by the group of fine-structure bands typical of aromatic systems. Azulene and its derivatives have complicated spectra consisting of a number of relatively intense bands throughout most of the ultraviolet region (up to 360 mμ) and a number of relatively weak bands throughout most of the visible region (500–700 mμ). As a consequence of the latter, azulene and most of its derivatives are blue.

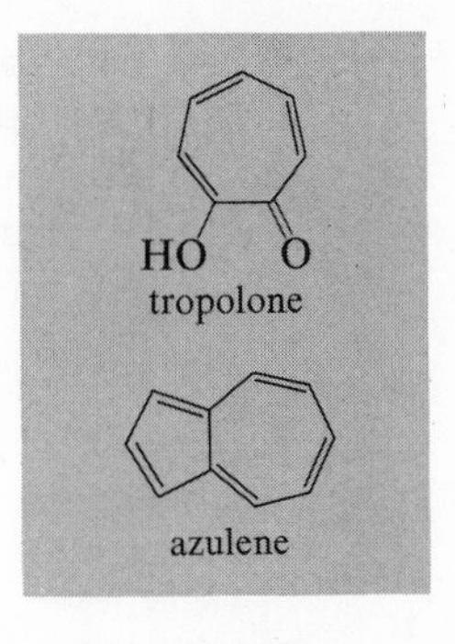

The spectra of simple heterocyclic aromatic compounds grossly resemble spectra of benzenoid compounds in that they consist of an absorption peak of relatively large extinction coefficient (ε 5,000–15,000) at short wavelength (λ_{max} 190–240 mμ) and a series of fine-structure bands of lower intensity (ε 1–400) at longer wavelengths (λ_{max} 240–300 mμ).

2.7 STEREOCHEMISTRY

The absorptions by compounds containing extended conjugation are caused by $\pi \rightarrow \pi^*$ transitions that arise from the delocalized π electron systems present. The intensities and positions of these peaks depend on the lengths of the conjugated systems; the longer such a system, the longer the wavelength of the absorption and the larger the extinction coefficient. When the π electron system is prevented from achieving coplanarity, the degree of overlap of the π electron system will be diminished; a marked effect on the ultraviolet spectrum results.

Hindered rotation in biphenyls is readily studied by ultraviolet spectroscopy. Then $\pi \rightarrow \pi^*$ transition of biphenyl, which readily achieves coplanarity, results in λ_{max} 246 mμ, ε 16,300. If large groups are present in *ortho* positions, coplanarity is restricted and the length of the π electron system is effectively diminished. For example, dimesityl (2,4,6,2′,4′,6′-hexamethylbiphenyl) shows λ_{max} 267 mμ, ε 545, an extinction coefficient essentially only twice that of mesitylene itself, λ_{max} 266 mμ, ε 260. Another example of steric hindrance to coplanarity may be found in nitrobenzene derivatives (data for heptane solutions): nitrobenzene, λ_{max} 252 mμ, ε 8,620; *o*-nitrotoluene, λ_{max} 250 mμ, ε 5,950; *o*-nitrocumene, λ_{max} 247 mμ, ε 3,760; for *o*-nitro-*t*-butylbenzene, there is no λ_{max} in this region, but at 250 mμ, ε is 1,450. Because the λ_{max} of nitrobenzene is dependent on the polarity of the solvent used, the activated structure has been shown to have charge-transfer character, as shown by **5.** The presence of increasingly bulky *ortho* substituents effectively hinders the coplanarity that the nitro group achieves with the benzene ring.

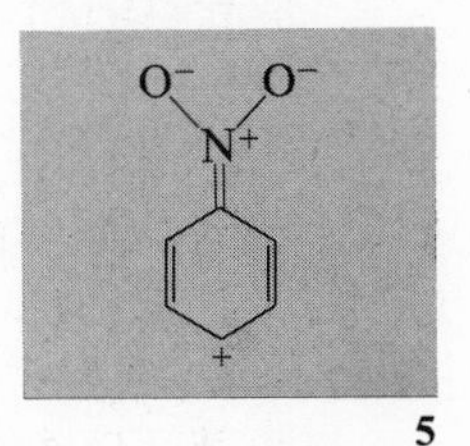

5

Of a pair of geometrical isomers, the *cis* form would be expected to be more sterically hindered, and the *trans* form would be expected to achieve coplanarity of the π electron system more readily. Data obtained for *cis* and *trans* isomers quite generally show that absorption due to the $\pi \rightarrow \pi^*$ transition of the *trans* isomer occurs at longer wavelength and has a larger extinction coefficient than that of the *cis* isomer. Data in Table 2-6 demonstrate this effect.

Table 2-6

ULTRAVIOLET ABSORPTION OF SOME *cis* AND *trans* ISOMERS

Compound	*cis*-Isomer λ_{max}, mμ	*cis*-Isomer ε_{max}	*trans*-Isomer λ_{max}, mμ	*trans*-Isomer ε_{max}
Cinnamic acid	268	10,700	272	15,900
Stilbene	278	9,350	294	24,000

2.8 PROBLEMS

1. The following α,β-unsaturated ketones have λ_{max} at 241 mμ (ε 4,700), 254 mμ (ε 9,550), and 259 mμ (ε 10,790) in ethanol. Which is which?

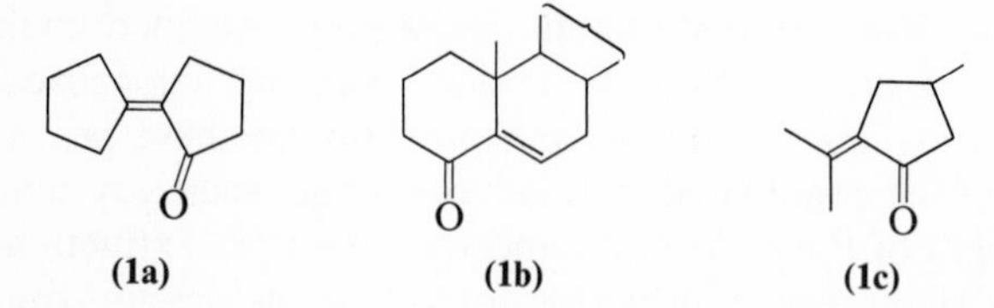

2. The following dienes have λ_{max} at 231 mμ (ε 21,000), 236 mμ (ε 12,000), 245 mμ (ε 18,000), 265 mμ (ε 6,400), and 282 mμ (ε 11,900) in ethanol. Which is which?

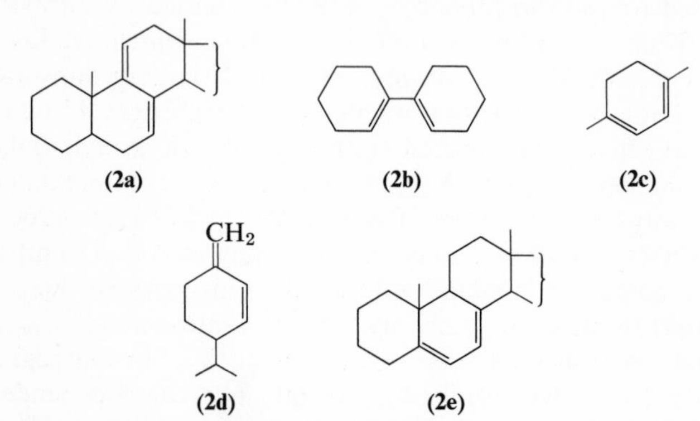

3. The following polyenes have λ_{max} at 306 mμ (ε 14,500), 315 mμ (ε 19,800), and 355 mμ (ε 19,700) in ethanol. Which is which?

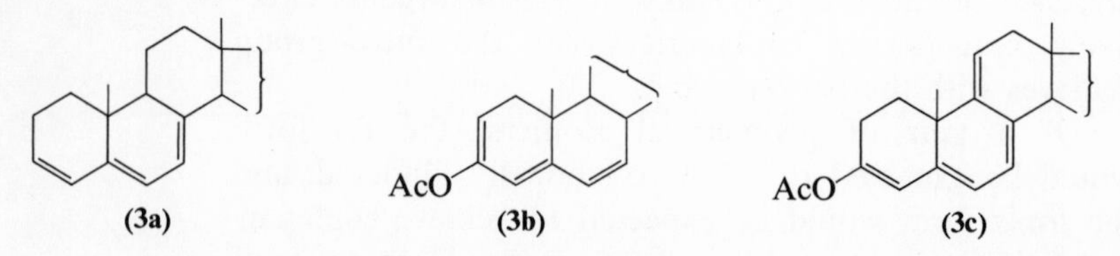

4. The following polyenones have λ_{max} at 284 mμ (ε 28,000), 315 mμ (ε 7,000), and 348 mμ (ε 26,500) in ethanol. Which is which?

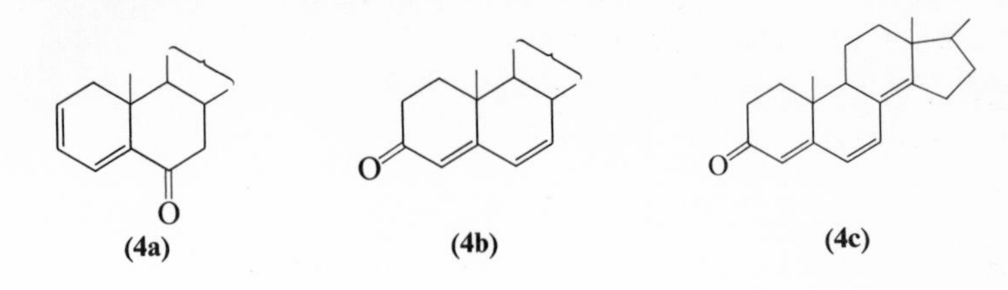

(4a) (4b) (4c)

SELECTED REFERENCES

E. A. Braude, "Ultraviolet Absorption and Structure of Organic Compounds," *Ann. Repts. Chem. Soc.,* **42,** 105 (1945).

E. A. Braude, in *Determination of Organic Structures by Physical Methods,* E. A. Braude and F. C. Nachod, eds. New York: Academic Press, 1955, pp. 131–93.

R. A. Friedel and M. Orchin, *Ultraviolet Spectra of Aromatic Compounds.* New York: John Wiley and Sons, 1951.

A. Gillam and E. S. Stern, *An Introduction to Electronic Absorption Spectroscopy in Organic Chemistry.* London: Arnold, 1957.

H. M. Hershenson, *Ultraviolet and Visible Spectra Index for 1930–1954.* New York: Academic Press, 1956.

H. M. Hershenson, *Ultraviolet and Visible Spectra Index for 1955–1959.* New York: Academic Press, 1961.

W. West in *Physical Methods of Organic Chemistry,* A. Weissberger, ed., Vol. I, Part III, 3rd ed. New York: Interscience Publishers, 1959, pp. 1799–1958.

H. H. Jaffé and M. Orchin, *Theory and Applications of Ultraviolet Spectroscopy.* New York: John Wiley and Sons, 1962.

L. Láng, *Absorption Spectra in the Ultraviolet and Visible Region.* New York: Academic Press, 1961.

American Petroleum Institute, Research Project 44, Compilation of Ultraviolet Spectral Data.

R. P. Bauman, *Absorption Spectroscopy.* New York: John Wiley and Sons, 1962.

Organic Electronic Spectral Data, Vol. I (1946–52), M. J. Kamlet, ed.; Vol. II (1953–55), H. E. Ungnade, ed.; Vol. IV (1958–59), J. P. Phillips and F. C. Nachod, eds. New York: Interscience Publishers.

S. F. Mason, "Molecular Absorption Spectra," *Quart. Revs.,* **15,** 287 (1961).

3 Infrared Spectroscopy

In contrast to the relatively few absorption peaks observed in the ultraviolet region for most organic compounds, the infrared spectrum provides a rich array of absorption bands. Many of the absorption bands cannot be assigned accurately; those that can, however, provide a wealth of structural information about a molecule.

Either the wavelength (μ) or wave number (cm^{-1}) (see p. 1) is used to measure the position of a given infrared absorption. The ordinary infrared region extends from 2.5 to 15 μ (4000 to 667 cm^{-1}); the region from 0.8 to 2.5 μ (12,500 to 4000 cm^{-1}) is called the *near infrared* and the region from 15 to 200 μ (667 to 50 cm^{-1}) is called the *far infrared.* As is the case in ultraviolet spectroscopy, absorptions that occur at shorter wavelengths (higher frequency) are of higher energy. The wave number is directly proportional to the absorbed energy ($K = E/hc$), whereas the wavelength is inversely proportional to the absorbed energy ($\lambda = hc/E$; $\lambda = 1/K$).

3.1 MOLECULAR VIBRATION

A molecule is not a rigid assemblage of atoms. A molecule can be said to resemble a system of balls of varying masses, corresponding to the atoms of a molecule, and springs of varying strengths, corresponding to the chemical bonds of a molecule. There are two kinds of fundamental vibrations for molecules: *stretching,* in which the distance between two atoms increases or decreases, but the atoms remain in the same bond axis, and *bending* (or deformation), in which the position of the atom changes relative to the original bond axis. The various stretching and bending vibrations of a bond occur at certain quantized frequencies. *When infrared light of that same frequency is incident on the molecule, energy is absorbed and the amplitude of that vibration is increased.* When the molecule reverts from the excited state to the original ground state, the absorbed energy is released as heat.

A nonlinear molecule that contains n atoms has $3n - 6$ possible *fundamental* vibrational modes that can be responsible for the absorption of infrared light. Thus, such simple molecules as methane and benzene have, theoretically, nine and thirty possible fundamental absorption bands, respectively. In order for a particular vibration to result in the absorption of infrared energy, that vibration must cause a change in the dipole moment of the molecule. Thus, molecules that contain certain symmetry elements will display somewhat simplified spectra. The C═C stretching vibration of ethylene and the symmetrical C—H stretching of the four C—H bonds of methane do not result in an absorption band in the infrared region. The predicted number of peaks will not be observed also if the absorption occurs outside the region ordinarily examined, if the vibrations result in absorptions that are so close that they cannot be resolved, or if the absorption is of very weak intensity.

Additional (nonfundamental) absorption bands may occur because of the presence of overtones (or harmonics) that occur with greatly reduced intensity, at $\frac{1}{2}$, $\frac{1}{3}$, . . . of the wavelength (twice, three times, . . . the wave number), combination bands (the sum of two or more different wave numbers), and difference bands (the difference of two or more different wave numbers).

Some of the various stretching and bending vibrations that can exist within a molecule are shown schematically in Fig. 3-1. Bending vibrations generally require less energy and occur at longer wavelength (lower wave number) than stretching vibrations. Stretching vibrations are found to occur in the order of bond strengths. The triple bond (absorption at 4.4–5.0 μ, 2300–2000 cm^{-1}) is stronger than the double bond (absorption at 5.3–6.7 μ, 1900–1500 cm^{-1}), which in turn is stronger than the single bond (C—C, C—N, and C—O absorption at 7.7–12.5 μ, 1300–800 cm^{-1}). When the single bond involves the very small proton (C—H, O—H, or N—H), stretching vibrations occur at much higher frequency (2.7–3.8 μ, 3700–2630 cm^{-1}). The O—H bond absorbs near 2.8 μ (3570 cm^{-1}) and

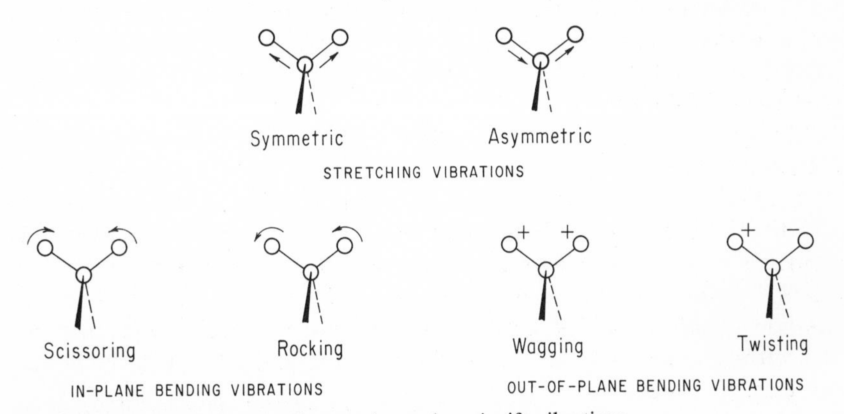

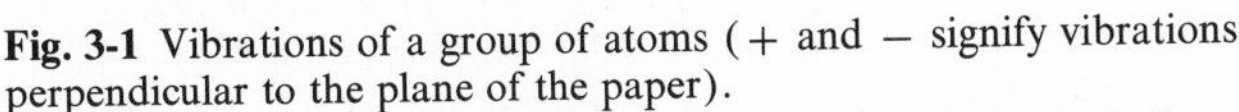
Fig. 3-1 Vibrations of a group of atoms (+ and − signify vibrations perpendicular to the plane of the paper).

the O—D bond absorbs near 3.8 μ (2630 cm^{-1}); in this case the strengths of the bonds are nearly the same but the mass of one atom is doubled.

An approximate value for the stretching frequency (ν, in cm^{-1}) of a bond is related to the masses of the two atoms (M_x and M_y, in grams), the velocity of light (c), and the force constant of the bond (k, in dynes/cm):

$$\nu = \frac{1}{2\pi c}\sqrt{\frac{k}{M_x M_y/(M_x + M_y)}}$$

Single, double, and triple bonds have force constants that are approximately 5, 10, and 15 $\times 10^5$ dynes/cm, respectively.

The magnitude of the molar extinction coefficient in infrared spectroscopy varies from near zero to around 2,000. The value is proportional to the square of the change in the dipole moment of the molecule that the particular vibration causes. Absorption peaks caused by stretching vibrations are usually the most intense peaks in the spectrum.

3.2 MECHANICS OF MEASUREMENT

Infrared absorption spectra are usually obtained by placing the sample in one beam of a double-beam infrared spectrophotometer and measuring the relative intensity of transmitted (and therefore absorbed) light energy versus wavelength (or wave number). A common light source for infrared radiation is the Nernst glower, a molded rod containing a mixture of zirconium oxide, yttrium oxide, and erbium oxide that is heated to around 1,500° by electrical means. Either optical prisms or gratings are used to obtain approximately monochromatic light; grating spectrophotometers give higher resolution. Glass and quartz absorb strongly throughout most of the infrared region, so they cannot be used as cell containers or as optical prisms. Metal halides (e.g., sodium chloride) are commonly used for these purposes. Recording spectrophotometers are available such that a complete spectrum (2.5–25 μ, 4000–400 cm^{-1}) may be obtained in a matter of minutes.

When the spectrum is determined, a calibration line is usually recorded on the paper.† This is necessary because the recorder paper is fitted on a drum of the ordinary spectrophotometer, and it is not possible to place the paper in exactly the same position every time. One of several absorption peaks of polystyrene (Fig. 3-2) is commonly used for this purpose: 3.509 μ (2850 cm^{-1}), 6.238 μ (1603 cm^{-1}), or 11.035 μ (906 cm^{-1}).

The spectrum may be determined if the sample is a gas, a solid, a liquid, or in solution. The sample should be dry, because water absorbs

† All infrared spectra here reproduced were recorded on a Perkin-Elmer Model 137 Infracord instrument; the 6.238 μ (1603 cm^{-1}) polystyrene absorption was used to calibrate all spectra and appears on them.

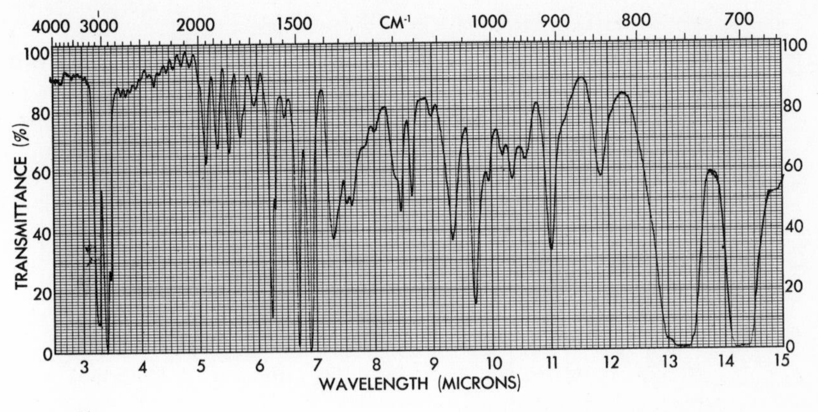

Fig. 3-2 Polystyrene, film.

strongly near 2.7 μ (~3710 cm^{-1}) and near 6.15 μ (~1630 cm^{-1}). These absorptions may obscure absorptions of the substance being analyzed or may, more frequently, lead to erroneous assignments. The most commonly used cells are constructed by using sodium chloride windows. Cells for the determination of the spectra of gaseous samples are available with path lengths up to several meters.

The spectrum of a solid sample is frequently best determined as an alkali halide "pellet." About 1 mg of the substance and 100–200 mg of an alkali halide (potassium bromide is commonly used) are ground together finely (or a solution of the sample and potassium bromide is freeze-dried), dried to remove moisture, and pressed at elevated temperature under high pressure (at least 25,000 psi) into a small disc that measures about 10 mm in diameter and 1–2 mm in thickness. Ideally, a clear pellet is obtained which actually consists of a solid solution of the substance in potassium bromide. Since potassium bromide does not absorb infrared light in the region 2.5–15 μ, a complete spectrum of the sample is obtained. The spectra of solids can also be determined by depositing on an alkali halide disc a thin film of the substance by evaporation of a solution of the solid.

The spectrum of a solid sample may also be determined conveniently as a mull. In this determination, about 5 mg of the solid is ground to a very fine dispersion with a drop of a suitable mulling agent; the spectrum of the mixture is then determined after being placed between two sodium chloride plates. The most commonly used mulling agent is nujol (Fig. 3-3), a mixture of high molecular weight liquid paraffinic hydrocarbons; absorptions present are caused by C—H stretching, 3.3–3.5 μ (3030–2860 cm^{-1}) and C—H bending, *ca* 6.85 μ (~1460 cm^{-1}) and *ca* 7.28 μ (~1374 cm^{-1}). Clearly, when nujol is used as the mulling agent, no information can be derived about absorptions of the sample in these regions. Another

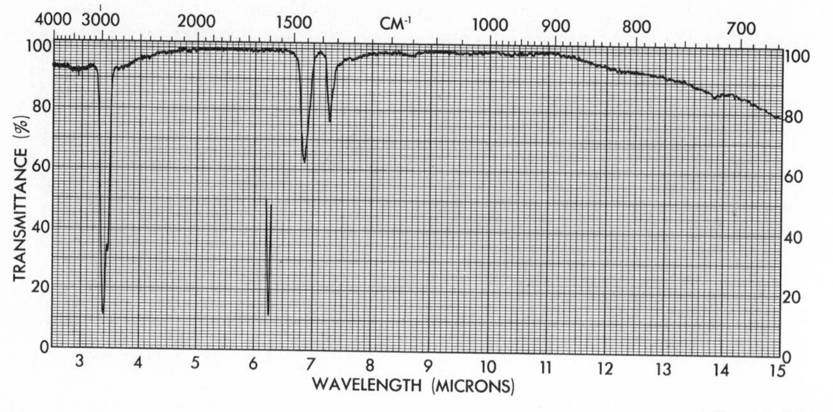

Fig. 3-3 Nujol, liquid film.

mulling agent is hexachlorobutadiene (Fig. 3-4); although many absorptions are present, the compound contains no C—H bonds and hence is transparent in those regions where nujol absorbs. A complete spectrum of the dispersed solid sample may be obtained through the combined use of nujol and hexachlorobutadiene.

A complete spectrum of a liquid material may be obtained without solvent interferences when it is determined as a liquid film. For this determination, a small drop of the liquid is placed on a sodium chloride plate (a crystal of sodium chloride that has been cut such that it is about 25 mm in diameter and 5 mm thick). Another sodium chloride plate is placed on top of the drop, and the plates are placed in a holder and the spectrum is determined. In addition, a sample of a solid with a low melting point can be melted on one plate, and the spectrum can be determined as a solid film.

It is frequently desirable to determine the spectrum of a substance in solution. It has been seen that there are a number of solvents that may

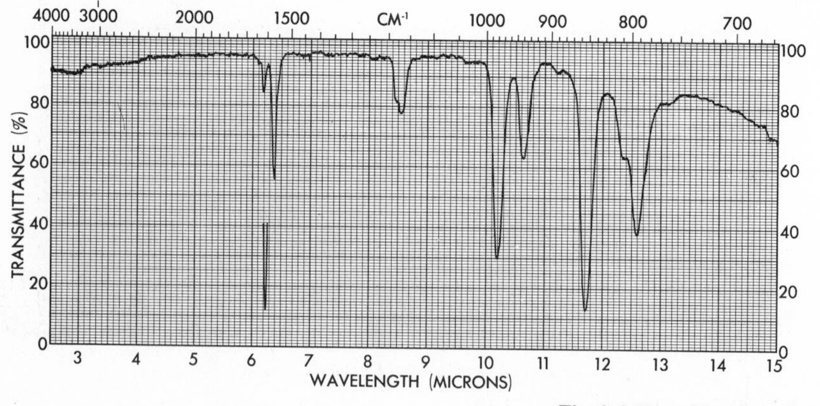

Fig. 3-4 Hexachlorobutadiene, liquid film.

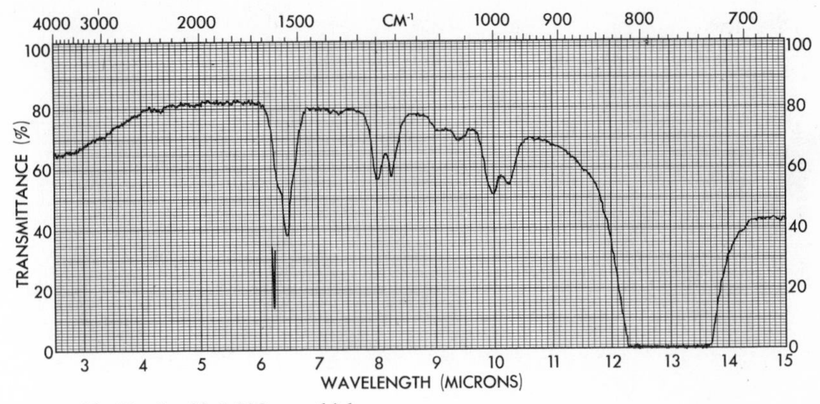

Fig. 3-5 Carbon tetrachloride, liquid, 0.025 mm thickness.

be used for ultraviolet spectroscopy. This is not the case in the infrared region. All solvents absorb strongly in at least several regions of the infrared spectrum. As a consequence of this, in order to minimize solvent absorption, and in spite of the fact that a cell with pure solvent is used in the reference beam, concentrated solutions and cells with a short path are used. The most commonly used cells for solution spectra have a path length of 0.1 mm. If 0.1 mm cells are used, a 10% solution (20 mg in 0.2 ml of solvent) generally gives a satisfactory spectrum.

In order to be desirable as a solvent, a liquid should have few absorptions itself. The most commonly used solvents in infrared spectroscopy are carbon tetrachloride (Fig. 3-5), carbon disulfide (Fig. 3-6), and chloroform (Fig. 3-7). Figures 3-5, 3-6, and 3-7 were recorded using 0.025 mm thickness cells versus air. When matched cells are used, the concentration of solvent will always be higher in the reference cell than in the sample cell; the spectral result is that in regions of the spectrum excludable because of solvent absorption, the per cent transmittance will be 100%, or

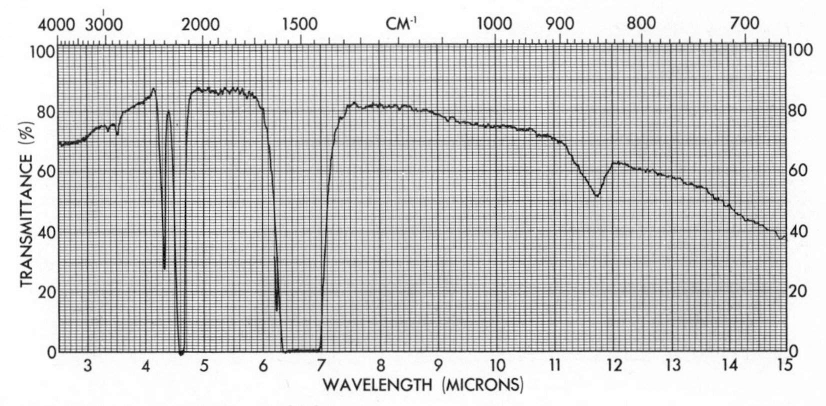

Fig. 3-6 Carbon disulfide, liquid, 0.025 mm thickness.

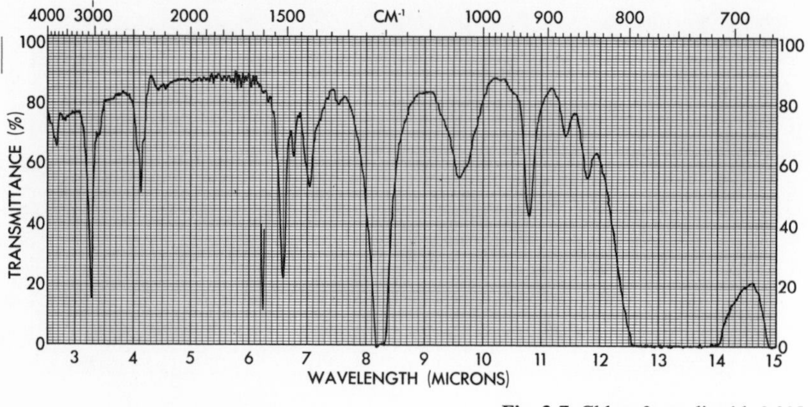

Fig. 3-7 Chloroform, liquid, 0.025 mm thickness.

nearly so. If 0.1 mm or 0.5 mm cells are used with a solvent blank in the reference beam, the effect owing to unequal absorption by solvent in the two cells will not be as marked as that shown in Figs. 3-5, 3-6, and 3-7. The region of the spectrum that is excluded by the solvent is indicated by the spectrum of the pure liquid measured at 0.025 mm thickness. Thus, the region 11.9–14.3 μ (834–700 cm^{-1}) is excluded when carbon tetrachloride is used as the solvent. Determination of spectra of the substance in both carbon tetrachloride and carbon disulfide provides the complete spectrum of the substance in solution. Although the spectrum of chloroform shows more absorptions, as it is a less symmetrical molecule than carbon tetrachloride or carbon disulfide, it is frequently used because it is a better solvent.

Water absorbs strongly in several regions of the infrared spectrum; furthermore, it dissolves the cell windows commonly used. Hence, it is not frequently used as a solvent. It may be used as a solvent when the cell windows are constructed from water-insoluble salts (for example, silver chloride) that are transparent to infrared light.

It is frequently desirable to determine spectra of a sample under different conditions of physical state or concentration. In very dilute solution or in the vapor phase, effects owing to molecular association are minimized, whereas in the solid phase or in concentrated solution, molecular-association effects become important. Effects caused by hydrogen bonding are frequently studied in this way. For example, a free (unassociated) alcoholic hydroxyl group absorbs (O—H stretching) as a sharp band of variable intensity near 2.77 μ (3610 cm^{-1}); in polymeric association, the hydroxyl group absorbs as a broad, strong band near 3.03 μ (3300 cm^{-1}). The relative strengths of these two absorptions change on dilution with an inert solvent. Another example is found in acetic acid, which absorbs (C=O stretching) at 5.82 μ (1718 cm^{-1}) as the pure liquid and at 5.77 μ (1733 cm^{-1}) and 5.60 μ (1786 cm^{-1}) in the vapor state; the latter two absorptions are attributed to the presence of both monomer and dimer, whereas that in the pure liquid is due only to the dimer. Hydrogen bonding generally decreases stretching frequencies and increases bending frequencies.

3.3 APPLICATIONS OF INFRARED SPECTROSCOPY

With an adequate number of examples of secure precedence, the chemist will usually know very closely what absorption position to expect from a certain functional group in a given environment. In the absence of steric or electrical effects that would affect the vibrational frequency of a given group, that group will absorb infrared energy of very nearly the same wavelength in all molecules. For example, the absorption owing to the carbonyl stretching vibration of acetone is at the same place as that for di-*n*-hexyl ketone. On the other hand, it is different for acetic acid (an electrical effect) and for cyclobutanone (a steric effect).

The infrared spectrum cannot commonly distinguish a pure sample from an impure sample. In general, however, the spectrum of a pure sample will have fairly sharp and well-resolved absorption bands. The spectrum of a crude preparation that contains many different kinds of molecules will display broad and poorly resolved absorption bands because of the many absorptions that are present. Materials of high molecular weight that contain many different kinds of functional groups generally give poor spectra.

The examination of the infrared spectrum can aid a chemical investigation in many ways. The progress of most organic reactions can be followed readily by examining spectra of aliquots withdrawn. For example, in the oxidation of a secondary alcohol to a ketone, one learns to expect the disappearance of hydroxyl (O—H) stretching near 2.8 μ ($\sim$3570 cm^{-1}) and the appearance of carbonyl (C=O) stretching near 5.8 μ ($\sim$1725 cm^{-1}). The progress of chromatographic fractionation can readily be monitored by examining the spectra of selected fractions.

Perhaps the most powerful function of infrared spectroscopy is establishing conclusively the identity of two samples that have identical spectra when determined in the same medium. The region 7–11 μ (1430–910 cm^{-1}) contains many absorptions caused by bending vibrations as well as absorptions caused by C—C, C—O, and C—N stretching vibrations. As there are many more bending vibrations in a molecule than stretching vibrations, this region of the spectrum is particularly rich in absorption bands and shoulders. For this reason, it is frequently called the *fingerprint region*. Although similar molecules may show very similar spectra in the region 2.5–7 μ (4000–1430 cm^{-1}), there will nearly always be discernible differences in the fingerprint region.

A number of characteristic group absorptions (compiled by N. B. Colthup) versus structural type are given as Fig. 3-8. This compilation is particularly useful when the spectrum of an unknown material has been

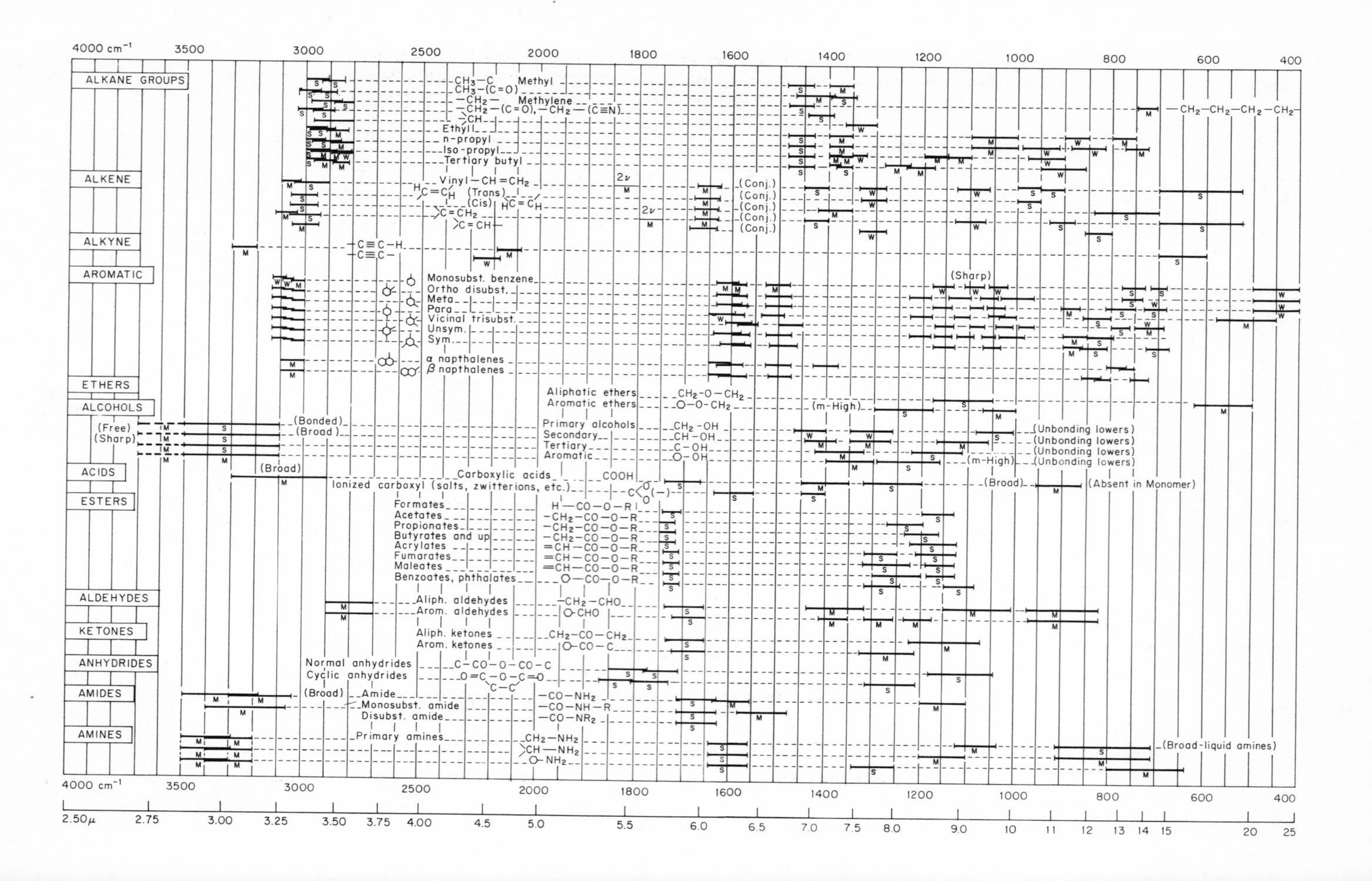

4000 cm⁻¹
3500
3000
2500
2000
1800
1600
1400
1200
1000
800
600
400
ALKANE GROUPS
Methyl
Methylene
Ethyl
n-propyl
Iso-propyl
Tertiary butyl
ALKENE
Vinyl
(Trans)
(Cis)
(Conj.)
2ν
ALKYNE
AROMATIC
Monosubst. benzene
Ortho disubst.
Meta
Para
Vicinal trisubst.
Unsym.
Sym.
α napthalenes
β napthalenes
(Sharp)
ETHERS
Aliphatic ethers
Aromatic ethers
(m-High)
ALCOHOLS
(Free)
(Sharp)
(Bonded)
(Broad)
Primary alcohols
Secondary
Tertiary
Aromatic
(Unbonding lowers)
(m-High)
ACIDS
(Broad)
Carboxylic acids
COOH
Ionized carboxyl (salts, zwitterions, etc.)
(Broad)
(Absent in Monomer)
ESTERS
Formates
Acetates
Propionates
Butyrates and up
Acrylates
Fumarates
Maleates
Benzoates, phthalates
ALDEHYDES
Aliph. aldehydes
Arom. aldehydes
KETONES
Aliph. ketones
Arom. ketones
ANHYDRIDES
Normal anhydrides
Cyclic anhydrides
AMIDES
(Broad)
Amide
Monosubst. amide
Disubst. amide
AMINES
Primary amines
(Broad-liquid amines)
2.50μ
2.75
3.00
3.25
3.50
3.75
4.00
4.5
5.0
5.5
6.0
6.5
7.0
7.5
8.0
9.0
10
11
12
13
14
15
20
25

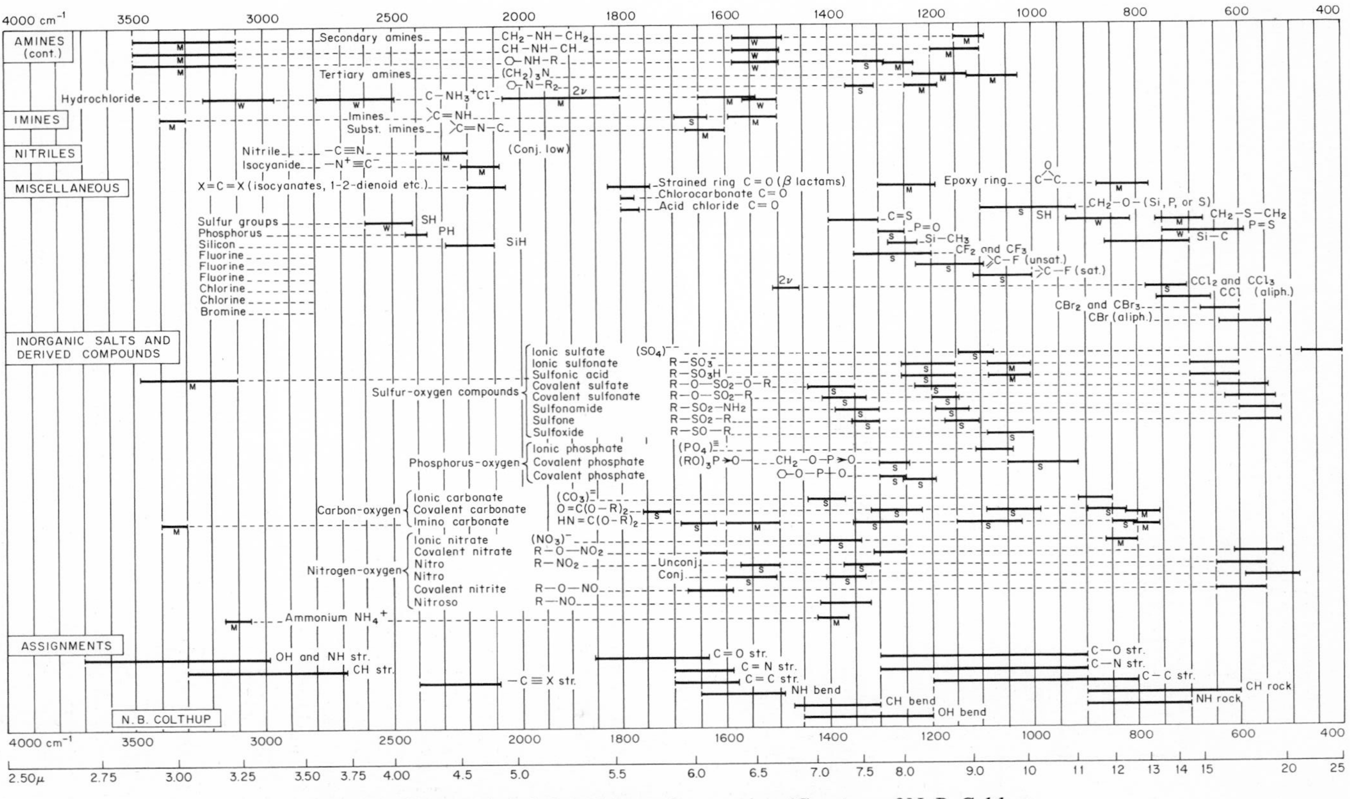

Fig. 3-8 Characteristic infrared group frequencies. (Courtesy of N. B. Colthup, Stamford Research Laboratories, American Cyanamid Company, and the editor of the Journal of the Optical Society.) Overtone bands are marked 2 ν.

obtained. For example, if the spectrum contains a strong band at 5.82 μ (1718 cm^{-1}), the compound almost certainly contains a carbonyl group. The spectrum by itself does not always provide further information as to the nature of the group; the compound could be an aldehyde, a ketone, an acid, an ester, or an amide. Thus, in order to define a functional group, the spectrum must be examined in detail for other diagnostic absorption bands and used in conjunction with (and cannot always replace) classical chemical reactions and solubility determinations. Conversely, the power of negative evidence cannot be overemphasized; *if the spectrum does not contain an absorption typical of a certain functional group, the molecule does not contain that functional group.* If the spectrum contains no absorption in the 5.4–6.3 μ (1850–1587 cm^{-1}) region, the sample does not contain a carbonyl group.

The systematic interpretation of the infrared spectrum can be of great help in determining, for example, whether a reaction has occurred to give the predicted product. One would expect the disappearance of absorptions of certain functional groups and the appearance of others. One should be alert, however, to the possibility of other reactions having occurred; the *entire* spectrum should be examined to determine if it is completely consistent with the structural formula anticipated. Most desirable, of course, is the availability of a spectrum of an authentic sample of the material for comparison.

When the spectrum of an unknown material is obtained, there are a number of questions that can be answered fairly rapidly: does it contain a carbonyl group? is it an acid or an aldehyde? is it aromatic? if so, what is the substitution type? Answers to questions such as these will give many clues for chemical work that can lead to the conclusive identification of the compound.

Most of the absorption bands that organic compounds show in the infrared region cannot be interpreted with assurance. The following section contains a listing (Table 3-1) of absorptions in those regions of the spectrum that can be readily interpreted. Because of the many bending vibrations, the easily interpreted absorptions are usually limited in practice to those caused by stretching vibrations.

3.4 ABSORPTIONS OF COMMON FUNCTIONAL GROUPS

Table 3-1 contains the easily interpreted absorption positions of the more common functional groups found in organic compounds, the variations to be expected with some changes in structural environments, and a qualitative indication of the intensity to be expected of the absorption peak. The appendix contains a table of reciprocals so that wavelengths and wave numbers may be easily interconverted. Organic chemists seem to be about equally divided in their preference for expressing infrared

Table 3-1

CHARACTERISTIC INFRARED ABSORPTIONS OF FUNCTIONAL GROUPS†

Group	Range μ	Intensity	Range cm^{-1}
A. Hydrocarbon chromophore			
1. C—H STRETCHING			
a. Alkane	3.38–3.51	(m–s)	2962–2853
b. Alkene, monosubstituted (vinyl)	3.29–3.32	(m)	3040–3010
	and 3.23–3.25	(m)	3095–3075
Alkene, disubstituted, *cis*	3.29–3.32	(m)	3040–3010
Alkene, disubstituted, *trans*	3.29–3.32	(m)	3040–3010
Alkene, disubstituted, *gem*	3.23–3.25	(m)	3095–3075
Alkene, trisubstituted	3.29–3.32	(m)	3040–3010
c. Alkyne	~3.03	(s)	~3300
d. Aromatic	~3.30	(v)	~3030
2. C—H BENDING			
a. Alkane, C—H	~7.46	(w)	~1340
Alkane, $—CH_2—$	6.74–6.92	(m)	1485–1445
Alkane, $—CH_3$	6.80–7.00	(m)	1470–1430
	and 7.25–7.30	(s)	1380–1370
Alkane, *gem*-dimethyl	7.22–7.25	(s)	1385–1380
	and 7.30–7.33	(s)	1370–1365
Alkane, *tert*-butyl	7.17–7.22	(m)	1395–1385
	and ~7.33	(s)	~1365
b. Alkene, monosubstituted (vinyl)	10.05–10.15	(s)	995–985
	10.93–11.05	(s)	915–905
	and 7.04–7.09	(s)	1420–1410
Alkene, disubstituted, *cis*	~14.5	(s)	~690
Alkene, disubstituted, *trans*	10.31–10.42	(s)	970–960
	and 7.64–7.72	(m)	1310–1295
Alkene, disubstituted, *gem*	11.17–11.30	(s)	895–885
	and 7.04–7.09	(s)	1420–1410
Alkene, trisubstituted	11.90–12.66	(s)	840–790
c. Alkyne	~15.9	(s)	~630
d. Aromatic, substitution type:‡			
five adjacent hydrogen atoms	~13.3	(v, s)	~750
	and ~14.3	(v, s)	~700
four adjacent hydrogen atoms	~13.3	(v, s)	~750
three adjacent hydrogen atoms	~12.8	(v, m)	~780
two adjacent hydrogen atoms	~12.0	(v, m)	~830
one hydrogen atom	~11.3	(v, w)	~880
3. C—C MULTIPLE BOND STRETCHING			
a. Alkene, nonconjugated	5.95–6.17	(v)	1680–1620
Alkene, monosubstituted (vinyl)	~6.08	(m)	~1645
Alkene, disubstituted, *cis*	~6.03	(m)	~1658
Alkene, disubstituted, *trans*	~5.97	(m)	~1675

† Abbreviations: s = strong, m = medium, w = weak, v = variable, b = broad, sh = sharp, ~ = approximately

‡ Substituted benzenes also show weak bands in the region 5.0–6.0 μ (2000–1670 cm^{-1}) region that are characteristic of the substitution type. See Fig. 3-30.

Table 3-1 (cont.)

CHARACTERISTIC INFRARED ABSORPTIONS OF FUNCTIONAL GROUPS†

Group	Range μ	Intensity	Range cm^{-1}
Alkene, disubstituted, *gem*	~6.05	(m)	~1653
Alkene, trisubstituted	~5.99	(m)	~1669
Alkene, tetrasubstituted	~5.99	(w)	~1669
Diene	~6.06	(w)	~1650
	and ~6.25	(w)	~1600
b. Alkyne, monosubstituted	4.67–4.76	(m)	2140–2100
Alkyne, disubstituted	4.42–4.57	(v, w)	2260–2190
c. Allene	~5.1	(m)	~1960
	and ~9.4	(m)	~1060
d. Aromatic	~6.25	(v)	~1600
	~6.33	(v)	~1580
	~6.67	(m)	~1500
	and ~6.90	(m)	~1450
B. Carbonyl chromophore			
1. KETONE STRETCHING VIBRATIONS			
a. Saturated, acyclic	5.80–5.87	(s)	1725–1705
b. Saturated, cyclic:			
6-membered ring (and higher)	5.80–5.87	(s)	1725–1705
5-membered ring	5.71–5.75	(s)	1750–1740
4-membered ring	~5.63	(s)	~1775
c. α,β-Unsaturated, acyclic	5.94–6.01	(s)	1685–1665
d. α,β-Unsaturated, cyclic:			
6-membered ring (and higher)	5.94–6.01	(s)	1685–1665
5-membered ring	5.80–5.85	(s)	1725–1708
e. α,β,α′,β′-Unsaturated, acyclic	5.99–6.01	(s)	1670–1663
f. Aryl	5.88–5.95	(s)	1700–1680
g. Diaryl	5.99–6.02	(s)	1670–1660
h. α-Diketones	5.78–5.85	(s)	1730–1710
i. β-Diketones (enolic)	6.10–6.50	(s)	1640–1540
j. 1,4-Quinones	5.92–6.02	(s)	1690–1660
k. Ketenes	~4.65	(s)	~2150
2. ALDEHYDES			
a. Carbonyl stretching vibrations			
Saturated, aliphatic	5.75–5.81	(s)	1740–1720
α,β-Unsaturated, aliphatic	5.87–5.95	(s)	1705–1680
α,β,γ,δ-Unsaturated, aliphatic	5.95–6.02	(s)	1680–1660
Aryl	5.83–5.90	(s)	1715–1695
b. C—H Stretching vibrations, two bands	3.45–3.55	(w)	2900–2820
	and 3.60–3.70	(w)	2775–2700
3. ESTER STRETCHING VIBRATIONS			
a. Saturated, acyclic	5.71–5.76	(s)	1750–1735
b. Saturated, cyclic:			
δ-lactones (and larger rings)	5.71–5.76	(s)	1750–1735
γ-lactones	5.62–5.68	(s)	1780–1760
β-lactones	~5.5	(s)	~1820

† Abbreviations: s = strong, m = medium, w = weak, v = variable, b = broad, sh = sharp, ~ = approximately

Table 3-1 (cont.)

CHARACTERISTIC INFRARED ABSORPTIONS OF FUNCTIONAL GROUPS

Group	Range μ	Intensity	Range cm^{-1}
c. Unsaturated:			
vinyl ester type	5.56–5.65	(s)	1800–1770
α,β-unsaturated and aryl	5.78–5.82	(s)	1730–1717
α,β-unsaturated δ-lactone	5.78–5.82	(s)	1730–1717
α,β-unsaturated γ-lactone	5.68–5.75	(s)	1760–1740
β,γ-unsaturated γ-lactone	~5.56	(s)	~1800
d. α-Ketoesters	5.70–5.75	(s)	1755–1740
e. β-Ketoesters (enolic)	~6.06	(s)	~1650
f. Carbonates	5.62–5.75	(s)	1780–1740
4. CARBOXYLIC ACIDS			
a. Carbonyl stretching vibrations:			
saturated aliphatic	5.80–5.88	(s)	1725–1700
α,β-unsaturated aliphatic	5.83–5.92	(s)	1715–1690
aryl	5.88–5.95	(s)	1700–1680
b. Hydroxyl stretching (bonded), several bands	3.70–4.00	(w)	2700–2500
c. Carboxylate anion stretching	6.21–6.45	(s)	1610–1550
	and 7.15–7.69	(s)	1400–1300
5. ANHYDRIDE STRETCHING VIBRATIONS			
a. Saturated, acyclic	5.41–5.56	(s)	1850–1800
	and 5.59–5.75	(s)	1790–1740
b. α,β-Unsaturated and aryl, acyclic	5.47–5.62	(s)	1830–1780
	and 5.65–5.81	(s)	1770–1720
c. Saturated, 5-membered ring	5.35–5.49	(s)	1870–1820
	and 5.56–5.71	(s)	1800–1750
d. α,β-Unsaturated, 5-membered ring	5.41–5.56	(s)	1850–1800
	and 5.47–5.62	(s)	1830–1780
6. ACYL HALIDE STRETCHING VIBRATIONS			
a. Acyl fluorides	~5.41	(s)	~1850
b. Acyl chlorides	~5.57	(s)	~1795
c. Acyl bromides	~5.53	(s)	~1810
d. α,β-Unsaturated and aryl	5.61–5.72	(s)	1780–1750
	and 5.72–5.82	(m)	1750–1720
e. COF_2	5.19	(s)	1928
f. $COCl_2$	5.47	(s)	1828
g. $COBr_2$	5.47	(s)	1828
7. AMIDES			
a. Carbonyl stretching vibrations			
Primary, solid and concentrated solution	~6.06	(s)	~1650
Primary, dilute solution	~5.92	(s)	~1690
Secondary, solid and concentrated solution	5.95–6.14	(s)	1680–1630
Secondary, dilute solution	5.88–5.99	(s)	1700–1670
Tertiary, solid and all solutions	5.99–6.14	(s)	1670–1630
Cyclic, δ-lactams, dilute solution	~5.95	(s)	~1680
Cyclic, γ-lactams, dilute solution	~5.88	(s)	~1700

Table 3-1 (cont.)

CHARACTERISTIC INFRARED ABSORPTIONS OF FUNCTIONAL GROUPS†

Group	Range μ	Intensity	Range cm^{-1}
Cyclic, γ-lactams, fused to another ring, dilute solution	5.71–5.88	(s)	1750–1700
Cyclic, β-lactams, dilute solution	5.68–5.78	(s)	1760–1730
Cyclic, β-lactams, fused to another ring, dilute solution	5.62–5.65	(s)	1780–1770
Ureas, acyclic	~6.02	(s)	~1660
Ureas, cyclic, 6-membered ring	~6.10	(s)	~1640
Ureas, cyclic, 5-membered ring	~5.81	(s)	~1720
Urethanes	5.75–5.92	(s)	1740–1690
Imides, acyclic	~5.85	(s)	~1710
	and ~5.88	(s)	~1700
Imides, cyclic, 6-membered ring	~5.85	(s)	~1710
	and ~5.88	(s)	~1700
Imides, cyclic, α,β-unsaturated, 6-membered ring	~5.78	(s)	~1730
	and ~5.99	(s)	~1670
Imides, cyclic, 5-membered ring	~5.65	(s)	~1770
	and ~5.88	(s)	~1700
Imides, cyclic, α,β-unsaturated, 5-membered ring	~5.59	(s)	~1790
	and ~5.85	(s)	~1710
b. N—H Stretching vibrations			
Primary, free; two bands	~2.86	(m)	~3500
	and ~2.94	(m)	~3400
Primary, bonded; two bands	~2.99	(m)	~3350
	and ~3.15	(m)	~3180
Secondary, free; one band	~2.92	(m)	~3430
Secondary, bonded; one band	3.0–3.2	(m)	3320–3140
c. N—H Bending vibrations			
Primary amides, dilute solution	6.17–6.29	(s)	1620–1590
Secondary amides, dilute solution	6.45–6.62	(s)	1550–1510
C. Miscellaneous chromophoric groups			
1. ALCOHOLS AND PHENOLS			
a. O—H Stretching vibrations			
Free O—H	2.74–2.79	(v, sh)	3650–3590
Intermolecularly hydrogen bonded (change on dilution)			
single bridge compounds	2.82–2.90	(v, sh)	3550–3450
polymeric association	2.94–3.13	(s, b)	3400–3200
Intramolecularly hydrogen bonded (no change on dilution)			
single bridge compounds	2.80–2.90	(v, sh)	3570–3450
chelate compounds	3.1–4.0	(w, b)	3200–2500

† Abbreviations: s = strong, m = medium, w = weak, v = variable, b = broad, sh = sharp, ~ = approximately

Table 3-1 (cont.)

CHARACTERISTIC INFRARED ABSORPTIONS OF FUNCTIONAL GROUPS

Group	Range μ	Intensity	Range cm^{-1}
b. O—H Bending and C—O stretching vibrations			
Primary alcohols	~9.5	(s)	~1050
	and 7.4–7.9	(s)	1350–1260
Secondary alcohols	~9.1	(s)	~1100
	and 7.4–7.9	(s)	1350–1260
Tertiary alcohols	~8.7	(s)	~1150
	and 7.1–7.6	(s)	1410–1310
Phenols	~8.3	(s)	~1200
	and 7.1–7.6	(s)	1410–1310
2. AMINES			
a. N—H Stretching vibrations			
Primary, free; two bands	~2.86	(m)	~3500
	and ~2.94	(m)	~3400
Secondary, free; one band	2.86–3.02	(m)	3500–3310
Imines (=N—H); one band	2.94–3.03	(m)	3400–3300
Amine salts	3.2–3.3	(m)	3130–3030
b. N—H Bending vibrations			
Primary	6.06–6.29	(s–m)	1650–1590
Secondary	6.06–6.45	(w)	1650–1550
Amine salts	6.25–6.35	(s)	1600–1575
	and ~6.67	(s)	~1500
c. C—N Vibrations			
Aromatic, primary	7.46–8.00	(s)	1340–1250
Aromatic, secondary	7.41–7.81	(s)	1350–1280
Aromatic, tertiary	7.36–7.64	(s)	1360–1310
Aliphatic	8.2–9.8	(w)	1220–1020
	and ~7.1	(w)	~1410
3. UNSATURATED NITROGEN COMPOUNDS			
a. C≡N Stretching vibrations			
Alkyl nitriles	4.42–4.46	(m)	2260–2240
α,β-Unsaturated alkyl nitriles	4.47–4.51	(m)	2235–2215
Aryl nitriles	4.46–4.50	(m)	2240–2220
Isocyanates	4.40–4.46	(m)	2275–2240
Isocyanides	4.50–4.83	(m)	2220–2070
b. >C=N— Stretching vibrations (imines, oximes)			
Alkyl compounds	5.92–6.10	(v)	1690–1640
α,β-Unsaturated compounds	6.02–6.14	(v)	1660–1630
c. —N=N— Stretching vibrations, azo compounds	6.14–6.35	(v)	1630–1575
d. —N=C=N— Stretching vibrations, diimides	4.64–4.70	(s)	2155–2130
e. $—N_3$ Stretching vibrations, azides	4.63–4.72	(s)	2160–2120
	and 7.46–8.48	(w)	1340–1180

Table 3-1 (cont.)

CHARACTERISTIC INFRARED ABSORPTIONS OF FUNCTIONAL GROUPS†

Group	Range μ	Intensity	Range cm^{-1}
f. C—NO_2, Nitro compounds:			
aromatic	6.37–6.67	(s)	1570–1500
	and 7.30–7.70	(s)	1370–1300
aliphatic	6.37–6.45	(s)	1570–1550
	and 7.25–7.30	(s)	1380–1370
g. O—NO_2, Nitrates	6.06–6.25	(s)	1650–1600
	and 7.70–8.00	(s)	1300–1250
h. C—NO, Nitroso compounds	6.25–6.67	(s)	1600–1500
i. O—NO, Nitrites	5.95–6.06	(s)	1680–1650
	and 6.15–6.21	(s)	1625–1610
4. HALOGEN COMPOUNDS, C—X STRETCHING VIBRATIONS			
a. C—F	7.1–10.0	(s)	1400–1000
b. C—Cl	12.5–16.6	(s)	800–600
c. C—Br	16.6–20.0	(s)	600–500
d. C—I	~20	(s)	~500
5. SULFUR COMPOUNDS			
a. S—H Stretching vibrations	3.85–3.92	(w)	2600–2550
b. C=S Stretching vibrations	8.33–9.52	(s)	1200–1050
c. S=O Stretching vibrations:			
sulfoxides	9.35–9.71	(s)	1070–1030
sulfones	8.62–8.77	(s)	1160–1140
	and 7.41–7.69	(s)	1350–1300
sulfites	8.13–8.70	(s)	1230–1150
	and 7.00–7.41	(s)	1430–1350
sulfonyl chlorides	8.44–8.59	(s)	1185–1165
	and 7.30–7.46	(s)	1370–1340
sulfonamides	8.48–8.77	(s)	1180–1140
	and 7.41–7.69	(s)	1350–1300
sulfonic acids	8.27–8.70	(s)	1210–1150
	9.43–9.71	(s)	1060–1030
	and ~15.4	(s)	~650

† Abbreviations: s = strong, m = medium, w = weak, v = variable, b = broad, sh = sharp, ~ = approximately

absorptions in terms of wavelengths or wave numbers. The remainder of this section is devoted to an examination of a number of infrared spectra. Significant structural features and absorptions are indicated.

The infrared spectrum of nujol (Fig. 3-3), a mixture of saturated hydrocarbons, contains absorptions resulting from vibrations typical of groups that are present in such molecules, i.e., C—H stretching (~3.39 and ~3.54 μ, ~2950 and ~2820 cm^{-1}), —CH_2— bending (~6.86 μ, ~1458 cm^{-1}), and C—CH_3 bending (~6.86 and 7.28 μ, ~1458 and

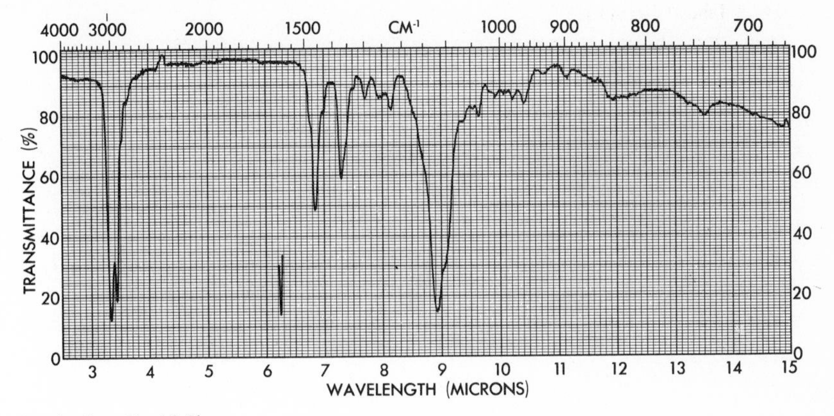

Fig. 3-9 Di-*n*-butyl ether, liquid film.

~1380 cm^{-1}). Weak absorption near 13.85 μ (722 cm^{-1}) is caused by bending vibrations of the group $-(CH_2)_n-$, where $n \geq 4$.

Simple replacement of a methylene group of a saturated hydrocarbon by an oxygen atom causes the appearance of absorption caused by strong C—O stretching vibrations near 9 μ (~1110 cm^{-1}). This is shown by the spectrum of di-*n*-butyl ether (Fig. 3-9). When a hydrogen atom of a hydrocarbon is exchanged for a hydroxyl group, the spectrum changes in a very predictable way; it now shows absorptions owing to O—H and C—O stretching vibrations in addition to the hydrocarbon chromophoric groups present. The spectrum of lauryl alcohol, $CH_3-(CH_2)_{10}-CH_2OH$, Fig. 3-10, is an example; absorption owing to O—H stretching vibration is present at ~2.9 μ (~3448 cm^{-1}) as a strong absorption typical of the polymeric association of hydroxyl groups. Absorption centered at ~9.5 μ (~1053 cm^{-1}) is typical of the C—O stretching vibration of a primary alcohol. The spectrum of isoborneol (Fig. 3-11), determined in carbon

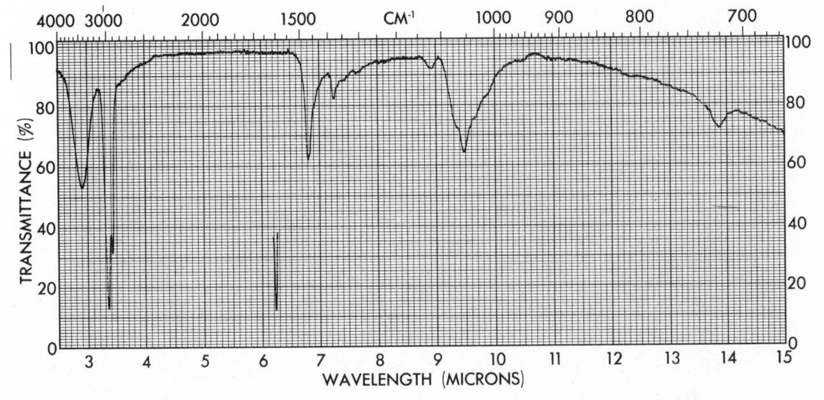

Fig. 3-10 Lauryl alcohol, liquid film.

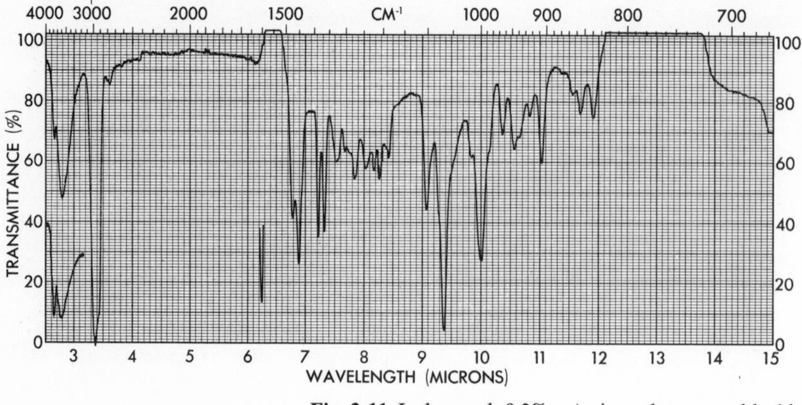

Fig. 3-11 Isoborneol, 8.2% w/w in carbon tetrachloride, 0.1 mm path; 2.5–3.2 μ insert, 1.5% w/w in carbon tetrachloride, 0.5 mm path.

tetrachloride solution (8.2% w/w, 0.1 mm cells), shows absorption resulting from the presence of both free O—H stretching (2.64 μ, 3788 cm^{-1}) and bonded O—H stretching (2.80 μ, 3571 cm^{-1}). In the case of polymeric association, the degree of association changes on dilution; a larger fraction of unassociated groups is present in more dilute solutions. The 2.5–3.2 μ insert in Fig. 3-11 (isoborneol, 1.5% w/w in carbon tetrachloride, 0.5 mm cells) shows this effect. The spectrum of the more dilute solution indicates relatively more free hydroxyl. The spectrum of isoborneol shows a complexity in the 7.5–12 μ (1333–833 cm^{-1}) region typical of the many stretching and bending vibrations present in organic compounds. Since isoborneol contains a *gem*-dimethyl group [$(CH_3)_2C\langle$], its spectrum displays a sharp doublet at 7.22 and 7.32 μ (1385 and 1366 cm^{-1}) resulting from symmetric and asymmetric C—CH_3 stretching vibrations. This absorption is quite characteristic of compounds containing the *gem*-dimethyl group.

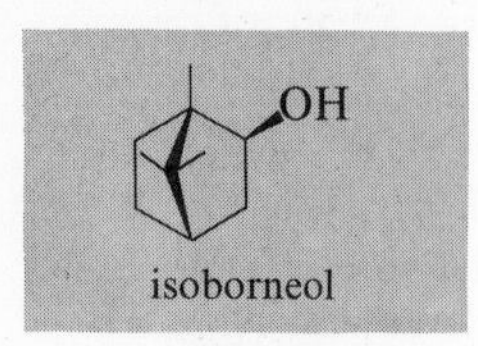

If a compound contains a carbonyl group, the absorption caused by C=O stretching is generally among the strongest present. If the nature of the carbonyl group can be established by classical chemical tests or by other infrared absorptions present, a great deal of structural information can be derived from the exact position of the carbonyl stretching absorption peak.

Carbonyl groups of ketones generally absorb in the region 5.7–6.0 μ (1754–1667 cm^{-1}); the position of absorption is sensitive to ring size and to the degree of conjugated unsaturation, among other factors. The carbonyl groups of cyclohexanones generally absorb at the same position as the carbonyl groups of saturated aliphatic ketones: cyclohexanone, Fig.

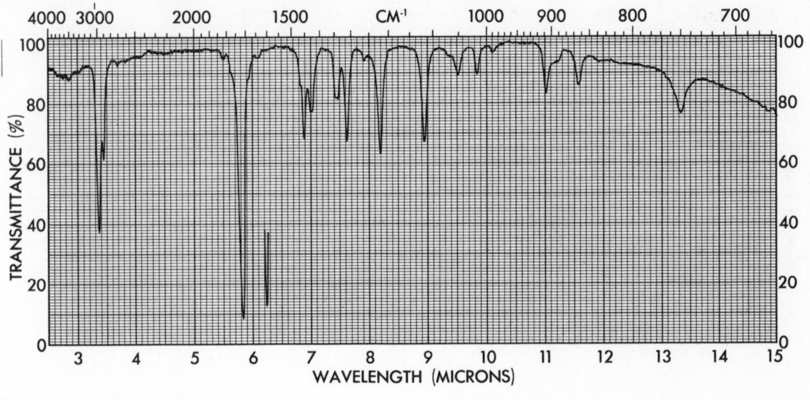

Fig. 3-12 Cyclohexanone, liquid film.

3-12, 5.83 μ (1715 cm^{-1}); 3-octanone, 5.82 μ (1718 cm^{-1}). The carbonyl absorption of a cyclopentanone is shifted about 0.1 μ to shorter wavelength (~30 cm^{-1} to higher wave number) when compared with the acyclic aliphatic analogue: cyclopentanone, Fig. 3-13, 5.71 μ (1751 cm^{-1}). The carbonyl absorption of an α,β-unsaturated ketone or an aryl ketone is shifted about 0.1 μ to longer wavelength (~30 cm^{-1} to lower wave number) when compared with the saturated analogue: acetophenone, Fig. 3-14, 5.92 μ (1689 cm^{-1}). The effects of ring size and conjugated unsaturation appear to be additive; thus the absorption resulting from carbonyl stretching vibrations of cyclohexanone and 2-cyclopentenone are at about the same position. A halogen on a carbon atom α- to the ketone function shortens the wavelength (raises the wave number) of C=O stretching absorption by about 0.07 μ (~20 cm^{-1}). This α-halogen effect is observed only if the C—*X* bond can become coplanar with the C=O bond. Thus, α,α-dihalogen compounds show only the effect of an α-halogen com-

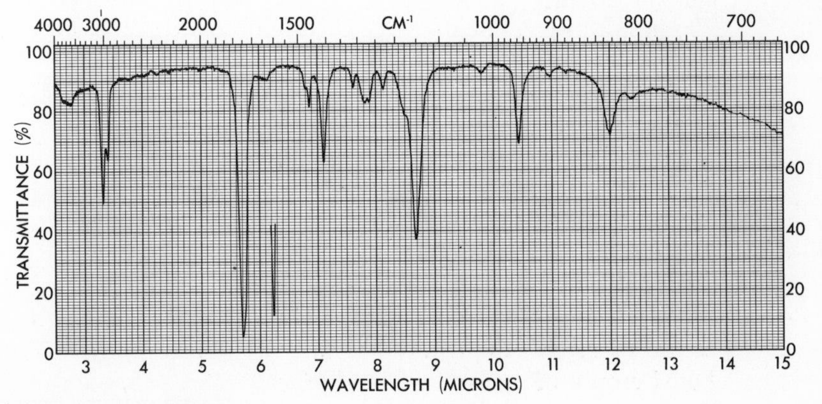

Fig. 3-13 Cyclopentanone, liquid film.

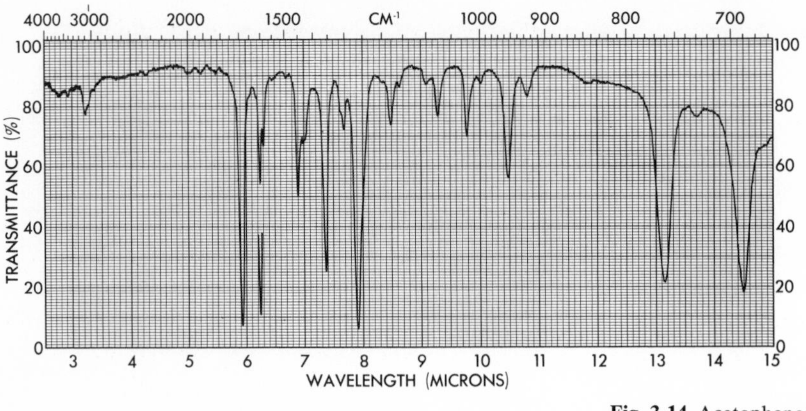

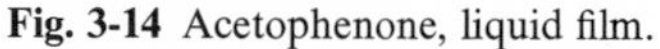
Fig. 3-14 Acetophenone, liquid film.

pound, α,α'-dihalogen compounds show twice the effect, and equatorial, but not axial, halogen groups in rigid cyclohexane systems show the effect.

The absorption owing to the carbonyl stretching vibration of aldehydes appears in the same general region as that of ketones. The absorption is also shifted to longer wavelength (lower wave number), when compared with the saturated analogue, if conjugated with an unsaturated linkage. The other striking characteristic of the aldehyde functional group absorption is the presence of two weak bands owing to C—H stretching vibrations. The wavelength of this absorption is increased (the wave number is lowered) from the normal C—H stretching position near 3.4 μ ($\sim$2940 cm^{-1}) to about 3.55 and 3.68 μ ($\sim$2820 and 2720 cm^{-1}). The presence of two absorption bands in this region is due to the symmetric and asymmetric stretching modes of the C—H bond with the C=O bond. Frequently the peak at shorter wavelength (higher wave number) is not readily observed, because it may be obscured by strong absorptions owing

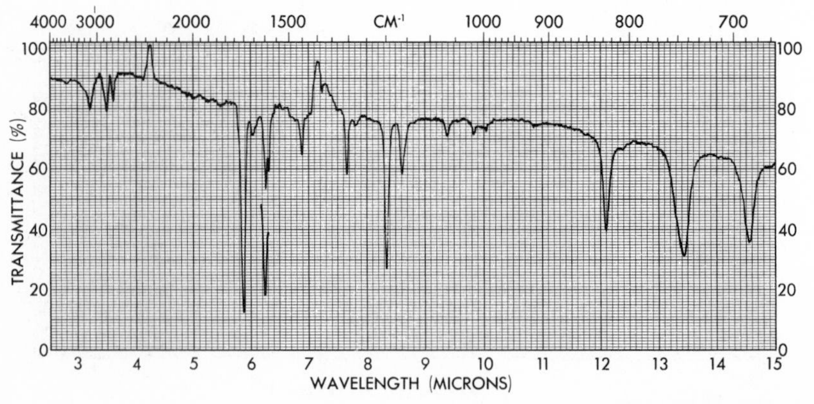

Fig. 3-15 Benzaldehyde, liquid film.

to C—H stretching vibrations in other parts of the molecule. These aldehyde absorptions are shown in the spectrum of benzaldehyde (Fig. 3-15): 3.52 and 3.62 μ (2841 and 2762 cm^{-1}). In this case both bands are easily seen because the molecule has no aliphatic C—H stretching vibration; the absorptions owing to aromatic C—H stretching vibrations occur near 3.24 μ ($\sim$3086 cm^{-1}). The absorption owing to carbonyl stretching vibration of benzaldehyde is seen to be at 5.89 μ (1698 cm^{-1}).

The position of absorption of the carbonyl stretching vibration of esters and lactones is dependent, as with ketones, on conjugated unsaturation and ring size. The position of absorption of normal aliphatic esters (methyl phenylacetate, Fig. 3-16, 5.73 μ, 1745 cm^{-1}) shows that there is an electrical effect operative in the change from the ketone $—CH_2—C(=O)—CH_2—$ to the ester $—CH_2—C(=O)—O—$ which shortens the wavelength of absorption about 0.1 μ (raises the wave number $\sim$30 cm^{-1}) owing to the exchange of a $—CH_2—$ group for the more electronegative oxygen group. The carbonyl absorption of an α,β-unsaturated or aryl ester is shifted about 0.1 μ to longer wavelength ($\sim$30 cm^{-1} to lower wave number) when compared with the saturated analogue; an example is ethyl benzoate, Fig. 3-17, 5.79 μ (1727 cm^{-1}). It is readily seen that the two isomeric esters, methyl phenylacetate (Fig. 3-16) and ethyl benzoate (Fig. 3-17), are distinguished by the different positions of their carbonyl stretching absorptions, as well as by many differences in the fingerprint region. As with ketones, when the carbonyl group of an ester is present in a five-membered ring, absorption owing to the stretching vibration occurs at $\sim$0.1 μ shorter wavelength ($\sim$30 cm^{-1} higher wave number): butyrolactone, Fig. 3-18, 5.63 μ (1776 cm^{-1}). The infrared spectrum of a β-ketoester that exists as

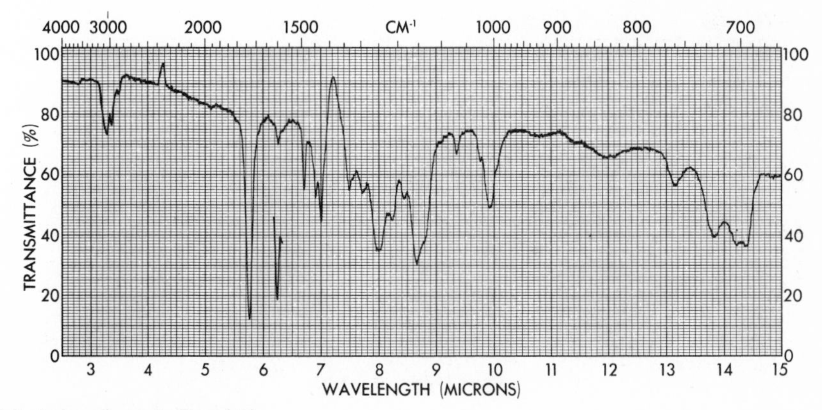

Fig. 3-16 Methyl phenylacetate, liquid film.

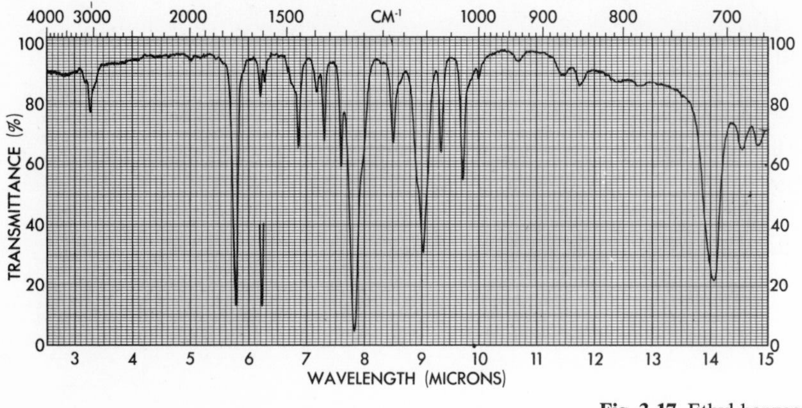

Fig. 3-17 Ethyl benzoate, liquid film.

an equilibrium mixture of keto and enol forms shows absorptions due to both forms. The spectrum of ethyl acetoacetate (Fig. 3-19), which contains 92% of the keto form at equilibrium as the neat liquid, shows keto (5.80 μ, 1724 cm^{-1}) and ester (5.72 μ, 1748 cm^{-1}) carbonyl stretching vibrations, as well as a band attributed to the β-hydroxy-α,β-unsaturated ester carbonyl (6.06 μ, 1650 cm^{-1}) of the enol form that is hydrogen bonded to the enolic hydroxyl group.

The absorption owing to the carbonyl stretching vibration of a saturated carboxylic acid (nonanoic acid, Fig. 3-20, 5.83 μ, 1715 cm^{-1}) is shifted to longer wavelength (lower wave number) if conjugated with an unsaturated group (benzoic acid, Fig. 3-21, 5.88 μ, 1701 cm^{-1}). As ordinarily determined (solid or fairly concentrated solution), the carbonyl absorption observed for carboxylic acids is that resulting from vibrations of the dimeric form. On extensive dilution with an inert solvent, two carbonyl absorptions may be observed, one resulting from the presence

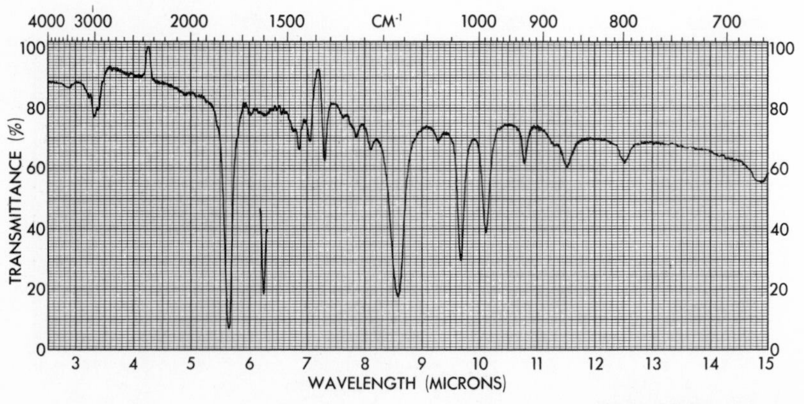

Fig. 3-18 Butyrolactone, liquid film.

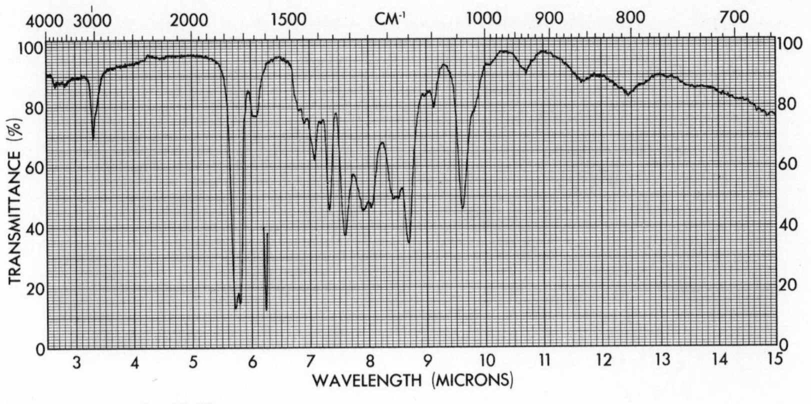

Fig. 3-19 Ethyl acetoacetate, liquid film.

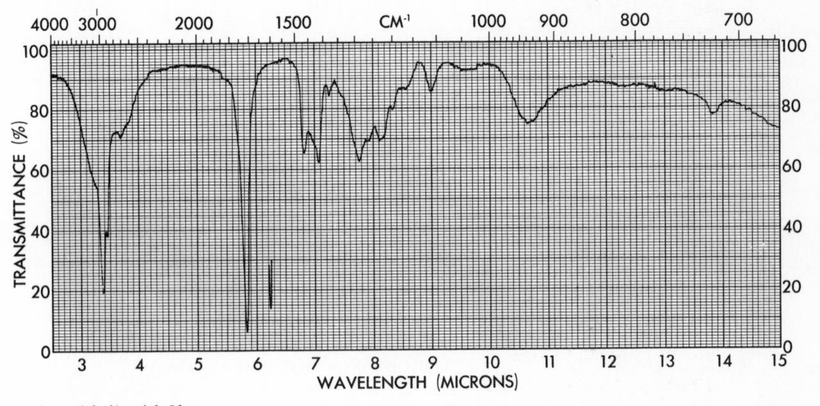

Fig. 3-20 Nonanoic acid, liquid film.

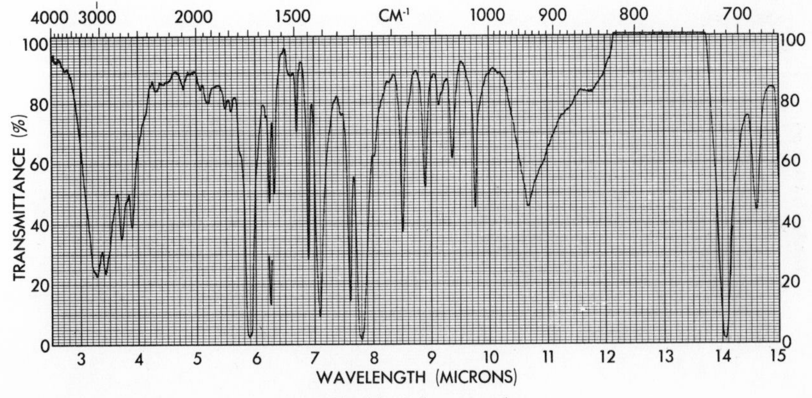

Fig. 3-21 Benzoic acid, 3.1% w/w in carbon tetrachloride, 0.1 mm path.

of the monomer and the other resulting from the presence of the dimer; these are reported to absorb near 5.68 μ (1761 cm^{-1}) and 5.82 μ (1718 cm^{-1}), respectively. In very dilute solution, absorption caused by free O—H stretching is observed in the region near 2.8 μ (~3570 cm^{-1}); absorption owing to bonded O—H stretching, such as that which is present in the dimeric species, absorbs in the region 3.7–4.0 μ (~2700–2500 cm^{-1}). This latter absorption is usually diagnostic of the carboxylic acid functional group and may be seen in the spectra of nonanoic acid and benzoic acid (Figs. 3-20 and 3-21). Salts of carboxylic acids do not show absorption in the region 5.8–6.0 μ (1724–1667 cm^{-1}). Instead, two absorptions, near 6.33 and 7.36 μ (~1580 and ~1359 cm^{-1}), are observed that are caused by the symmetric and asymmetric >C═O stretching vibrations of the resonance stabilized carboxylate anion group. An example of this is seen in the spectrum of *L*-aspartic acid (α-aminosuccinic acid, Fig. 3-22). This compound shows absorptions owing to the free carboxylic acid group at 5.94 μ (1684 cm^{-1}) and 3.6–4.0 μ (2778–2500 cm^{-1}) and absorptions owing to the carboxylic anion at 6.26 μ and 7.30 μ (1597 and 1370 cm^{-1}).

Carboxylic acid anhydrides all show two absorption bands in the region 5.35–5.75 μ (1870–1740 cm^{-1}). The absorption at shorter wavelength (higher wave number) is usually the more intense; the positions of the bands depend, as is the case with cyclic ketones and lactones, on the ring size of the anhydride as well as on the presence of conjugated unsaturation. An example is seen in acetic anhydride (Fig. 3-23, 5.46 and 5.68 μ, 1832 and 1761 cm^{-1}). A relatively intense and diagnostic absorption owing to a C—O stretching vibration is always present in the regions 8.5–9.5 μ (~1175–1050 cm^{-1}) for acyclic anhydrides and 7.7–8.3 μ (~1300–1200 cm^{-1}) for cyclic anhydrides.

All amides show strong absorption owing to carbonyl stretching

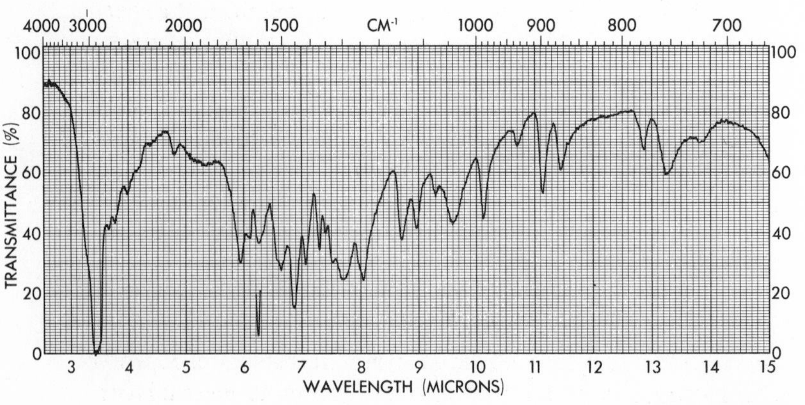

Fig. 3-22 Aspartic acid, nujol mull.

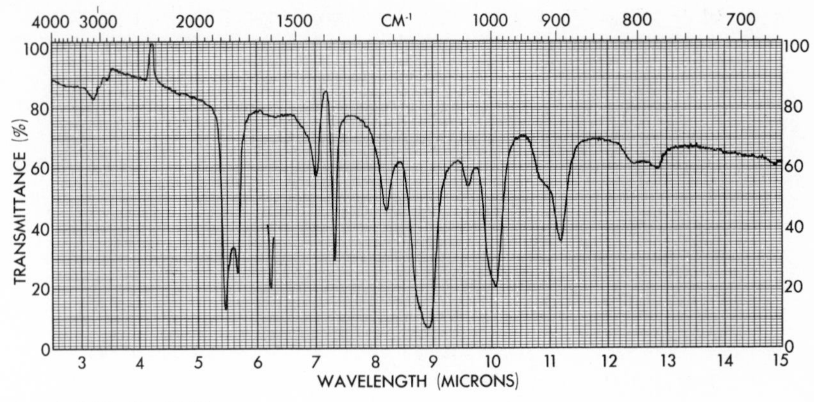

Fig. 3-23 Acetic anhydride, liquid film.

vibrations in the region 5.60–6.15 μ (1786–1626 cm^{-1}). The absorption owing to the carbonyl stretching vibration of amides is very markedly dependent upon the method of determination. *N*-Methylacetamide is reported to absorb at 5.82 μ (1718 cm^{-1}) in the vapor state, at 5.88 μ (1701 cm^{-1}) in dilute chloroform solution, and at 6.06 μ (1650 cm^{-1}) as the pure liquid; only one absorption band resulting from C=O stretching vibrations is present, but its position is clearly concentration dependent. This variation is due to the degree of hydrogen bonding present, which is maximum in the solid state (as, for example, when determined as a mull) or as the pure liquid. The carbonyl absorptions of tertiary amides, which contain no N—H group, do not show nearly as marked a shift with concentration; this indicates, as would be anticipated, that hydrogen bonding is not so important in these compounds as in primary and secondary amides. Absorptions resulting from N—H stretching vibrations of primary and secondary amides are in the 2.8–3.2 μ (~3570–3125 cm^{-1}) region. The complexity observed in this region is dependent on the method of determination and the degree of hydrogen bonding present. If the spectrum is determined in reasonably dilute solution, the number of peaks found in this region provides valuable structural information. The spectra of primary amides show two sharp peaks in the region 2.85–2.95 μ (3509–3390 cm^{-1}) owing to symmetric and asymmetric N—H stretching vibrations. Secondary amides show only one absorption in this region, and tertiary amides show none. The spectrum of *o*-methoxyacetanilide (Fig. 3-24) shows carbonyl stretching at 5.88 μ (1701 cm^{-1}) and N—H stretching at 2.83 μ (3534 cm^{-1}).

The most characteristic absorption of amines is that owing to N—H stretching vibrations in the region 2.8–3.0 μ (~3570–3333 cm^{-1}). As with alcohols and amides, the complexity of the spectrum in this region depends on the degree of hydrogen bonding. In dilute solution in an inert solvent, the spectra of primary amines have two sharp bands in this region, owing

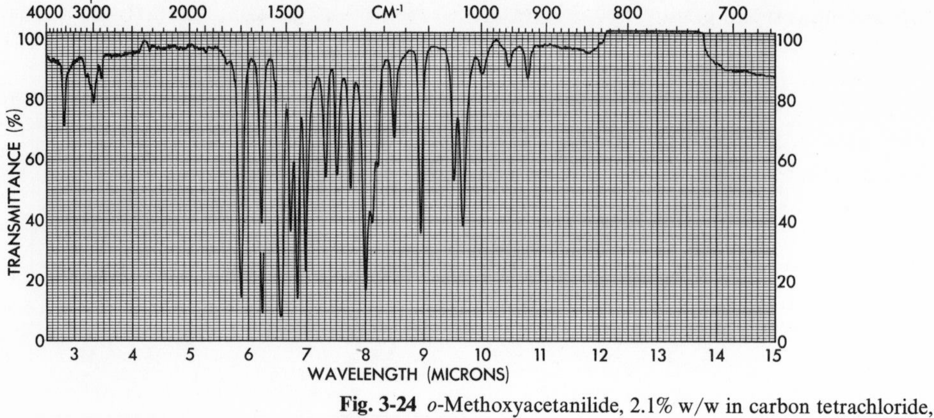

Fig. 3-24 *o*-Methoxyacetanilide, 2.1% w/w in carbon tetrachloride, 0.1 mm path.

to symmetric and asymmetric N—H stretching vibrations; the spectra of secondary amines have only one band in this region, and tertiary amines do not absorb in this region. Aliphatic amines tend to hydrogen-bond much more effectively than aromatic amines, since they are stronger bases; consequently, their absorption in this region is broad unless determined as very dilute solutions. The spectrum of *o*-methoxyaniline (Fig. 3-25) shows absorption caused by free N—H stretching vibrations at 2.78 and 2.86 μ (3597 and 3497 cm^{-1}). It is interesting to note the very remarkable changes, especially in the fingerprint region, that are brought about in the infrared spectrum by simple acetylation of *o*-methoxyaniline (Fig. 3-25), which yields *o*-methoxyacetanilide (Fig. 3-24). Amine salts, $-\overset{|}{\underset{|}{N}}{}^{\pm}-H$, show absorption owing to N—H stretching vibrations in the region near 3.25 μ ($\sim$3077 cm^{-1}) and absorption owing to N—H bending vibrations at 6.03–6.22 μ (1658–1608 cm^{-1}) and 6.45–6.74 μ (1550–1484 cm^{-1}). Absorptions owing to the N—H bending vibrations of the substi-

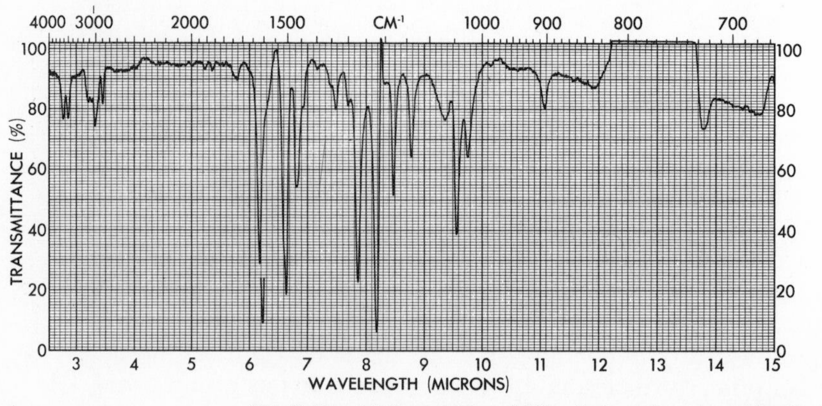

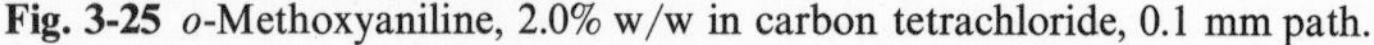
Fig. 3-25 *o*-Methoxyaniline, 2.0% w/w in carbon tetrachloride, 0.1 mm path.

tuted ammonium group of aspartic acid (Fig. 3-22) occur at 6.10 μ (1639 cm^{-1}) and at 6.64 μ (1506 cm^{-1}).

The molar extinction coefficient of an infrared absorption band can be measured accurately only when the spectrum is determined by using a solution of known composition in a cell of precisely known path length. Because the path length of the cell is usually not accurately known, the extinction coefficients are not usually measured, as is the case in ultraviolet spectroscopy. It has been indicated that the intensity of a given absorption is dependent upon the change in the dipole moment of the molecule that a given vibration causes. Within a given group of substances containing the same functional group, there will be variations in the magnitude of the extinction coefficient. Some average values of the extinction coefficients (ε) for the absorption owing to the stretching vibrations of certain functional groups are ketone and aldehyde C═O (500), ester C═O (800), carboxylic acid and amide C═O (1,300), alkane C—H (50), and free alcohol O—H (70).

The extinction coefficient for C═C stretching vibrations of alkenes is 10–300 times less than that of ketones. The extinction coefficients for mono- and *gem*-disubstituted ($>C{=}CH_2$) olefins ($\varepsilon \sim 40$) are larger than those for other olefin types ($\varepsilon \sim 5$). As a consequence of the weak intensity of the C═C stretching vibration absorption, concentrated solutions of the olefins should be used; the absorptions occur in the 5.95–6.17 (~1680–1620 cm^{-1}) region. The absorptions are more intense if the olefinic bond is conjugated with some unsaturated group. The spectrum of limonene (Fig. 3-26) contains several absorptions worthy of comment. The absorption at 6.08 μ (1645 cm^{-1}) is due to the *gem*-disubstituted C═C stretching vibration; that due to the trisubstituted olefin at 5.97 μ (1675 cm^{-1}) appears as only a small shoulder. Absorption owing to olefinic C—H stretching vibration is observed as a small peak at 3.19 μ (3135 cm^{-1}) near the larger alkane C—H stretching vibration absorption.

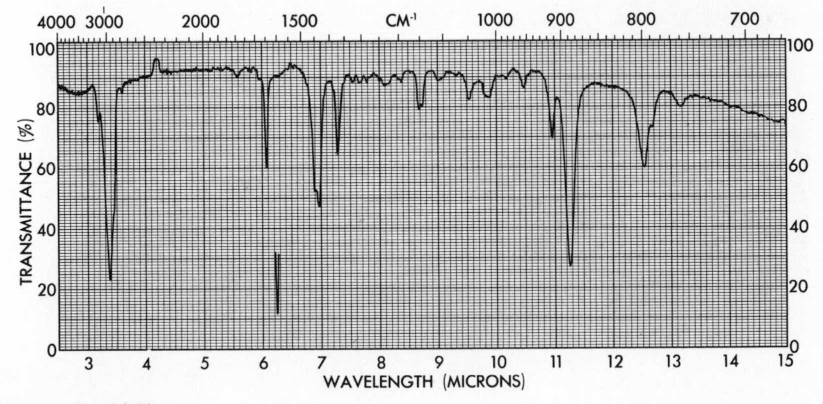

Fig. 3-26 Limonene, liquid film.

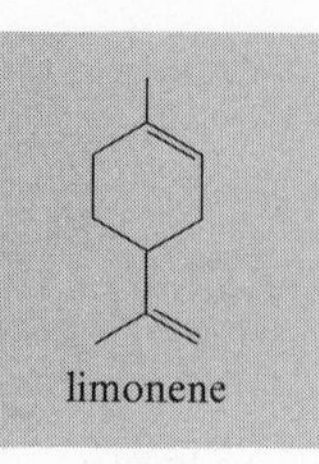

Absorptions owing to bending vibrations of olefinic C—H groups are more intense than those caused by C=C stretching vibrations and may be used to determine the number and nature of substituent groups present. Absorption of limonene at 11.27 μ (887 cm^{-1}) is caused by the C—H bending vibration of the *gem*-disubstituted olefinic group, and absorption at 12.53 μ (798 cm^{-1}) is caused by the C—H bending vibration of the trisubstituted olefinic group. *Cis* and *trans* olefins may be distinguished by examining this region of the spectrum. Tetrasubstituted olefinic groups are difficult to detect, because absorption caused by the C=C stretching vibration is very weak, and they show no C—H stretching or bending vibrations.

Absorptions resulting from the C≡C stretching vibrations of acetylenic compounds occur in the region 4.4–4.8 μ (~2275–2085 cm^{-1}). The absorption is weak, especially if the acetylenic linkage is nonterminal. The stretching vibration results only in a linear expansion and contraction of the molecule, and hence the dipole moment is not much affected. Absorption caused by the acetylenic C—H stretching vibration occurs as a fairly strong, sharp band near 3.0 μ (~3333 cm^{-1}). The spectrum of phenylacetylene (Fig. 3-27) shows C≡C stretching at 4.72 μ (2119 cm^{-1}), acetylenic C—H stretching at 3.02 μ (3311 cm^{-1}), and aromatic C—H stretching at 3.24 μ (3086 cm^{-1}).

The absorption caused by the stretching vibration of the triple bond of nitriles occurs in about the same region as that of acetylenes, but the absorption is much more intense. This absorption of benzonitrile (Fig. 3-28) appears at 4.44 μ (2252 cm^{-1}). The remarkable similarity in the spectra of benzonitrile (Fig. 3-28) and phenylacetylene (Fig. 3-27) is to be anticipated, as the molecules differ only by the interchange of ≡N and ≡C—H groups.

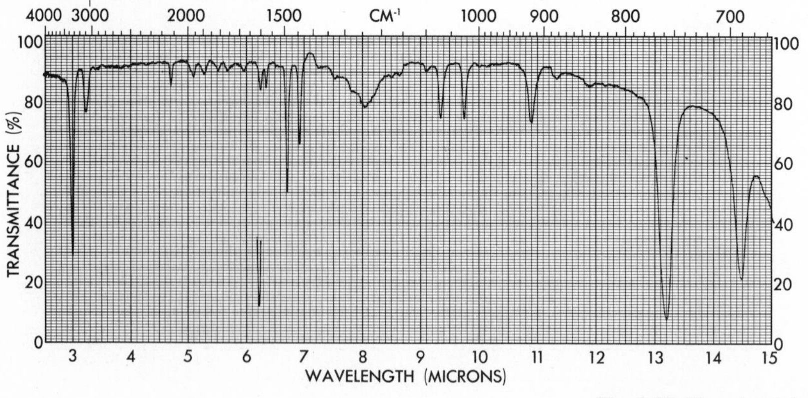

Fig. 3-27 Phenylacetylene, liquid film.

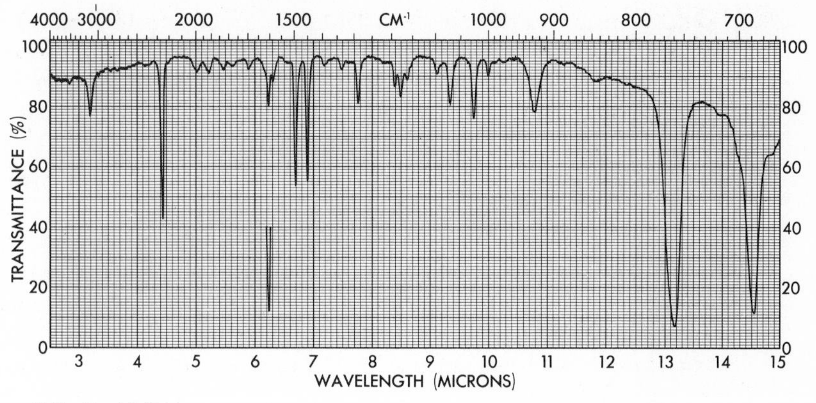

Fig. 3-28 Benzonitrile, liquid film.

Aromatic compounds show characteristic absorptions in several regions of the spectrum. Absorptions owing to the C—H stretching vibrations of aromatic compounds occur near 3.3 μ ($\sim$3030 cm^{-1}).

There are four absorption bands in the 6–7 μ (1667–1429 cm^{-1}) region that are particularly diagnostic of aromatic structure. These occur near 6.25, 6.32, 6.67, and 6.90 μ ($\sim$1600, 1580, 1500, and 1450 cm^{-1}) and are caused by C=C skeletal in-plane vibrations. The second band is frequently observed only as a shoulder of the first, but is intensified if the aromatic nucleus is conjugated with some unsaturated group; the fourth band is frequently obscured by strong absorptions resulting from $—CH_2—$ bending vibrations if aliphatic groups are present. These bands are observable in the spectra of polystyrene (Fig. 3-2), benzoic acid (Fig. 3-21), phenylacetylene (Fig. 3-27), benzonitrile (Fig. 3-28), and biphenyl (Fig. 3-29), among others. The absence of absorption by a compound in these regions is fair assurance that the compound is not aromatic.

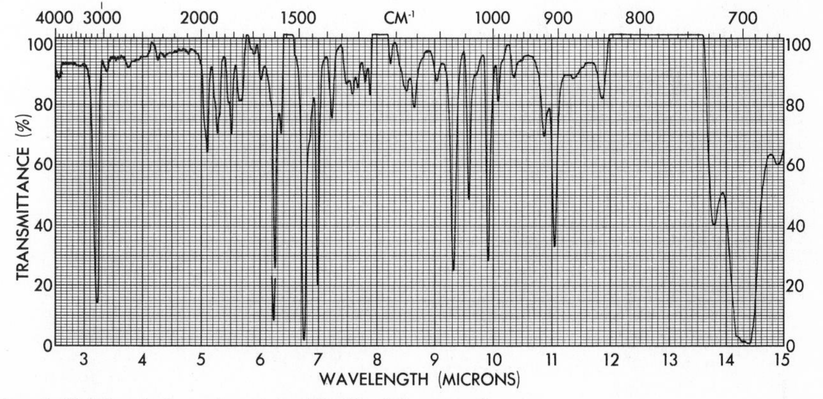

Fig. 3-29 Biphenyl, 20.2% w/w in carbon tetrachloride, 0.1 mm path.

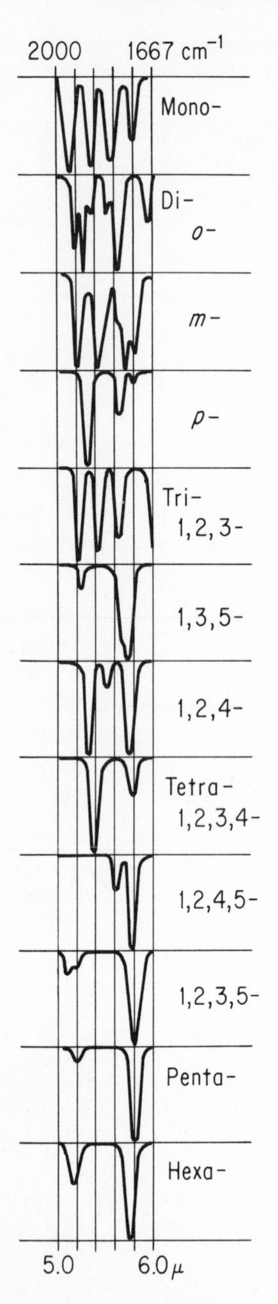

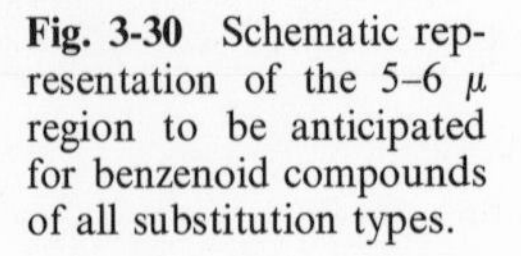

Fig. 3-30 Schematic representation of the 5–6 μ region to be anticipated for benzenoid compounds of all substitution types.

A number of absorption bands of variable intensity appear in the 10–15 μ (1000–670 cm^{-1}) region that are caused by C—H bending vibrations. These absorptions depend on the number of adjacent free hydrogen atoms that an aromatic nucleus contains. An aromatic compound containing five adjacent hydrogen atoms absorbs strongly in both the 13.3 and 14.3 μ regions (~750 and 700 cm^{-1}); if the compound contains four adjacent hydrogen atoms, as, for example, an *o*-disubstituted benzene, it absorbs strongly only near 13.3 μ (~750 cm^{-1}). The remaining absorptions owing to fewer adjacent hydrogen atoms (higher degree of substitution on the aromatic nucleus) are usually weak and not easily assigned. Of particular importance for benzene compounds is the absorption near 14.3 μ (~700 cm^{-1}); if the compound does not absorb strongly in this region, it cannot be a monosubstituted benzene compound. The spectra of biphenyl (Fig. 3-29) and other monosubstituted benzene compounds show these absorptions.

The region 5–6 μ (2000–1670 cm^{-1}) of the spectra of benzenoid compounds contains absorption bands of low intensity that are overtone or combination bands. The number and relative position of these bands are remarkably dependent upon the particular substitution type of the benzene ring. The general pattern of bands to be expected for the various substitution types is shown diagrammatically in Fig. 3-30. As these bands have low intensity, relatively concentrated solutions must be used to observe them adequately. If it is properly analyzed and if no interfering absorption is present (for example, a carbonyl group), this region provides one of the most reliable means of determining the substitution pattern on the benzene ring. These bands are seen in the spectra of biphenyl (Fig. 3-29) and polystyrene (Fig. 3-2), among others.

3.5 PROBLEMS

1. Compound **1** was obtained as a crystalline solid, m.p. 93–94°, b.p. 223°/746 mm, and was found to contain C, H, N, and Cl. Analytical data were obtained (61.1% C, 2.9% H, and 10.2% N) and the infrared spectrum was determined (Fig. 3-31). Deduce the structure of the compound.

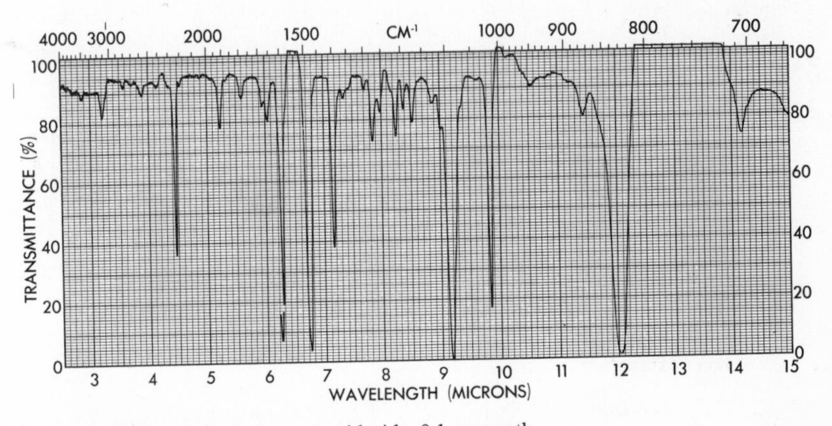

Fig. 3-31 Compound **1**, 9.9% w/w in carbon tetrachloride, 0.1 mm path.

2. Compound **2** (infrared spectrum, Fig. 3-32), on heating with dilute aqueous mineral acid gave ethyl alcohol, acetic acid, carbon dioxide, and ammonia in equimolar amounts. Deduce the structure of the compound.

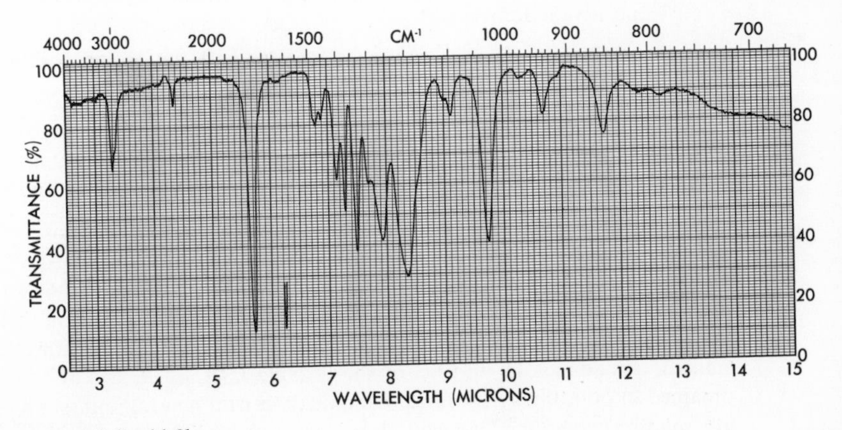

Fig. 3-32 Compound **2**, liquid film.

3. Compound **3a** (infrared spectrum, Fig. 3-33), $C_6H_{10}O$, $[\alpha]_D$ +17°, on reduction (hydrogen, platinum, ethanol), gave compound **3b,** $C_6H_{14}O$, $[\alpha]_D$ 0°. Deduce the structures of compounds **3a** and **3b.**

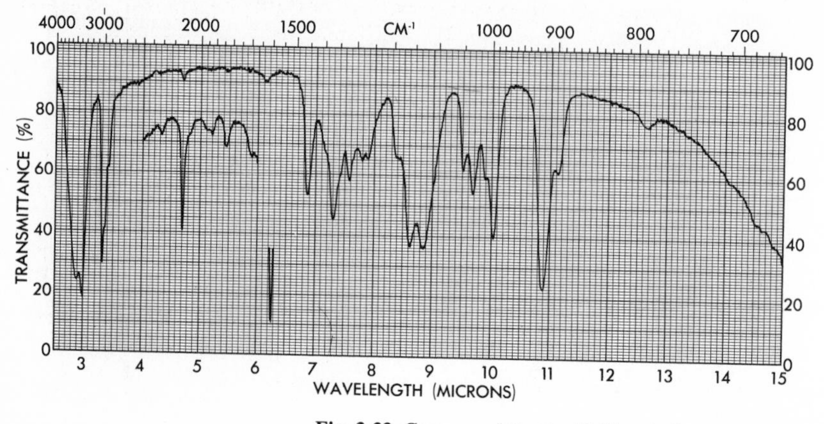

Fig. 3-33 Compound **3a,** liquid film; 4–6 μ insert, 0.025 mm thickness.

4. Give structural formulas of compounds that are consistent with the following sets of data:

a. Compound **4a,** $C_6H_{10}O$, λ_{max}^{EtOH} 228 mμ, ε 7,900, λ_{max} 5.95 μ (1681 cm^{-1}), negative iodoform test.

b. Compound **4b,** $C_{13}H_{20}O$, λ_{max}^{EtOH} 255 mμ, ε 11,400, λ_{max} 5.95 μ (1681 cm^{-1}), 0.0 C—CH_3 determination.

c. Compound **4c,** $C_7H_{10}O$, λ_{max}^{EtOH} 227 mμ, ε 8,400, λ_{max} 5.84 μ (1712 cm^{-1}), 1.5 C—CH_3 determination.

d. Compound **4d,** $C_6H_8O_2$, λ_{max} 5.82 μ (1718 cm^{-1}), $[\alpha]_D$ 64°, 0.0 active hydrogen determination.

e. Compound **4e,** $C_8H_{12}O$, λ_{max}^{EtOH} 239 mμ, ε 9,400, λ_{max} 5.93 μ (1686 cm^{-1}), positive iodoform test.

f. Compound **4f,** $C_9H_{14}O$, λ_{max} 5.72 μ (1748 cm^{-1}), no reaction with hot alkaline permanganate solution.

5. Compound **5a,** $C_{13}H_{12}O$ (infrared spectrum, Fig. 3-34), on oxidation with chromium oxide in acetic acid gave compound **5b** (infrared spectrum, Fig. 3-35) as the only organic product. Deduce the structures of compounds **5a** and **5b.**

6. Compound **6a,** $C_{10}H_{16}O$, may be isolated from oils derived from plants of the *Labiatae* family; its infrared spectrum is given as Fig. 3-36. It showed λ_{max}^{EtOH} 253 mμ, ε 8,150 and λ_{max}^{EtOH} 316 mμ, ε 85; it had $[\alpha]_D$ + 21°. When compound **6a** was subjected to the action of sodium borohydride, then warm phosphoric acid, and then hydrogen in the presence of platinum and acetic acid, there resulted a mixture of two substances, compounds **6b** and **6c,** of the formula $C_{10}H_{20}$, neither of which could be obtained in optically active form. On oxidation with neutral potassium permanganate solution, compound **6a** was degraded, and gave acetone and an acidic substance, compound **6d,** $C_7H_{12}O_4$, N.E. 80 ± 3, $[\alpha]_D$ +57°, 0.67 C—CH_3 determination. Derive structural formulas for compounds **6a** through **6d.**

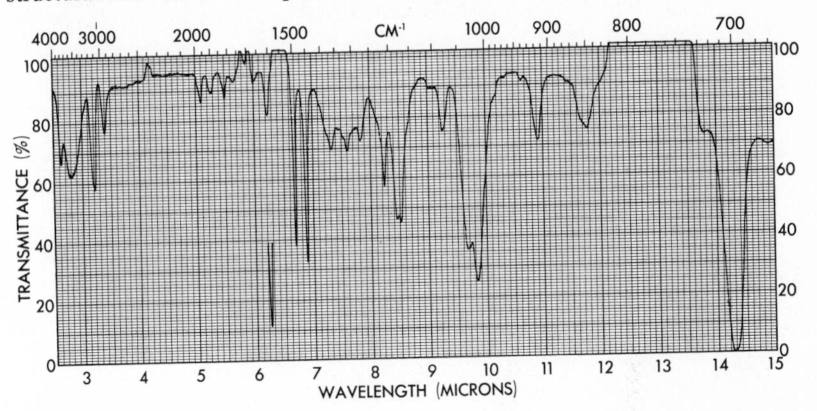

Fig. 3-34 Compound **5a,** 5.0% w/w in carbon tetrachloride, 0.1 mm path.

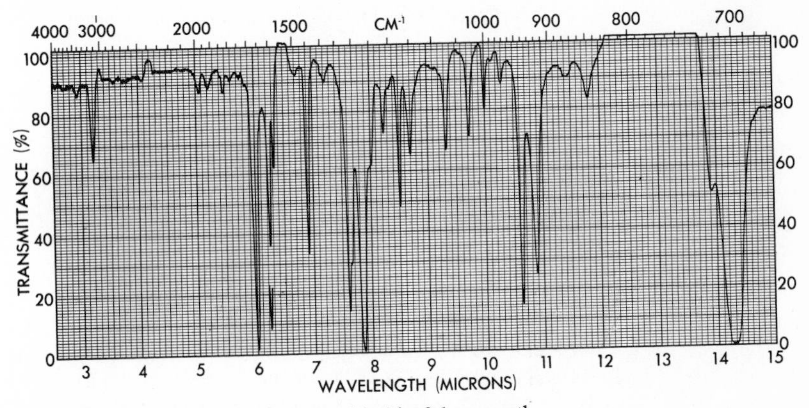

Fig. 3-35 Compound **5b,** 4.9% w/w in carbon tetrachloride, 0.1 mm path.

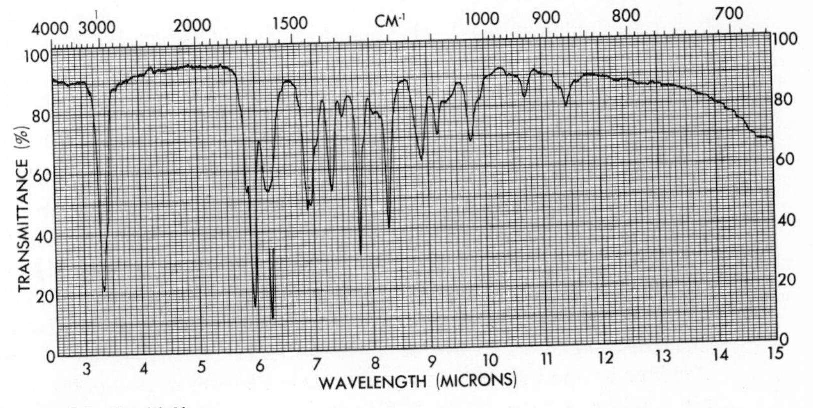

Fig. 3-36 Compound **6a,** liquid film.

7. By chromatographic fractionation of oil of caraway, liquid compound **7a,** $C_{10}H_{16}O$, b.p. 228°, can be obtained. Compound **7a** showed the following properties: $[\alpha]_D$ 213°, 0.82 active hydrogen determination, 1.52 C—CH_3 determination, λ_{max} 2.80, 6.01, and 6.06 μ (3571, 1664, and 1650 cm^{-1}), no λ_{max} between 5 and 6 μ (2000 and 1667 cm^{-1}), no λ_{max} of high extinction above 210 mμ in the ultraviolet region, negative iodoform test. On catalytic hydrogenation (platinum in acetic acid), compound **7a** consumed 1.92 moles of hydrogen. By reaction with chromium (VI) oxide in acetic acid, compound **7a** was converted into compound **7b,** $C_{10}H_{14}O$, $[\alpha]_D$ 67°, λ_{max} 5.93 μ (1686 cm^{-1}), λ_{max}^{EtOH} 235 mμ, ε 19,000. On oxidation with hot potassium permanganate solution kept neutral by magnesium sulfate, either compound **7a** or **7b** gave rise to an acid, compound **7c,** $C_7H_{10}O_5$, N.E. 85 ± 3, which was optically inactive and could not be resolved into optically active isomers. By reaction of compound **7c** with iodine in sodium hydroxide solution, a yellow precipitate, compound **7d,** was obtained, as well as an acid, compound **7e,** $C_6H_8O_6$, N.E. 60 ± 3. On heating above its melting point for some time, compound **7e** showed no tendency to lose carbon dioxide, but did give rise to a new acid, compound **7f,** $C_6H_6O_5$, N.E. 160 ± 2, which reverted to compound **7e** when heated with aqueous acid or base. Give structural formulas for compounds **7a** through **7f** that are consistent with the data given.

8. Compound **8a** is obtained as the major odoriferous principle of vetiver, an East Indian grass whose roots are used in the perfume industry. It had the formula $C_{15}H_{22}O$, m.p. 44°, $[\alpha]_D$ −24°, and showed λ_{max} 5.93 μ (1686 cm^{-1}), λ_{max}^{EtOH} 236 mμ, ε 11,800; ozonolysis gave acetone, and on reaction with semicarbazide, a semicarbazone, $C_{16}H_{25}ON_3$, m.p. 229°, was formed. On reduction with sodium amalgam at *p*H 4, compound **8a** yielded compound **8b,** $C_{15}H_{24}O$, $[\alpha]_D$ 0°, which could not be resolved into optically active forms and which yielded an oxime, $C_{15}H_{25}ON$, on treatment with hydroxylamine and a compound, $C_{29}H_{32}O$, when treated with benzaldehyde and sodium hydroxide in ethanolic solution. On reaction with ozone followed by oxidative work-up (hydrogen peroxide in acetic acid), compound **8b** gave acetone and compound **8c,** $C_{12}H_{18}O_2$, λ_{max} 5.74 and 5.86 μ (1742 and 1706 cm^{-1}), 1.35 C—CH_3 determination. Compound **8b,** on reduction (hydrogen, platinum in ethanol), gave compound **8d,** $C_{15}H_{26}O$, which gave an oxime, $C_{15}H_{27}ON$, with hydroxylamine, but did not react with ozone. Give stereochemically correct structures for compounds **8a** through **8d.**

9. Compound **9a,** $C_6H_6O_3$, an antibiotic isolated from natural sources, was an optically inactive, unstable oil that polymerized rapidly on standing at room temperature and showed λ_{max} 2.9–3.1, 5.68, and 6.25 μ (3448–3226, 1761, and 1600 cm^{-1}) and λ_{max}^{EtOH} 245 mμ, ε 7,800. On treatment with dilute aqueous barium hydroxide solution at room temperature, compound **9a** yielded crystalline compound **9b,** $(C_6H_5O_3)_2Ba \cdot H_2O$, λ_{max} 2.9–3.1, 6.05, and 6.35 μ (3448–3226, 1653, and 1575 cm^{-1}), λ_{max}^{EtOH} 272 mμ, ε 20,500. On reduction (hydrogen, palladium on carbon in ethyl acetate), compound **9a** yielded compound **9c,** $C_6H_{10}O_3$, λ_{max} 2.9–3.2 and 5.65 μ (3448–3125 and 1770 cm^{-1}), which yielded, on treatment with semicarbazide, a semicarbazone, compound **9d,** $C_7H_{13}O_3N_3$, found to be a titratable acid. Compound **9c,** on oxidation with nitric acid, silver oxide, or hydrogen peroxide, gave an acid, compound **9e,** $C_6H_{10}O_4$, N.E. 73. Give structural formulas for compounds **9a** through **9e** that are consistent with the above information.

SELECTED REFERENCES

H. M. Randall, R. G. Fowler, N. Fuson, and J. R. Dangl, *Infrared Determination of Organic Structures*. New York: D. Van Nostrand, 1949.

F. A. Miller, "Applications of Infrared and Ultraviolet Spectra to Organic Chemistry," Vol. III, in H. Gilman, *Organic Chemistry, An Advanced Treatise*. New York: John Wiley and Sons, Inc., 1953, pp. 122–77.

R. N. Jones and C. Sandorfy, "The Application of Infrared and Raman Spectroscopy to the Elucidation of Molecular Structure," Chap. IV, Vol. IX, in A. Weissberger, *Technique of Organic Chemistry*. New York: Interscience, 1956, pp. 247–580.

L. J. Bellamy, *The Infrared Spectra of Complex Organic Molecules,* 2nd ed. New York: John Wiley and Sons, Inc., 1958.

H. M. Hershenson, *Infrared Absorption Spectra Index for 1945–1957*. New York: Academic Press, 1959.

Infrared Spectral Data, American Petroleum Institute Research Project 44.

An Index of Published Spectra. London: Ministry of Aviation, Her Majesty's Stationery Office, Vols. I and II, 1960.

A. D. Cross, *Introduction to Practical Infrared Spectroscopy*. London: Butterworths Scientific Publications, 1960.

R. P. Bauman, *Absorption Spectroscopy*. New York: John Wiley and Sons, Inc., 1962.

W. Brugel, *An Introduction to Infrared Spectroscopy*. London: Methuen and Co., Ltd., 1962.

M. K. Wilson, "Infrared and Raman Spectroscopy," Chap. 3, Vol. 2, in F. C. Nachod and W. D. Phillips, *Determination of Organic Structures by Physical Methods*. New York: Academic Press, 1962, pp. 181–243.

4 Nuclear Magnetic Resonance Spectroscopy

The organic chemist will quite possibly find nuclear magnetic resonance (n.m.r.) spectroscopy to be a more powerful tool than ultraviolet or infrared spectroscopy in terms of structural information derived from the spectrum. The method cannot, however, replace these older methods; instead, it is complementary to them. From a knowledgeable use of the three, a great deal of structural information about a substance can be obtained.

The organic chemist usually treats ultraviolet and infrared data rather empirically because theory will, in the usual case, not be of much help in the qualitative interpretation of spectra. He ordinarily relies on compilations of spectral data with which to compare his experimental results. A comparatively better understanding of the theoretical basis of the nuclear resonance phenomenon is desirable for an adequate interpretation of the results than is necessary in ultraviolet and infrared spectroscopy.

4.1 MAGNETIC PROPERTIES OF NUCLEI

Nuclei of certain isotopes possess a mechanical spin, or angular momentum. The total angular momentum depends on the nuclear spin, or spin number I, which may have values of 0, $\frac{1}{2}$, 1, $\frac{3}{2}$, . . . (depending on the particular nucleus). The numerical value of the spin number I is related to the mass number and the atomic number as follows:

Mass number	Atomic number	Spin number, I
odd	even or odd	$\frac{1}{2}, \frac{3}{2}, \frac{5}{2}, \ldots$
even	even	0
even	odd	1, 2, 3, . . .

Since an electric charge is associated with an atomic nucleus, the spinning nucleus gives rise to a magnetic field whose axis is coincident with the axis of spin. Thus the nucleus is equivalent to a minute magnet of magnetic moment μ. Each nucleus for which $I > 0$ will have a characteristic magnetic moment. The proton has a spin number of $\frac{1}{2}$ (ordinary carbon, C^{12}, and oxygen, O^{16}, are nonmagnetic, and have $I = 0$). If a magnetic nucleus is placed in a uniform magnetic field, it is found that the magnetic dipole assumes only a discrete set of orientations. The system is said to be *quantized.* The magnetic nucleus may assume any one of $(2I + 1)$ orientations with respect to the direction of the applied magnetic field. Thus, a proton ($I = \frac{1}{2}$) will be able to assume only one of two possible orientations that correspond to energy levels of $\pm\mu H$ in an applied magnetic field, where H is the strength of the external magnetic field. For nuclei with $I > \frac{1}{2}$, a larger number of orientations (energy levels) are obviously possible. The numerical value of I indicates the number of orientations that a given nucleus may assume in a uniform magnetic field; μ determines the energies. The transition of a proton from one possible orientation to another may be affected by the absorption or emission of a discrete amount of energy such that $E = h\nu = 2\mu H$, where ν is the frequency of electromagnetic radiation absorbed or emitted. For protons in a magnetic field of 14,000 gauss, the frequency of such energy is in the radio-frequency region—about 60 megacycles per second (60 Mc).

Unless the axis of the nuclear magnet is oriented exactly parallel or antiparallel with the applied magnetic field, there will be a certain force by the external field to so orient it. But because the nucleus is spinning, the effect is that its rotational axis draws out a circle perpendicular to the applied field. Such an effect is shown in Fig. 4-1. This motion of the nucleus is called *precession.* An example of this type of gyroscopic motion is a common top, which precesses when spun with an initial axis of rota-

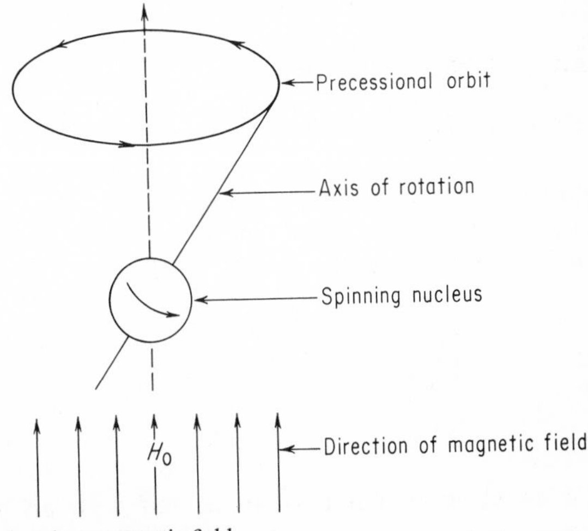

Fig. 4-1 Motion of a nucleus in a magnetic field.

tion different from the earth's gravitational field. The frequency of precession, it will be seen, is of exceptional importance in the nuclear resonance phenomenon.

4.2 THEORY OF NUCLEAR RESONANCE

A proton in a static external magnetic field may assume only two orientations corresponding to energies of $\pm\mu H$. The low-energy orientation corresponds to that state in which the nuclear magnetic moment is aligned parallel to the external magnetic field, and the high-energy orientation corresponds to that state in which the nuclear magnetic moment is aligned antiparallel (opposed) to the external magnetic field. It is possible to induce transitions between these two orientations; the frequency ν of electromagnetic radiation necessary for such a transition is given by $\nu = 2\mu H_o/h$, where H_o is the strength of the external magnetic field.

The precessional frequency of the spinning nucleus is exactly equal to the frequency of electromagnetic radiation necessary to induce a transition from one nuclear spin state to another. The nuclear transition corresponds to a change in the angle that the axis of the nuclear magnet makes with the applied magnetic field. This change can be brought about through the application of electromagnetic radiation whose magnetic vector component is rotating in a plane perpendicular to the main magnetic field. When the frequency of the rotating magnetic field and the frequency of the precessing nucleus become equal, they are said to be in *resonance,* and absorption or emission of energy by the nucleus can occur. Thus, nuclear resonance (absorption or emission of energy) will occur when a nucleus ($I > 0$) is placed in a stable magnetic field and subjected to electromagnetic radiation of appropriate frequency.

The theory of electromagnetic radiation indicates that the probability of an upward transition by absorption of energy from the magnetic field is exactly equal to the probability of a downward transition by a process stimulated by the field. Further, the theory shows that a spontaneous transition from a higher-energy state to a lower-energy state is negligible in the radio-frequency region. Thus, if the two possible spin states in a collection of nuclei were populated exactly equally, the probability of an upward transition (absorption) would exactly equal that of a downward transition (emission), and there would be no observable nuclear resonance effect. Under ordinary conditions in a magnetic field, however, there is a very slight excess of nuclei in the lower spin state (low-energy orientation); they take up a Boltzmann distribution (under ordinary conditions the Boltzmann factor is about 0.001%). It is this very small but finite excess of nuclei in a lower-energy state that gives rise to *net* absorption of energy in the radio-frequency region. Without this small excess, there would be no nuclear resonance phenomenon. As the collection of nuclei continually absorbs radio-frequency radiation, the excess of nuclei originally in a lower state may diminish; accordingly, the intensity of the absorption signal may diminish and may, under certain circumstances, vanish entirely. Such a phenomenon is known as *saturation*; the populations of nuclei in the two spin states become equal. Were it not for other mechanisms by which a nucleus in a higher-energy state could return to a lower-energy state, a very great length of time would be required for the initial excess of nuclei in a lower state to be reformed.

The various types of radiationless transitions by which a nucleus in an upper spin state returns to a lower spin state are called *relaxation processes*. There are two kinds of relaxation processes, spin-spin relaxation and spin-lattice relaxation. Spin-spin relaxation is effected by the mutual exchange of spins by two precessing nuclei in close proximity to one another. Associated with each precessing nucleus there is a magnetic vector component rotating in a plane perpendicular to the main field. If two nuclei are in very close proximity, this small rotating magnetic field is exactly what is required to induce a transition in the neighboring nucleus. Although this mutual exchange of spins (spin-spin relaxation, sometimes called transverse relaxation) shortens the lifetime of an individual nucleus in the higher state, it does not contribute to the maintenance of the required excess of nuclei in a lower spin state.

The term *lattice* refers to the framework of molecules (sample and solvent, liquid, gas, or solid) containing the precessing nuclei. All of these molecules are undergoing translational, rotational, and vibrational motions and have magnetic properties. Hence, a variety of small magnetic fields is present in the lattice. A particular small magnetic field, properly oriented in the lattice, can induce a transition in a particular precessing nuclear magnet from an upper state to a lower state. The energy from this transition is transferred to the components of the lattice as additional translational, rotational, and vibrational energy (spin-lattice relaxation, sometimes referred to as longitudinal relaxation); the total energy of the system remains unchanged. Thus, a nucleus is returned to a lower state from an upper state. This process maintains an excess of nuclei in a lower state, which is the condition necessary for the observation of the nuclear resonance phenomenon.

The natural width of a spectral line is inversely proportional to the average time the system spends in the excited state. Thus, sharp resonance lines are observed for states of extended excitation, and broad lines are observed for short-lived excited states. Both spin-lattice relaxation and spin-spin relaxation processes contribute to the width of a spectral line. In solids and very viscous liquids, molecular motions are greatly restricted, so properly oriented magnetic nuclei, which may effect spin-lattice relaxation, are present relatively infrequently. Accordingly, most solids and viscous liquids exhibit very long spin-lattice relaxation times. On the other hand, solids and very viscous liquids usually provide properly oriented nuclei in lower spin states which may exchange spins with nuclei in higher spin states, so spin-spin relaxation times are very short. Solids and viscous liquids usually display broad resonance lines for this reason. The effective magnetic field that a precessing nucleus experiences is a combination of the static applied field and local fields developed within the lattice. In solids and viscous liquids these local fields are frequently fairly stable, so the precessing nuclear magnets experience a spread in the effective magnetic field. Hence, these resonance lines are broadened for this reason also. Relaxation times for most nonviscous organic liquids and solids in solution are of the order of one second; this gives rise to a natural line width of about 1 cps.

Two additional factors influence the width of a spectral line. Paramagnetic broadening results from the presence of paramagnetic molecules (for example, dissolved oxygen) or ions in the sample. Greatly reduced spin-lattice relaxation times result, owing to the large magnetic fields associated with the paramagnetic lattice components (the electron magnetic moment is more than a thousand times greater than nuclear magnetic moments). It is thus desirable that the sample be deoxygenated before the spectrum is determined. Resonance signals for protons attached to an element that has an electric quadrupole moment will frequently be broadened. The magnitude of the electric quadrupole moment is a measure of the nonspherical nature of the electric charge distribution of the nucleus. Only nuclei with spin numbers greater than $\frac{1}{2}$ have electric quadrupole moments. The nitrogen nucleus ($I = 1$) is the most common example of this phenomenon. Molecules that contain nuclei with $I > \frac{1}{2}$ frequently have unsymmetric local electrostatic fields. A nitrogen nucleus in an excited spin state, by interaction of its quadrupole with the electrostatic fields, transfers its spin energy to the lattice. Thus, nuclei with quadrupole moments usually have short spin-lattice relaxation times; absorption signals of these nuclei or protons attached to these nuclei are consequently broadened.

4.3 THE CHEMICAL SHIFT

We have seen that the precessional frequencies of magnetic nuclei in a magnetic field are directly dependent upon the strength of the magnetic field and that absorption of electromagnetic radiation by the nucleus will result when the frequency of a rotating magnetic field perpendicular to the main field reaches the precessional frequency of the nucleus. Thus, it is possible to induce a nuclear transition in one of two ways: (1) the strength of the applied magnetic field can be maintained at a constant value and the frequency of the rotating magnetic field can be slowly changed, or (2) the frequency of the rotating magnetic field can be maintained at a constant value and the strength of the applied magnetic field can be changed over a very small range. Construction of instruments employing the latter process is easier.

The most important single feature of the nuclear magnetic resonance spectrometer is the magnet itself. The magnet is required to produce the condition necessary for the absorption of radio-frequency radiation. In order to obtain high-resolution spectra, the field produced by the magnet must be homogeneous over a considerable area between the pole faces (that is, the strength of the field should not vary from point to point). If the magnetic field is inhomogeneous, nuclei in different parts of the sample will experience different magnetic fields; they will precess over a range of frequencies, and broadened absorption signals will result. As the resolution of precessional frequencies desired is one part in 10^8 or even 10^9, the homogeneity of the magnetic field must be of this same order in the region of the sample. The volume of homogeneity of the magnetic field ordinarily achieved is small, so the volume of sample which can be used is small.

The remaining components of the magnetic resonance spectrometer have their counterparts in other methods of absorption spectroscopy. These are a method of continually varying the magnetic field strength over a very small range, a radio-frequency oscillator, and a radio-frequency receiver.

If the resonance frequencies for all protons in a molecule were the same, the nuclear resonance technique would be of little use to the organic chemist—one would observe only one peak for the compound, regardless of the number or nature of protons present. The utility of the nuclear resonance phenomenon to organic chemists depends on the fact that nuclear magnetic resonance frequencies are to a small degree dependent on the molecular environment of the nucleus. The surrounding electrons *shield* the nucleus, so the effective magnetic field felt by the nucleus is not quite the same as the applied field. Electronic shielding arises from an induced circulation of electrons about a nucleus. These circulations are induced by the applied field and are in a plane perpendicular to the applied magnetic field. They produce a magnetic field that, in the region of the nucleus, is usually in a direction *opposed* to the direction of the applied field. *The magnitude of this induced field is directly proportional to the magnitude of the applied field.* The effective magnetic field experienced by the nucleus is changed by this small local field such that $H_{\text{eff}} = H_o - \sigma H_o$, where σH_o is the induced field owing to electronic circulations. Protons in different environments are shielded by the circulations of surrounding electrons to different extents. Hence, different values of σH_o, each dependent on the magnitude of the applied field H_o are obtained for different protons. A more detailed discussion of shielding is given in Sec. 4.7.

Protons in the usual types of organic compounds absorb at frequencies (directly proportional to H_o) spread over about 700 cycles per second (cps) at a field strength of about 14,000 gauss. At this field strength, protons absorb at a frequency of about 60×10^6 cps. The accurate measurement of the position of absorption of protons in various environments is without doubt a very important aspect of proton resonance spectroscopy. If the position of absorption of a given proton is to be determined with an accuracy of about ± 1 cps (out of about 60×10^6 cps), the instrument required must be able to discriminate frequencies of the order of one part in 10^8. Because the strength of the applied magnetic field cannot be determined to the required degree of accuracy (one part in 10^8), the absolute position of absorption cannot be obtained directly from the instrument, as is the case with ultraviolet and infrared spectrophotometers. However, *relative* proton frequencies can readily be determined with an accuracy of about ± 1 cps. The separation of resonance frequencies of nuclei in different structural environments from some arbitrarily chosen standard is termed the *chemical shift*.

As only relative absorption values can be obtained, a suitable standard must be used. The chemical shift values of the protons in a particular compound are then determined with reference to this standard. A standard may be used in one of two ways: as an external reference (the standard is usually placed in a small capillary contained within the sample tube) and as an internal reference (the standard is dissolved in a solution of the sample to be measured). It has been found that when an external reference is used, the magnetic field experienced by the sample is not exactly the same as that experienced by the reference compound and that this difference varies from compound to compound. In order to obtain reliable chemical shift values when an external reference is used, it has been found necessary to make a number of determinations and to extrapolate the chemical shift value to infinite dilution. As this consumes considerable time, most proton resonance spectra are recorded using internal reference compounds. The reference compound is dissolved in the same solution as the sample, so both experience the same magnetic field; reliable chemical shift values are obtained, provided reasonably dilute ($<15\%$) solutions are used.

Several organic liquids were initially used as reference compounds, but it now appears that tetramethylsilane (TMS) is the reference compound of choice. TMS meets the criteria of a good standard: it is chemically inert, magnetically isotropic, volatile (b.p. 27°)—so that precious sample materials may be recovered readily—and miscible with most organic solvents used; it gives a single sharp absorption line, and, furthermore, absorbs at higher frequency than all common types of organic protons. Because TMS is insoluble in deuterium oxide, it cannot be used with this solvent. A suitable reference for aqueous solutions appears to be the methyl groups of sodium 2,2-dimethyl-2-silapentane-5-sulfonate (DSS). This standard has the disadvantage that it is nonvolatile and has absorptions other than CH_3—Si. These other absorptions are readily determined and offer no real hindrance to interpretation of spectra. Any water-soluble substance that gives a strong, sharp resonance line may be used as a standard. Acetone, dioxane, and *t*-butyl alcohol, among others, are occasionally used.

Since electronic shielding (σH_o) is directly proportional to the strength of the applied field, the chemical shift value is proportional to the field strength. The oscillators of most commercially available instruments are 30, 40, 60, or 100 Mc. Because instruments with different field strengths are available, it is desirable that the chemical shift position be expressed in some form independent of the field strength. The chemical shift parameter δ is used, which is defined as $\delta = (H_r - H_s)/H_r$, where H_s and H_r are the field strengths corresponding to resonance for a particular nucleus in the sample (H_s) and reference (H_r). Since spectra are usually calibrated in cycles per second (cps), the equation may be rewritten as

$$\delta = \frac{\Delta\nu \times 10^6}{\text{oscillator frequency (cps)}}$$

where $\Delta\nu$ is the difference in absorption frequencies of the sample and the reference in cps; the oscillator frequency is characteristic of the instrument: a 60 Mc instrument has an oscillator frequency of 60×10^6 cps. The factor 10^6 is included simply for convenience; δ, which is dimensionless, is expressed as parts per million (ppm). As TMS appears to be an acceptable standard, reference to it is made by the symbol τ, where $\tau = 10 - \delta$. All but very acidic protons, or protons in very electronegative environments, have positive τ values. The larger the numerical value of τ, the greater the magnetic shielding of the nucleus to which it refers.

Throughout the literature, nuclear magnetic resonance values are expressed in any of three ways: (1) cps—the reference compound must be quoted and the oscillator frequency given, (2) δ—the reference compound must be quoted (δ is independent of the oscillator frequency), and (3) τ [independent of both the oscillator frequency and the reference compound (TMS or DSS is assumed)].

All spectra reproduced here were recorded using a Varian A-60 (60 Mc) instrument; TMS was used as an internal reference for solutions in organic solvents, and DSS was used for solutions in deuterium oxide. The absorption of the reference is adjusted so that it falls on "zero" (cps or ppm, 10 τ) at the right end of the chart paper. The spectrum is then determined, usually by sweeping from left to right (lower field to higher field), one of the available sweep widths of 1000, 500, 250, 100, or 50 cps being used. The chemical shift values in cps for the various sweep widths are given in the top portion of each chart. The numbers across the bottom of the chart are δ values (remember: $\tau = 10 - \delta$) and are applicable only when the 500 cps sweep width is used. When other sweep widths are used, the absorption positions are read in cps from the chart paper and are converted to τ values in the usual way. Thus, when the 500 cps sweep width is used, the spectrum from 1.7 to 10.0 τ is determined, and when the 1000 cps sweep width is used, the spectrum from -6.6 to 10.0 τ is determined. Each square of the calibrated chart paper at 50 cps sweep width is 0.5 cps, and each square at 500 cps sweep width is 5.0 cps, etc.

4.4 SPIN-SPIN INTERACTIONS

Very nearly the same energy for a given spin transition is involved for each proton in a molecule. Provided the efficiency of spin-lattice relaxation is such that the Boltzmann distribution is maintained, the ratio of the intensities of the absorption bands, as measured by the areas that they enclose, is the ratio of the number of protons in each group. The low resolution spectrum of ethanol (Fig. 4-2) shows three absorption peaks in an area ratio of 1:2:3, corresponding to —OH, —CH_2—, and —CH_3, respectively.

Under higher resolution the peaks of ethyl alcohol (Fig. 4-3) attributed to methylene and methyl protons appear as multiplets, whose relative total areas are still 2:3. The protons of acidified ethanol (Fig. 4-3) absorb as follows: —OH, 322 cps downfield from TMS (4.63 τ), —CH_2—, centered (the chemical shift value of any proton whose absorption is a multiplet is obtained only by mathematical analysis of the spectral data

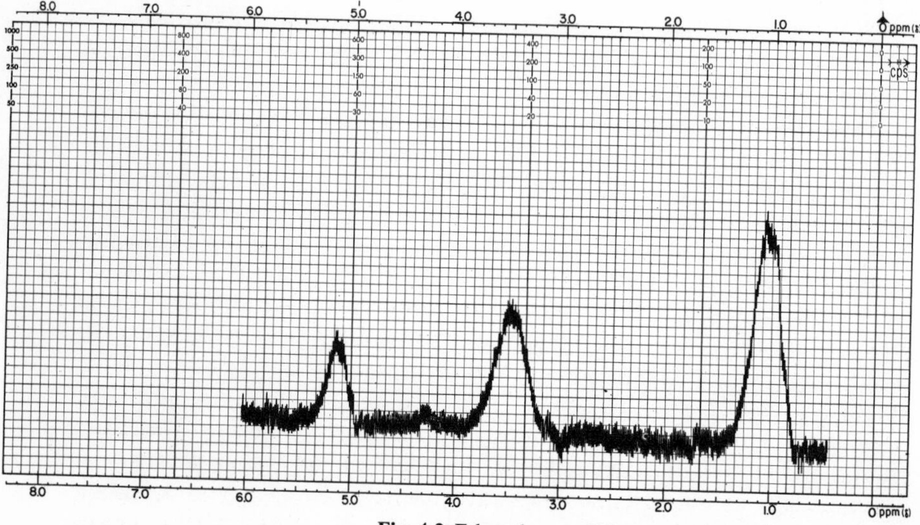

Fig. 4-2 Ethanol, neat, 500 cps sweep width, low resolution. CH_3—CH_2—OH

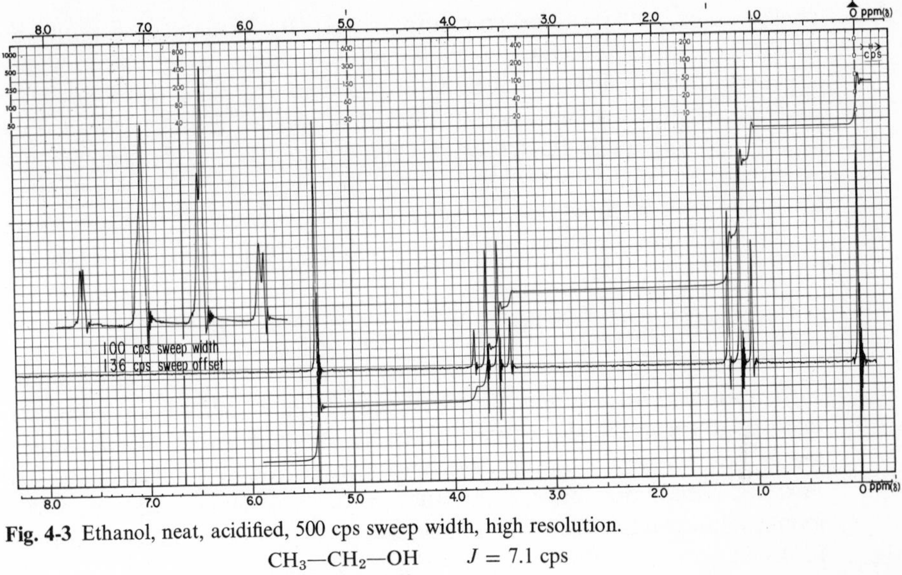

Fig. 4-3 Ethanol, neat, acidified, 500 cps sweep width, high resolution.

CH_3—CH_2—OH $J = 7.1$ cps

8.83 τ 6.38 τ 4.63 τ

but is approximated by the center of gravity of the multiplet) at 217 cps (6.38 τ), and —CH_3, 70 cps (8.83 τ). After the spectrum is determined, it is integrated so as to determine the relative number of protons in each absorption. The integral tracing is usually recorded from left to right. The height that the tracing rises for each group of protons is proportional to the area enclosed by the peak and, therefore, to the number of protons responsible for that absorption. In the spectrum of ethanol (Fig. 4-3) the integral tracing rises 6.0, 12.4, and 17.8 squares for the —OH, —CH_2—, and —CH_3 groups, respectively. This corresponds to a relative proton count of 1.00:2.07:2.97.

From the spectrum of acidified ethanol, it is seen that the methyl absorption is split into a triplet (relative areas *ca* 1:2:1), and the methylene absorption is split into a quartet (relative areas *ca* 1:3:3:1). The spacing (in cps) of the three components of the methyl group triplet is found to be equal to the spacing of the four components of the methylene group quartet. The observation of these splitting patterns is explained by assuming that the magnetic field experienced by the protons of one group is influenced by the spin arrangements of the protons in the adjacent group. For the two protons of the methylene group of ethanol, there are three possible combinations of spin orientations that may affect the resonance frequencies of the protons of the methyl group. These are shown in Fig. 4-4. It is seen that if the effect of the instantaneous spin arrangements of the protons of the methylene group can be transmitted to the protons of the methyl group, the protons of the methyl group would be split into three peaks (a triplet) having relative areas of 1:2:1.

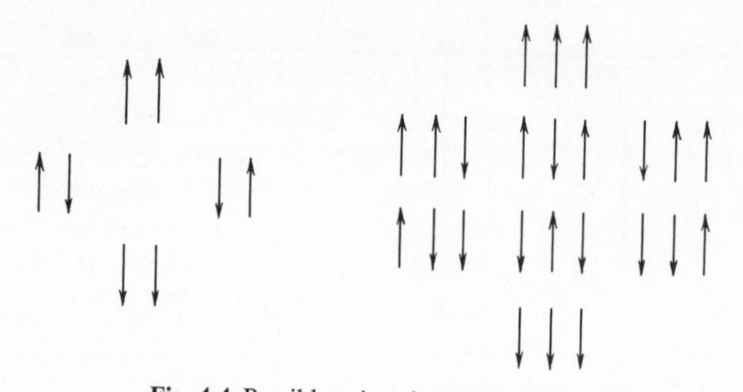

Fig. 4-4 Possible spin orientations of the protons of an ethyl group: left, the methylene protons; right, the methyl protons.

If the spin orientations of the methyl group (Fig. 4-4) have a similar effect on the protons of the methylene group, the protons of the methylene group will be split into four peaks (a quartet) having relative areas of 1:3:3:1. Interaction between protons within a group of equivalent protons (for example, the methylene group protons and the methyl group protons) is not ordinarily observed, and is discussed in Sec. 4.10.

Since local fields are averaged to zero in liquids, owing to rapid molecular motions, the direct transmission of instantaneous spin states through space is unlikely (this mechanism is, however, important in spectra of solids, where relatively stable local fields are possible). The explanation that appears most probable for liquids or solids in solution is that the nature of the instantaneous spin state is transmitted from one nucleus to another through the bonding electrons. In a given covalent bond the net electronic spin magnetic moment is zero, because the electron spins are paired. But a nuclear magnetic moment induces a small magnetic polarization of the bonding electrons, and this polarization effectively transmits the instantaneous spin arrangement of one nucleus to another.

The magnitude of multiplet separation resulting from spin-spin interactions is independent of the strength of the applied field. Although the absorption position of a group (in cps) changes with magnetic field strength, the spacings of spin-spin coupled multiplicities do not. This spacing, determined by the efficiency of the coupled interactions, is called the *spin-spin coupling constant,* and is denoted by the symbol J. Numerical values of J are always quoted in cycles per second (cps). For most ethyl groups, $J = 6\text{–}8$ cps. The magnitude of J decreases sharply with distance; it is about 1 cps for coupling through four covalent bonds. In special cases, observable coupling through five covalent bonds has been reported.

The value of the coupling constant can be more accurately determined if the multiplet is expanded. When the sweep-offset adjustment of the instrument is used, it is possible to change the region of the spectrum observed by 0–1000 cps downfield from TMS. For example, if a sweep offset of 500 cps and a sweep width of 1000 cps are used, the region 1500–500 cps (−15.0 to 1.67 τ) downfield from TMS is observed. When a sweep offset of 366 cps and a sweep width of 100 cps are used, the spectrum recorded is that of 366–466 cps downfield from TMS (2.23 to 3.90 τ). As seen in Fig. 4-3, the methylene quartet of ethanol is expanded on the upper left portion of the chart paper by using a sweep offset of 136 cps and a sweep width of 100 cps. A more accurate value for the coupling constant can then be determined and is seen to be 7.1 cps.

The observed multiplicity of a given group of equivalent protons clearly depends on the number of protons on adjacent atoms. The multiplicity of a given group is given by the expression $(n + 1)$ where n is the number of protons on adjacent atoms.† In simple cases of interacting nuclei, the relative intensities of a multiplet are symmetric about the midpoint and are numerically proportional to the coefficients of the terms in the expansion of $(r + 1)^n$. Thus, the following multiplicities are to be expected for the following compounds. 1-Bromopropane: a 3-proton triplet (1:2:1), a 2-proton sextet (1:5:10:10:5:1), and a 2-proton triplet (1:2:1); 2-bromopropane, a 6-proton doublet (1:1) and a 1-proton septet (1:6:15:20:15:6:1); methyl ethyl ether, a 3-proton triplet (1:2:1), a 2-proton quartet (1:3:3:1), and a 3-proton singlet.

These simple rules for determining the multiplicities for spin-spin interactions of adjacent groups hold *only* for cases in which the separation of resonance lines of interacting groups (the symbol $\Delta\nu$ is usually used, measured in cps) is *much larger than the coupling constant J* of the groups ($\Delta\nu \gg J$). In systems of interacting nuclei in which the coupling constant is of the same order of magnitude as the separation of resonance lines ($\Delta\nu \cong J$), the simple multiplicity rules no longer hold; more lines appear and simple patterns of spacings and intensities are no longer found. As will be seen in later sections, these simple systems are more the exception than the rule.

4.5 CHEMICAL EXCHANGE

The high resolution spectrum of ordinary ethanol (Fig. 4-3) shows only a singlet for the hydroxyl proton. If the spectrum of a very highly purified sample of ethanol is examined (Fig. 4-5), the expected multiplicity of the hydroxyl proton signal (a triplet, $J = 5.0$ cps) is observed, together with an increase in the multiplicity of the methylene absorption (discussed in Sec. 4.10). The exact shape of the hydroxyl proton signal

† The situation becomes more complicated if magnetic nuclei other than equivalent protons are present on adjacent atoms. The general expression for the multiplicity of a group of equivalent magnetic nuclei A is given by $(2n_BI_B + 1)(2n_CI_C + 1)\ldots$, where n_B and n_C are the number of other equivalent magnetic nuclei present and I_B and I_C are the spin numbers of these nuclei.

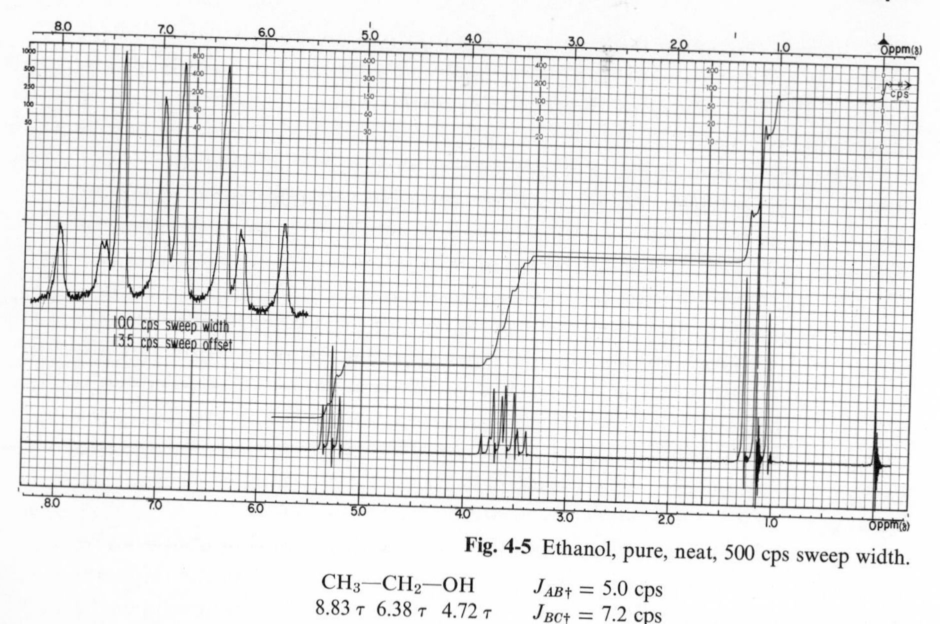

Fig. 4-5 Ethanol, pure, neat, 500 cps sweep width.

CH_3—CH_2—OH $\quad J_{AB}$† = 5.0 cps
8.83 τ 6.38 τ 4.72 τ $\quad J_{BC}$† = 7.2 cps

depends on the time that the proton spends on a given ethyl alcohol molecule. The term *chemical exchange* is used to describe the fact that, in a given period of time, a single hydroxyl proton may be attached to a number of different ethyl alcohol molecules. The rate of chemical exchange (proton transfer) in pure ethyl alcohol is relatively slow, but this rate is very markedly increased by acidic or basic impurities that are ordinarily present. If the rate of chemical exchange is very slow, the expected multiplicity of the hydroxyl proton signal is observed; if the rate of chemical exchange is rapid, a single sharp signal results. At intermediate rates of exchange the absorption may occur as a broad peak.

In a given period of time, if rapid chemical exchange exists, a particular proton will be attached to many different ethyl alcohol molecules, and the spin orientations of the methylene protons that the hydroxyl proton would otherwise experience will be averaged to a single value. This results in a sharp singlet for the absorption peak. Similarly, the absorption caused by the methylene protons will not be split by the hydroxyl proton if rapid chemical exchange exists. In other words, *rapid chemical exchange causes spin decoupling*. If the rate of chemical exchange is much slower than the frequency separation of the components of the multiplet in the absence of exchange, the anticipated multiplicity (of both the hydroxyl and methylene signals in the case of ethyl alcohol) will be observed. When the rate of chemical exchange is of the same order of magnitude as the frequency separation of the components of the multiplet in the absence

† The conventional labeling of nuclei (*A*, *B*, . . .) is explained in section 4.10, p. 98.

of exchange, the instantaneous spin orientations are only partially averaged, and a broad absorption peak results. The maximum width of this broad peak is the width of the multiplet observed in the absence of rapid chemical exchange.

When the components of the multiplet have just coalesced to a broad absorption peak, the average residence time (in seconds) for a proton at one site is given by the expression $\sqrt{2}/\pi\Delta$, where Δ is the separation of peaks (in cps) in the absence of chemical exchange. Spectra of molecules capable of chemical exchange are used to derive the rates of proton transfer, even though such processes may have half-lives of the order of only a hundredth of a second. From the spectrum of pure ethyl alcohol (Fig. 4-5) in which the hydroxyl absorption is a triplet ($J = 5.0$ cps), it may be calculated that hydroxylic protons of ordinary ethyl alcohol (Fig. 4-3) are exchanging very much more rapidly than eleven times a second (the average proton residence time at coalescence would be 0.090 sec).

The rate of chemical exchange increases with increasing temperature. Thus, spin decoupling can sometimes be observed by raising the temperature of the sample and, conversely, spin *coupling* can sometimes be observed by lowering the temperature of the sample. The spectrum of a particular sample of methyl alcohol, recorded at temperatures varying between $-40°$ and $+31°$ (Fig. 4-6), shows this effect. At $-40°$ the absorption caused by the hydroxyl proton is clearly a quartet ($J = 5.2$ cps) and that caused by the methyl group is clearly a doublet ($J = 5.2$ cps). This indicates that the rate of chemical exchange at $-40°$ is very slow. At $+31°$, both peaks are sharp singlets. This indicates that the rate of chemical exchange is rapid. The temperature at which the components of the multiplet appear to coalesce is about $-4°$. At this temperature the average hydroxyl proton residence time is $(\sqrt{2}/5.2\pi)$ 0.086 sec. In other words, at $-4°$ a given hydroxyl proton is changing from one methanol molecule to another an average of about twelve times a second in this particular sample.

If two hydroxylic species are present, such as in solutions of ethanol-water or acetic acid-water, rapid chemical exchange will usually occur. Instead of two resonance lines being observed for the different hydroxylic species present, only one results that is at an average, concentration-dependent position. If a single molecule contains both carboxyl and hydroxyl groups, chemical exchange usually causes the absorptions of these groups to lose their individuality.

4.6 MECHANICS OF MEASUREMENT

The sample is contained in a precision tube that has a 5 mm outside diameter and is about 15 cm high. In ordinary use, about 0.4 ml of sample

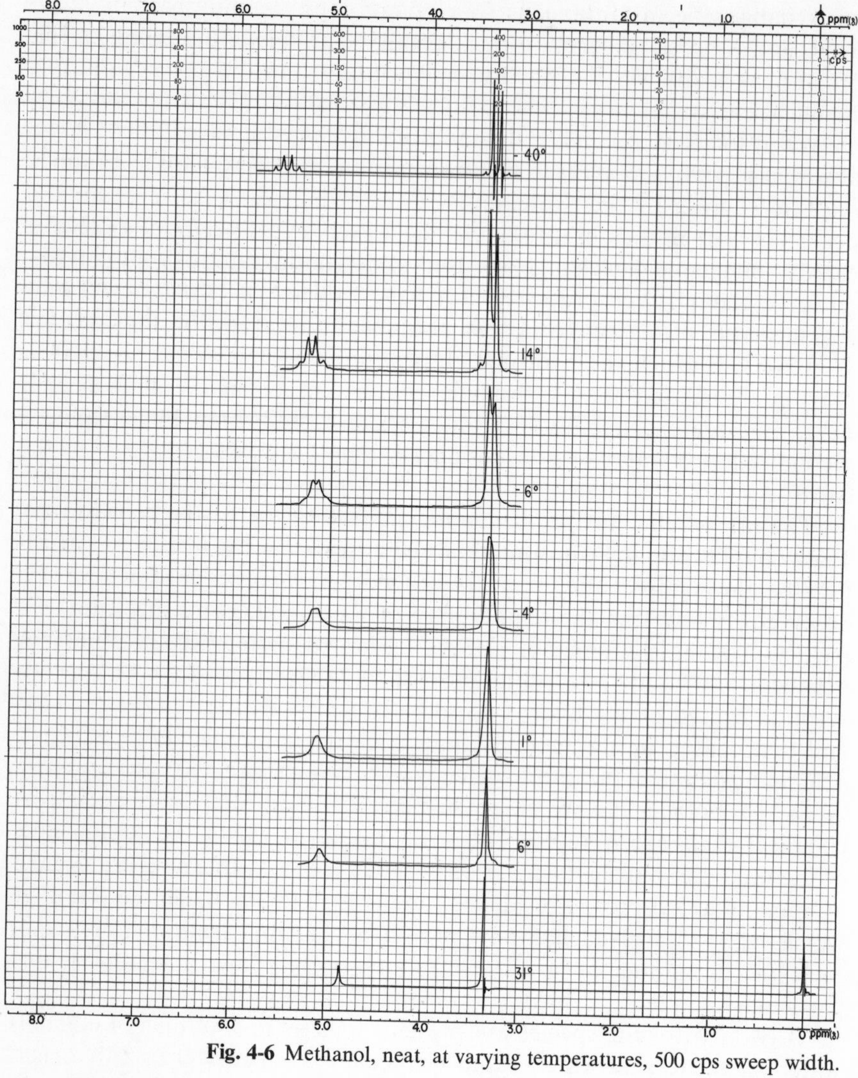

Fig. 4-6 Methanol, neat, at varying temperatures, 500 cps sweep width.
$CH_3—OH$ $J = 5.2$ cps

solution is required. The tube is placed between the pole faces of the magnet, and the spectrum is determined. For proton resonance spectroscopy, where absorption lines are usually sharp, the homogeneity of the magnetic field experienced by the sample is improved by spinning the sample several hundred times a minute about the vertical axis. Thus, inhomogeneities in the field perpendicular to the vertical axis are averaged. The rate of spinning should be in excess of the desired resolution. A rate of spinning of two times per second gives a maximum resolution of only 0.5 cps. If the rate of spinning is too slow, the averaging of the field is incomplete and the main absorption signal is accompanied by spinning side bands. The spacing of the spinning side bands is symmetric about the main band. These bands more frequently result from imperfect sample tubes that spin unevenly. Very rapid spinning can produce a vortex in the sample solution that effectively reduces the number of nuclei between the pole faces of the magnet.

If the spectrum is swept rapidly (that is, if the strength of the homogeneous magnetic field is changed rapidly within the small limit possible), some distortion of the absorption peaks results. The primary phenomenon is called *ringing* (or relaxation wiggles) and occurs after the magnetic field has passed through the particular resonance value. An example of ringing is shown by the quartet due to the C—H of acetaldehyde (Fig. 4-7); $J = 2.84 \pm 0.02$ cps. The ringing decays exponentially with time and is usually observed only with sharp absorption peaks. It is not shown by nuclei having very short relaxation times. At resonance, a portion of the nuclear magnetic moment appears as a rotating vector in a plane perpendicular to that of the applied field. As the field is swept, the rotational frequency of the rotating magnetic field is changed from the original resonance situation. The radio-frequency receiver is sensitive to the total signal; the rotating magnetic field combines with the horizontal magnetic vector component of the relaxing nuclei to produce an in-phase

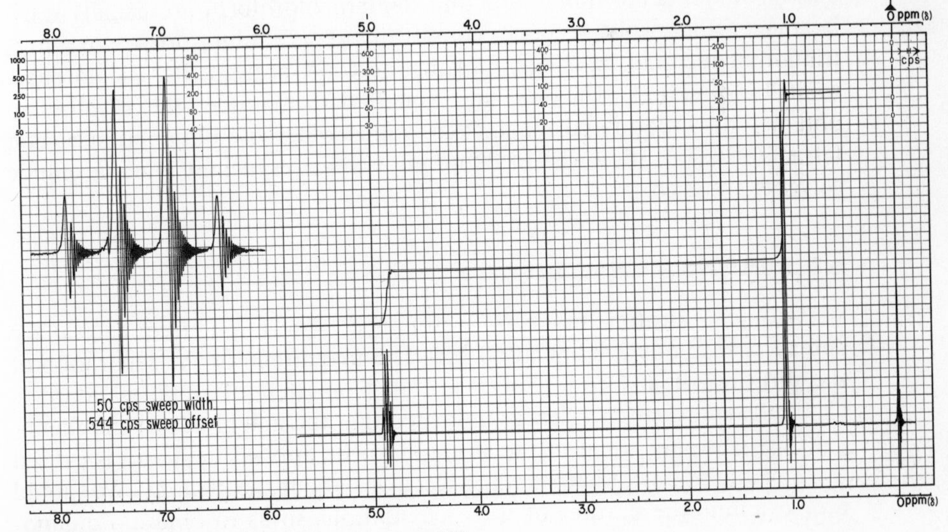

Fig. 4-7 Acetaldehyde, neat, 1000 cps sweep width.

O=C(H)–CH_3; H 0.32 τ; CH_3 7.85 τ

$J = 2.84$ cps

and out-of-phase magnetic component. The result is a characteristic wiggle, or ringing pattern. The shorter the relaxation times, the less will be the distortion from ringing. Since the spin-spin relaxation time depends partly on field homogeneity, a strong symmetrical pattern of ringing is a sign of good magnetic field homogeneity.

In order to obtain the best spectrum of a compound with the largest signal-to-noise ratio, it is desirable to use as concentrated a solution as possible. Organic liquids may be used directly without solvent, provided they are not viscous. Organic solids and viscous liquids must be dissolved in suitable solvents. Slurries of organic solids should not be used, because the presence of solids, as has been pointed out, broadens the resonance lines. Resonance values change somewhat with concentration. Hence, if very accurate resonance values are required, the spectra of dilute solutions (*ca* 10%) should be recorded—the resonance values possibly being extrapolated to infinite dilution. Absorption positions for protons in most organic compounds (with the exception of highly polar groups or alkyl groups attached to highly polar groups) decrease only about 0.05 ppm when the spectrum of a neat liquid is compared with the spectrum of a 10% solution in carbon tetrachloride.

The solvent chosen must dissolve the sample to a reasonable extent. It should also be chemically inert, magnetically isotropic, and preferably devoid of hydrogen atoms. Carbon tetrachloride is the ideal solvent. Carbon disulfide, deuterium oxide, and deuterochloroform are usually satisfactory. Other solvents occasionally used are chloroform, pyridine, trifluoroacetic acid, benzene, dioxane, acetone, acetonitrile, trichloroacetonitrile, dimethyl sulfoxide, and dimethyl formamide; the τ values so obtained may require corrections (to values otherwise obtained in carbon tetrachloride) of the order of 0.5 ppm or more, especially when aromatic solvents are used.

4.7 SHIELDING MECHANISMS

Ordinary proton magnetic resonance absorption frequencies are spread over about 700 cps at 60 Mc. The magnitude of the separation of the position of absorption of a proton from that of some standard is called the *chemical shift*. It was indicated that the magnitude of the chemical shift is proportional to the strength of the applied field and is caused by the circulations of surrounding electrons about the protons. We should now examine the natures of these circulations so as to obtain a qualitative understanding of the chemical shift values to expect from certain structural types within complex molecules. The shielding that a proton experiences is a combination of at least three types of electronic circulations: local diamagnetic effects, diamagnetic and paramagnetic effects from neighboring atoms, and effects from interatomic currents. The three factors have different relative importance in the shielding experienced by an individual atom.

Diamagnetism is an atomic property and is usually important when the atom has a symmetrical electronic structure and no permanent magnetic moment. Whereas the electronic distributions in the hydrogen atom, hydride ion, and free proton are spherically symmetrical, those for protons in organic molecules are not. A magnetic field induces electronic circulations about a nucleus in a plane perpendicular to the applied magnetic field. This diamagnetic circulation in turn produces a small magnetic field which, in the neighborhood of the nucleus, is opposed to the direction of the applied field. These circulations and the resultant effect are shown diagrammatically in Fig. 4-8.

Since the electronic distributions about protons in organic molecules cannot possess spherical symmetry, effects in addition to diamagnetic electronic circulations can become important. However, for molecules in which the protons are surrounded by very nearly spherical electron distributions, it appears that diamagnetic circulations are the most important of any electronic circulations in contributing to shielding. Diamagnetic shielding always *reduces* the apparent magnetic field at the proton, and consequently is a source of *positive* shielding. The degree of electronic shielding is clearly dependent on the electron density around the proton; the higher the electron density around the proton, the higher the shielding and the higher the field (higher τ value) at which the proton absorbs. It is not surprising to note a reasonable correlation of shielding characteristics and electronegativity of substituent groups in simple saturated molecules. The absorptions of the protons of the methyl halides (CH_3I, CH_3Br, CH_3Cl, CH_3F: 7.84, 7.32, 6.95, 5.74 τ, respectively) are in line with the electronegativity of the halogen atom. When the protons of

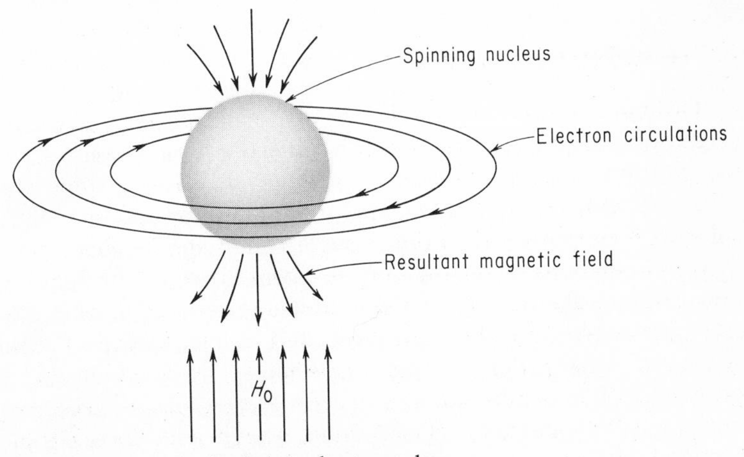

Fig. 4-8 Diamagnetic electronic circulations about a nucleus.

methane are successively replaced by phenyl groups, the pos
sorption of the aliphatic proton(s) changes in a regular way: C
$C_6H_5CH_3$, 7.66 τ; $(C_6H_5)_2CH_2$, 6.08 τ; $(C_6H_5)_3CH$, 4.37 τ.
worthy that the aliphatic proton of diphenylmethyl carbo
[$(C_6H_5)_2\overset{+}{C}H$], which is in a very electronegative environment,
at 0.3 τ. The absorptions of methyl protons attached to saturated
(*ca* 9.1 τ), nitrogen (*ca* 7.8 τ), and oxygen (*ca* 6.5 τ) are in line with
relative electronegativities of the attachment atoms. Similarly, the hydroxyl protons of alcohols are more shielded than those of phenols. Thus, one may conclude that if local diamagnetic currents only were responsible for shielding, the shielding characteristics would always be in line with the electronegativities of the attached atoms (the inductive effect).

If the diamagnetic effect were the only shielding mechanism operating, one would expect to find that the τ values for ethane, ethylene, and acetylene would decrease in a regular way, which would be in line with the electronegativities of the groups to which the protons are attached. Yet one finds that (for the liquid substances) ethane absorbs at 9.04 τ, ethylene at 4.16 τ, and acetylene at 7.12 τ; clearly, the shielding experienced by acetylene is not only the result of the diamagnetic effect—the shielding is *increased* more than what might be predicted on the basis of electronegativity.

In linear molecules similar to acetylene, and in other molecules at least to some extent, an important contribution to the total shielding a proton experiences is the result of a paramagnetic effect. Paramagnetic shielding arises from electronic circulations within molecules when they are specifically *oriented* with respect to the magnetic field. These electronic circulations about a nucleus produce a secondary magnetic field that is parallel to the applied magnetic field and frequently contributes to the shielding experienced by a neighboring nucleus. Local paramagnetic circulations do not contribute to the shielding of protons, but paramagnetic electronic circulations about atoms such as carbon, nitrogen, and oxygen may contribute to the shielding of an adjacent or neighboring proton. Such is the case for the acetylene molecule when it is oriented perpendicular to the applied magnetic field; the induced magnetic fields are paramagnetic at carbon but diamagnetic at the proton (Fig. 4-9). This paramagnetic effect is important in the shielding of other linear molecules, such as hydrogen cyanide and the hydrogen halides.

A proton may experience shielding effects caused by electronic circulations that originate in other parts of the molecule. Effects resulting from electronic currents in other molecules will not contribute to the shielding of a proton, because such effects will be averaged to zero by rapid thermal motions. Likewise, currents in the same molecule will not effect shielding of a proton if such currents are averaged to zero by rapid rotation about single bonds. But in a relatively rigid molecule such currents can effect

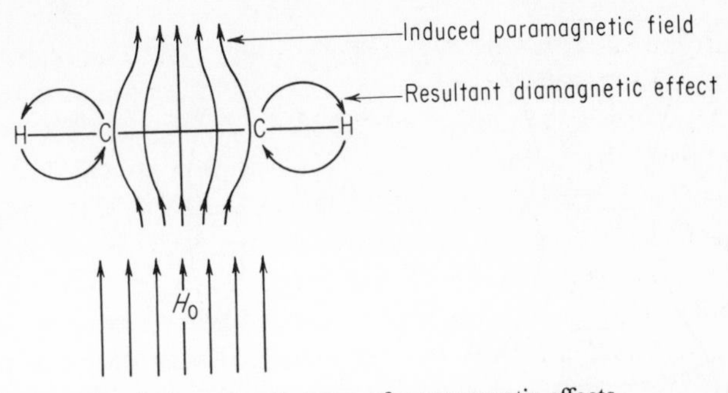

Fig. 4-9 Shielding of an acetylenic proton in terms of paramagnetic effects.

either shielding or deshielding of a proton. These effects depend on the *orientation* of the proton relative to the induced magnetic currents and are called *anisotropic effects*.

In addition to the paramagnetic effect in the acetylene molecule that results in a diamagnetic shielding of the proton, there is a diamagnetic anisotropic effect when the linear acetylene molecule is oriented parallel to the applied magnetic field. The electronic circulations within the cylindrical π electron cloud induce a diamagnetic shielding at the acetylenic proton (Fig. 4-10a). The proton of an aldehyde group absorbs at much lower field (*ca* 0.0 τ) than would be predicted on grounds of electronegativity or a simple atomic diamagnetic effect. When the carbonyl group is oriented such that the plane of the trigonal carbon atom is perpendicular to the field, diamagnetic circulations in the group produce an anisotropic effect at the proton that results in *deshielding* (Fig. 4-10b). Alkane and alkene protons differ in absorption position by about 4 ppm. This differ-

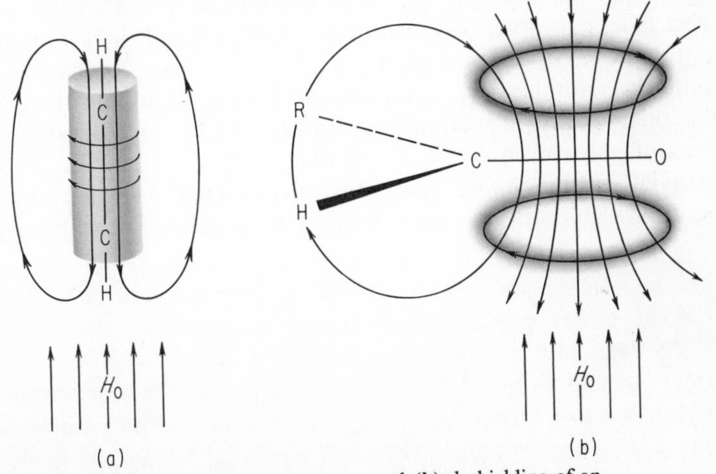

Fig. 4-10 (**a**) Shielding of an acetylenic proton and (**b**) deshielding of an aldehydic proton in terms of diamagnetic anisotropic effects.

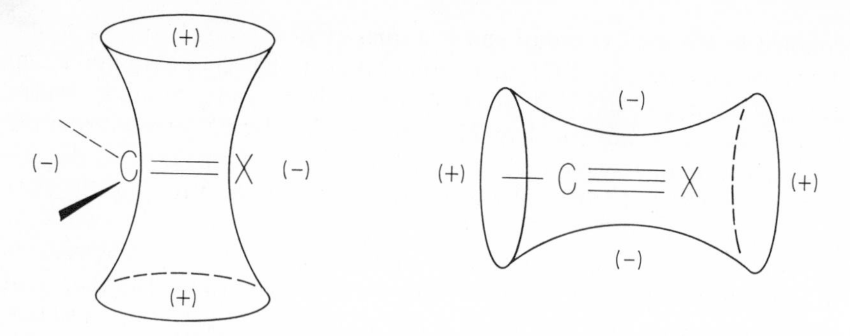

Fig. 4-11 Diamagnetic anisotropic shielding effects of unsaturated linkages.

ence is generally thought to be too large to be accounted for by a difference in the local diamagnetic shielding effect resulting from the electronegativity of the double bond. It is very probable that olefinic protons and, in fact, any group attached to the olefinic bond are deshielded because of diamagnetic anisotropic effects in the plane of the carbon-carbon double bond.

If molecules contain protons that are sterically oriented so that they are close to double- or triple-bonded groups, there will generally be a diamagnetic anisotropic effect of some kind. Such groups are exemplified by acetylenes, nitriles, olefins, aldehydes, ketones, esters, acids, oximes, etc. Figure 4-11 diagrammatically shows these effects. If a proton lies in the positive region, it will be shielded (shifted to a higher τ value), and if a proton lies in the negative region, it will be deshielded (shifted to a lower τ value). It is to be recognized that the diagrams in Fig. 4-11 are qualitative only; the magnitude of the effect is dependent upon the distance of the proton from the multiple bond and the exact orientation. That is, the effect is less at larger distances and greater toward the symmetry axis of the induced electronic circulations.

Common examples of diamagnetic deshielding by an anisotropic effect are the olefinic protons of α,β-unsaturated carbonyl compounds. The positions of absorption of the C_3 olefinic protons of ethyl 2-(4-methyl-3-pentenyl)-*cis*-2-butenoate and ethyl 2-(4-methyl-3-pentenyl)-*trans*-2-butenoate are given beside their structural formulas. Each absorption is

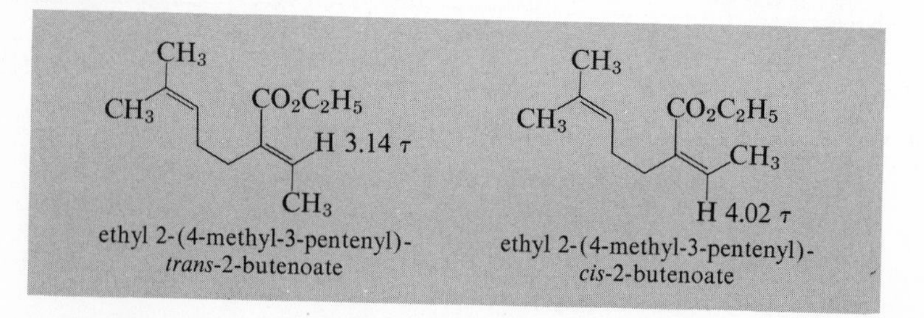

coupled to the methyl group and is a quartet ($J = 7$ cps). It is seen that the C_3 olefinic proton of the *trans* isomer is *cis* to the ester carbonyl group and is deshielded by 0.88 ppm, compared with the corresponding absorption of the *cis* isomer. In these compounds, the electronegativities of the conjugated systems would be expected to be about the same, so the difference observed is due totally to the diamagnetic anisotropy of the ester carbonyl group.

Other examples of diamagnetic deshielding are provided by protons in aromatic compounds that are *ortho* to a carbonyl group. The decreased shielding experienced by protons in this situation is at least in part caused by the electron withdrawing capacity of the carbonyl group (see Sec. 4.8), but is also the result of deshielding by the anisotropic effect of the carbonyl group. The spectrum of benzaldehyde (Fig. 4-12) shows that the two protons *ortho* to the formyl group absorb at 2.28 τ and the three other protons of the benzene ring absorb at about 2.60 τ. Thus, the *ortho* protons are deshielded by about 0.3 ppm. The spectrum of methyl *p*-toluate (Fig. 4-13) shows that the two protons *ortho* to the carbonyl group absorb at 2.14 τ and that the two other protons of the benzene ring absorb at 2.87 τ. In this case the *ortho* protons are deshielded by about 0.73 ppm.

In compounds that have rigid structures, such as bicyclic systems, diamagnetic anisotropic *shielding* effects may be observed in addition to

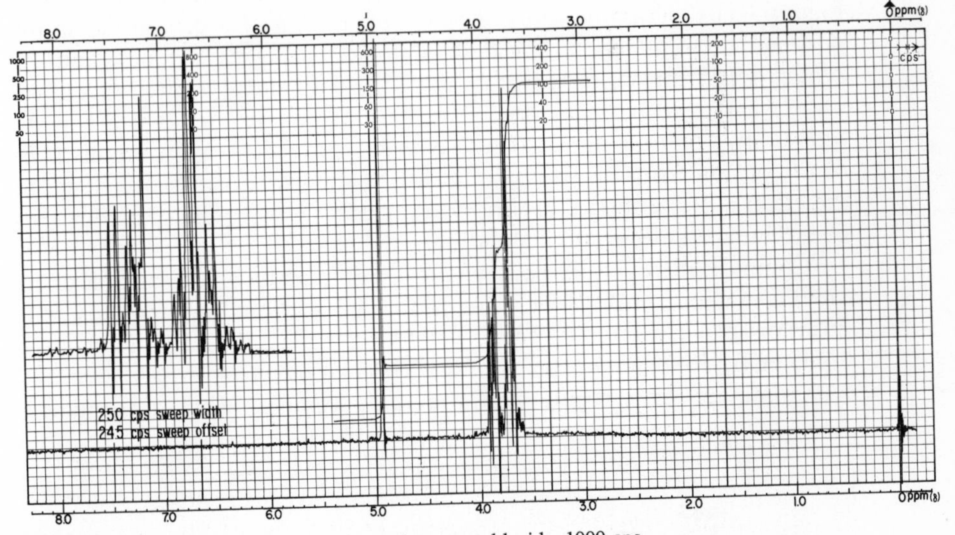

Fig. 4-12 Benzaldehyde, 15% (w/v) in carbon tetrachloride, 1000 cps sweep width.

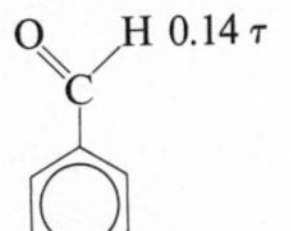

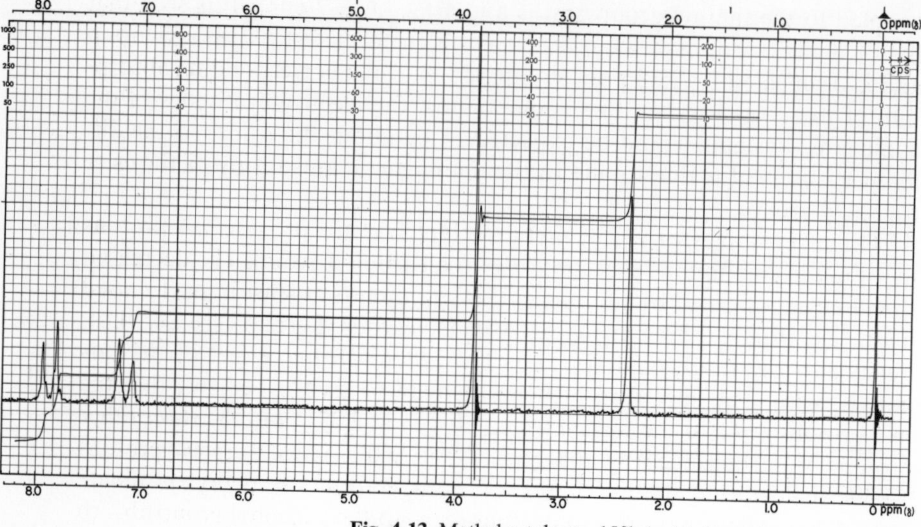

Fig. 4-13 Methyl *p*-toluate, 15% (w/v) in carbon tetrachloride, 500 cps sweep width.

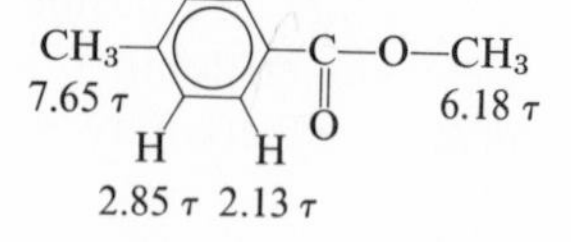

deshielding effects. The absorption positions for the methyl groups of pinane, α-pinene, and β-pinene are given beside their formulas. The spectrum of α-pinene (Fig. 4-14) shows that the methyl group attached to the double bond absorbs at 8.37 τ and is less shielded by 0.64 ppm compared to the absorption of the corresponding methyl group of pinane. This effect is the result of decreased diamagnetic shielding of the methyl group attached to the (more electronegative) double bond and also to diamagnetic anisotropic deshielding. The two methyl groups of the bridge isopropyl group of α-pinene absorb differently. One absorbs at 9.15 τ and is *shielded* by 0.16 ppm (when compared with the corresponding methyl group of pinane), because the rigid structure of the molecule forces it to

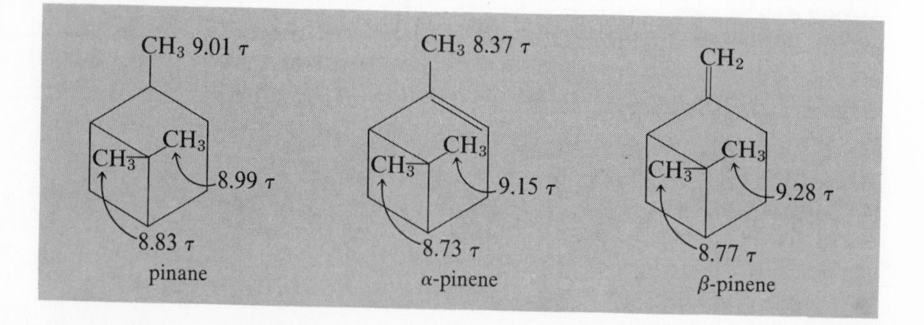

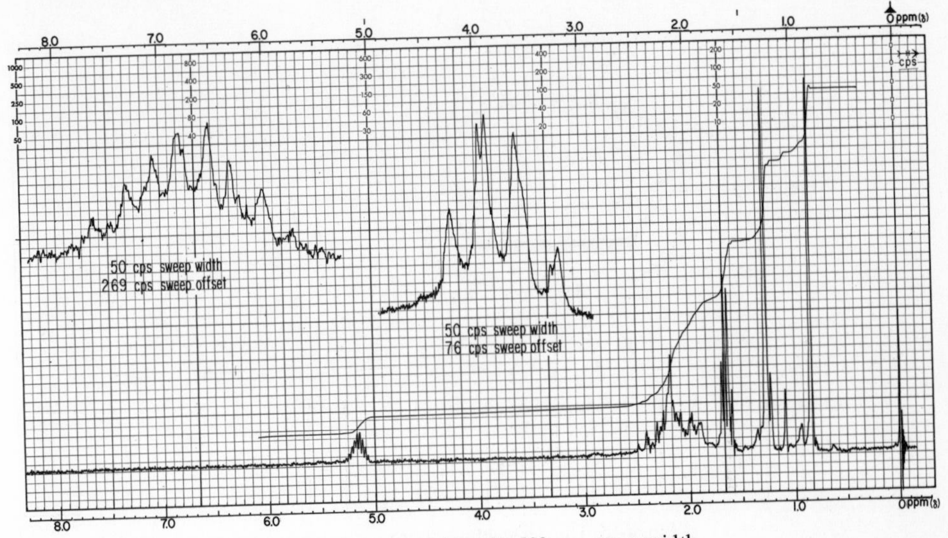

Fig. 4-14 α-Pinene, 15% (w/v) in carbon tetrachloride, 500 cps sweep width.

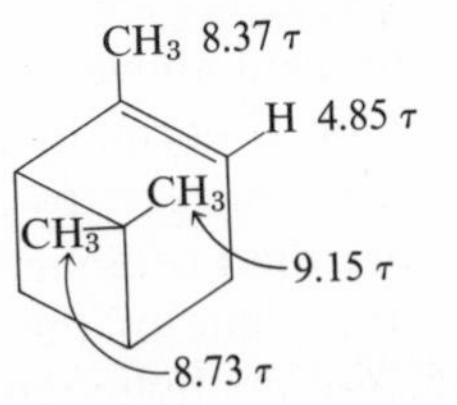

lie close above the π electron cloud of the double bond. The spectrum of β-pinene shows a similar abnormal shielding effect. One of the methyl groups of the bridge isopropyl group of β-pinene absorbs at 9.28 τ, which indicates that it experiences an enhanced shielding of 0.29 ppm. An examination of molecular models reveals that this methyl group is closer to the symmetry axis of the π electron cloud of the double bond in the case of β-pinene than in the case of α-pinene. Thus, the shielding would be expected to be greater.

Aromatic nuclei contain large closed loops of π electrons in which strong diamagnetic currents are induced by the magnetic field. This effect results in a *paramagnetic shielding* at the aromatic proton and is shown in Fig. 4-15. It is called the *ring current effect*. It is seen that this effect causes the *deshielding* of aromatic protons (shifted to lower τ value) or any group oriented such that it is contained in the plane of the benzene ring. Methyl groups attached to the benzene ring experience slightly reduced local diamagnetic shielding because of the weak electron release from alkyl group to the benzene ring. Such groups are also strongly deshielded because of the ring current effect (see methyl *p*-toluate, Fig. 4-13; Ar—CH_3 = 7.65 τ).

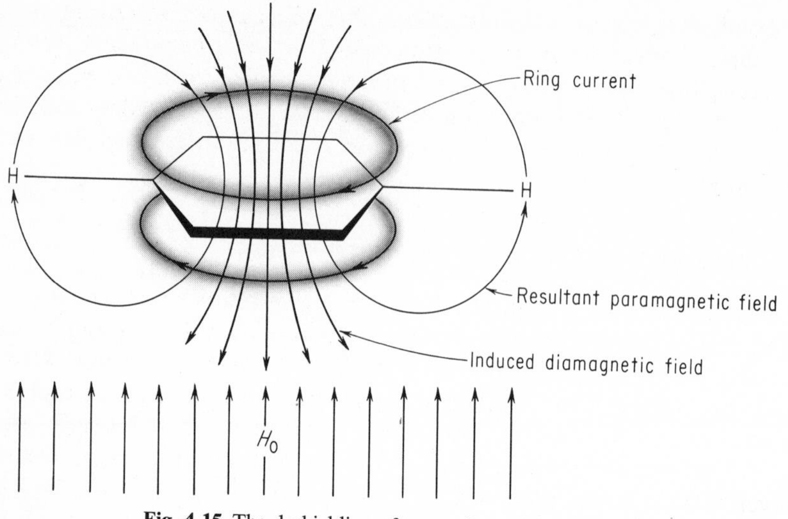

Fig. 4-15 The deshielding of aromatic protons due to a ring current effect.

Any group that is sterically held above or below the plane of the aromatic nucleus will, obviously, be abnormally *shielded* because of the ring current effect. The central methylene groups of [1.8]paracyclophane are shielded by about 1 ppm more than ordinary methylene groups because they are held rigidly above the plane of the benzene rings. The methyl groups of 15,16-dihydro-15,16-dimethylpyrene are found to absorb at 14.23 τ, which shows they are subject to a very remarkably increased shielding. This result also demonstrates that 15,16-dihydro-15,16-dimethylpyrene has a significant ring current, and therefore has aromatic character, even though it does not contain a classical benzenoid ring system.

A ring current effect appears to be operative in saturated cyclic hydrocarbons. Although such molecules contain no loop of π electrons, a diamagnetic current is apparently induced as a result of circulations of

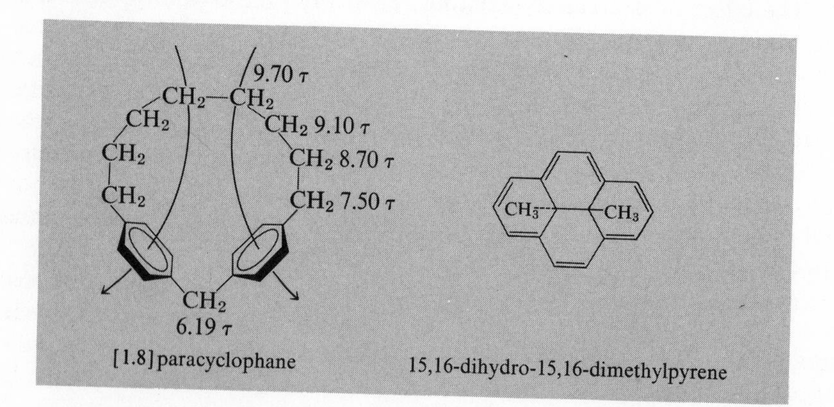

the bonding electrons. As anticipated, this effect is not so strong as the ring current effect in aromatic molecules, but it is responsible for the observed difference in the positions of absorption of axial and equatorial protons in cyclohexane compounds. Equatorial protons are deshielded by this mechanism. They generally absorb at about 0.5 ppm lower field than axial protons.

4.8 CORRELATIONS: HYDROGEN BOUND TO CARBON

Proton resonance frequencies can be measured with an accuracy of about ± 0.02 ppm relative to an internal standard. Figure 4-16 provides a general correlation of structural type with absorption position. Unless otherwise indicated, the functional groups listed in Fig. 4-16 are attached to saturated carbon atoms. All absorption values quoted herein are τ values. Absorption values quoted in the literature as δ or cps are easily converted to τ values (Sec. 4.3).

The total shielding that protons in organic molecules experience is the *sum* of all diamagnetic and paramagnetic effects present. When one attempts to rationalize the absorption of a given group or to derive structural information from a given absorption, it is necessary to consider all possible shielding effects. For saturated molecules, it appears that the diamagnetic contribution is most important and that the absorption positions of such protons are related to the electronegativity of the atom to which the groups are attached. Figure 4-17 very remarkably demonstrates this relationship for methyl compounds $[CH_3X(CH_3)_n]$. As these molecules are fully saturated, it would be expected that the shielding experienced by the methyl groups would be governed almost totally by the electronegativity of the atom X. A linear relationship appears to hold for elements in the same period *as well as* elements in the same group of the periodic chart. The shielding experienced by the protons in the hydrides XH_n does not, however, correlate at all well with the electronegativity of X.

The effect of decreased shielding caused by the proximity of a more electronegative group falls off rapidly with distance, and there is little effect on the absorption by a proton more than two saturated carbon atoms away. As was seen in Sec. 4.7, certain structural features can cause a significant paramagnetic contribution (shielding *or* deshielding) to the total shielding that a proton experiences. Paramagnetic effects are important in molecules that contain unsaturated groups. This effect depends not only on the distance of the proton from these groups but also on the specific orientation of the proton relative to the groups.

A given proton in different conformational isomers of a molecule will not necessarily experience the same shielding. A proton experiences a total shielding that is the weighted average of the shielding that it experiences in all different conformations of the molecule. In acyclic systems,

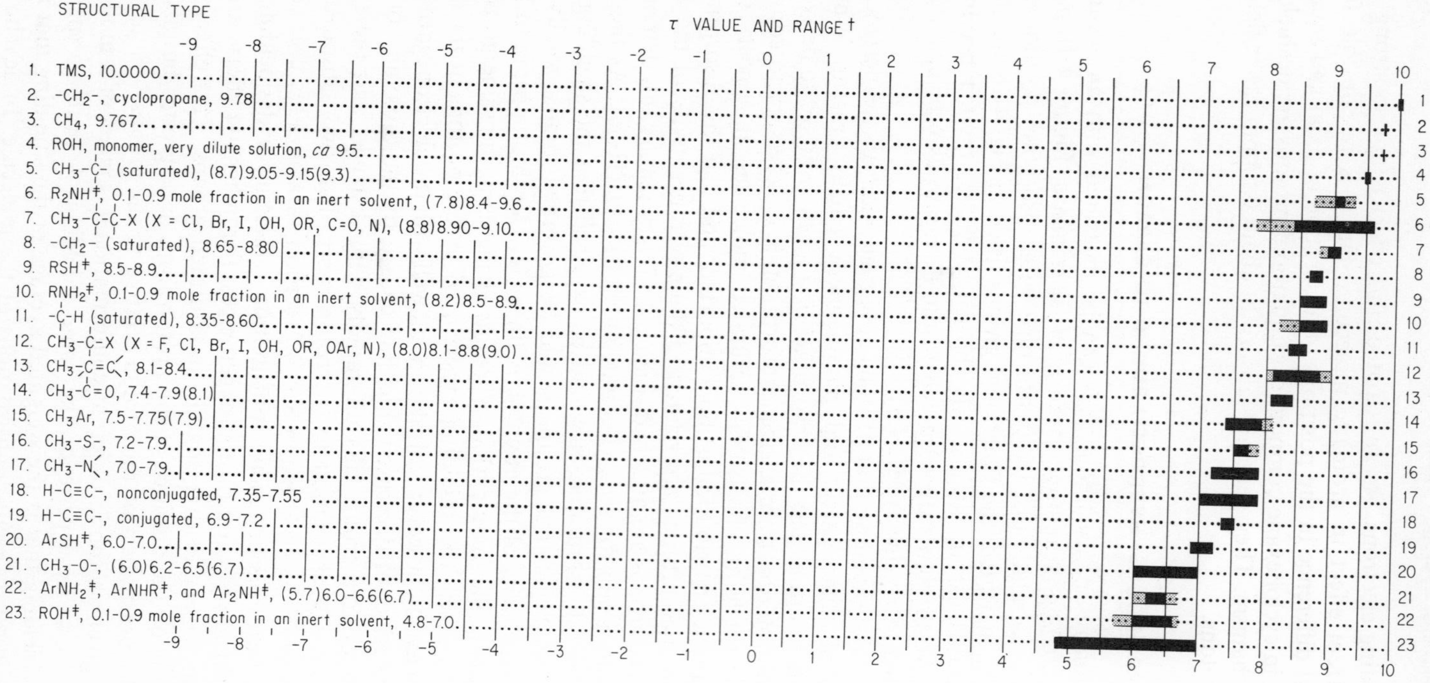
STRUCTURAL TYPE
τ VALUE AND RANGE†
-9 -8 -7 -6 -5 -4 -3 -2 -1 0 1 2 3 4 5 6 7 8 9 10
1. TMS, 10.0000
2. $-CH_2-$, cyclopropane, 9.78
3. CH_4, 9.767
4. ROH, monomer, very dilute solution, *ca* 9.5
5. $CH_3-\overset{|}{\underset{|}{C}}-$ (saturated), (8.7)9.05-9.15(9.3)
6. $R_2NH^{‡}$, 0.1-0.9 mole fraction in an inert solvent, (7.8)8.4-9.6
7. $CH_3-\overset{|}{\underset{|}{C}}-\overset{|}{\underset{|}{C}}-X$ (X = Cl, Br, I, OH, OR, C=O, N), (8.8)8.90-9.10
8. $-CH_2-$ (saturated), 8.65-8.80
9. $RSH^{‡}$, 8.5-8.9
10. $RNH_2^{‡}$, 0.1-0.9 mole fraction in an inert solvent, (8.2)8.5-8.9
11. $-\overset{|}{\underset{|}{C}}-H$ (saturated), 8.35-8.60
12. $CH_3-\overset{|}{\underset{|}{C}}-X$ (X = F, Cl, Br, I, OH, OR, OAr, N), (8.0)8.1-8.8(9.0)
13. $CH_3-\overset{|}{C}=C<$, 8.1-8.4
14. $CH_3-\overset{|}{C}=O$, 7.4-7.9(8.1)
15. CH_3Ar, 7.5-7.75(7.9)
16. CH_3-S-, 7.2-7.9
17. $CH_3-N<$, 7.0-7.9
18. $H-C\equiv C-$, nonconjugated, 7.35-7.55
19. $H-C\equiv C-$, conjugated, 6.9-7.2
20. $ArSH^{‡}$, 6.0-7.0
21. CH_3-O-, (6.0)6.2-6.5(6.7)
22. $ArNH_2^{‡}$, $ArNHR^{‡}$, and $Ar_2NH^{‡}$, (5.7)6.0-6.6(6.7)
23. $ROH^{‡}$, 0.1-0.9 mole fraction in an inert solvent, 4.8-7.0
1 2 3 4 5 6 7 8 9 10 11 12 13 14 15 16 17 18 19 20 21 22 23
-9 -8 -7 -6 -5 -4 -3 -2 -1 0 1 2 3 4 5 6 7 8 9 10

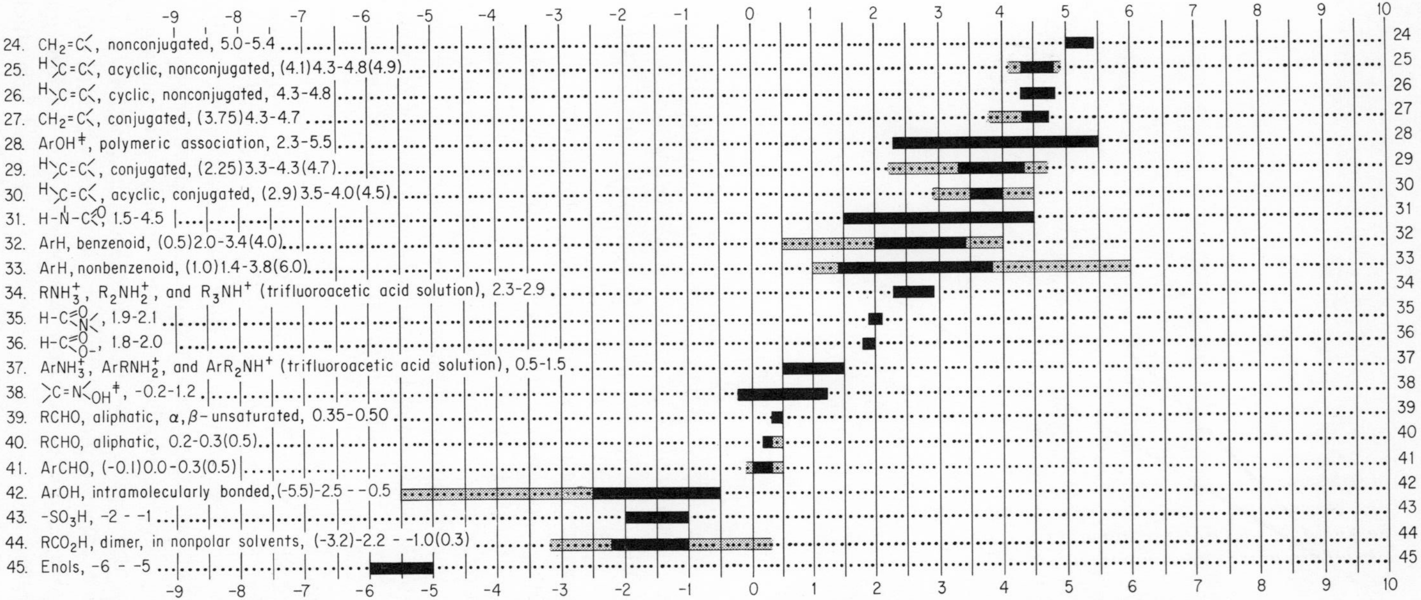

24. $CH_2=C\langle$, nonconjugated, 5.0-5.4
25. $^{H}\rangle C=C\langle$, acyclic, nonconjugated, (4.1)4.3-4.8(4.9)
26. $^{H}\rangle C=C\langle$, cyclic, nonconjugated, 4.3-4.8
27. $CH_2=C\langle$, conjugated, (3.75)4.3-4.7
28. ArOH‡, polymeric association, 2.3-5.5
29. $^{H}\rangle C=C\langle$, conjugated, (2.25)3.3-4.3(4.7)
30. $^{H}\rangle C=C\langle$, acyclic, conjugated, (2.9)3.5-4.0(4.5)
31. $H-\overset{|}{N}-C\overset{O}{\langle}$, 1.5-4.5
32. ArH, benzenoid, (0.5)2.0-3.4(4.0)
33. ArH, nonbenzenoid, (1.0)1.4-3.8(6.0)
34. RNH_3^+, $R_2NH_2^+$, and R_3NH^+ (trifluoroacetic acid solution), 2.3-2.9
35. $H-C\overset{O}{\underset{N\langle}{\lessgtr}}$, 1.9-2.1
36. $H-C\overset{O}{\underset{O-}{\lessgtr}}$, 1.8-2.0
37. $ArNH_3^+$, $ArRNH_2^+$, and ArR_2NH^+ (trifluoroacetic acid solution), 0.5-1.5
38. $\rangle C=N\langle_{OH}$‡, -0.2-1.2
39. RCHO, aliphatic, α,β-unsaturated, 0.35-0.50
40. RCHO, aliphatic, 0.2-0.3(0.5)
41. ArCHO, (-0.1)0.0-0.3(0.5)
42. ArOH, intramolecularly bonded, (-5.5)-2.5 - -0.5
43. $-SO_3H$, -2 - -1
44. RCO_2H, dimer, in nonpolar solvents, (-3.2)-2.2 - -1.0(0.3)
45. Enols, -6 - -5

(Scale: -9 to 10)

†Normally, absorptions for the functional groups indicated will be found within the range shown. Occasionally, a functional group will absorb outside this range. Approximate limits for this are indicated by absorption values in parentheses and by shading in the figure.

‡The absorption positions of these groups are concentration-dependent and are shifted to higher τ values in more dilute solutions.

Fig. 4-16 Absorption positions of protons in various structural environments.

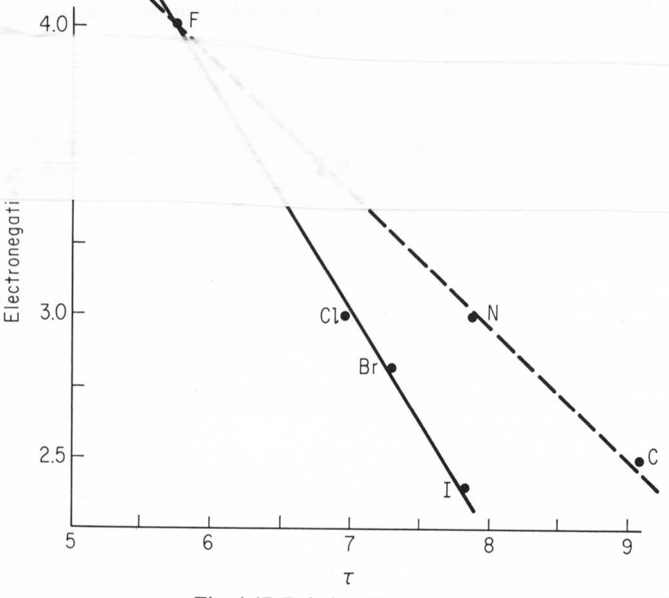

Fig. 4-17 Relationship of the electronegativity (Pauling) of X to the τ value of $CH_3—X(CH_3)_n$.

relatively free rotation about single bonds may usually be assumed, whereas in cyclic systems only one or several conformations may be important. Consequently, absorption values for cyclic systems frequently do not correlate well with those of acyclic systems.

Aliphatic protons, in the absence of any deshielding effects caused by neighboring groups or atoms, are usually the most highly shielded of all the common organic types. Methyl groups in a saturated hydrocarbon environment absorb near 9.1 τ. Acyclic methylene groups (*ca* 8.75 τ) are less shielded than methyl groups, and methine groups (*ca* 8.5 τ) are still less shielded. *This relationship is quite general.* The shielding of protons in cyclic systems depends markedly on the ring size: cyclopropane, 9.78 τ; cyclobutane, 8.03 τ; cyclopentane, 8.49 τ; cyclohexane, 8.57 τ; cycloheptane, 8.47 τ; cyclooctane, 8.47 τ.

A methylene group of ethylene oxides absorbs near 7.7 τ, which is at considerably higher field than ordinary $—CH_2—O—$ groups (near 6.4 τ). Epoxides, particularly when compared with their hydrolysis or reduction products, are particularly easily detected by n.m.r. spectroscopy.

Most methyl groups attached to carbonyl groups give strong three-proton singlets in the region 7.8–8.1 τ; acetaldehyde (Fig. 4-7), 7.85 τ, and acetone, 7.91 τ, are examples. Methyl aryl ketones, which absorb near 7.4 τ, are exceptions to this correlation. Methylene and methine groups attached to carbonyl groups are, as expected, somewhat less shielded. There are insufficient differences in the absorption values for alkyl groups adjacent to aldehyde, ketone, carboxylic acid, ester, and amide carbonyl groups to enable the absorptions of α-protons to be used in distinguishing these functional groups.

Methyl groups attached to isolated carbon-carbon double bonds absorb in the range 8.2–8.4 τ (α-pinene, Fig. 4-14, and limonene, Fig. 4-18). Conjugation of the double bond with some unsaturated group causes the methyl absorption to be shifted to lower field (7.9–8.2 τ). The magnitude of this shift depends on the geometrical isomerism about the double bond (a diamagnetic anisotropic effect). Methyl groups attached to aromatic nuclei absorb near 7.66 τ (methyl *p*-toluate, Fig. 4-13). Only the more powerful electron-withdrawing or electron-donating groups alter the positions of absorption of these methyl groups, and even this shift is not large (for example, the methyl group of *p*-nitrotoluene absorbs at 7.57 τ, and that of *p*-methoxytoluene absorbs at 7.75 τ).

When the position of absorption of the C_1-protons of an alcohol is compared with the corresponding absorption of the acetyl derivative, it is found that primary and secondary alcohol groups can be distinguished. Ordinarily, α-protons of a primary alcohol group ($-\underline{CH_2}-OH$) absorb near 6.4 τ, and those of the corresponding acetate ($-\underline{CH_2}-O-COCH_3$) absorb near 5.9 τ ($\Delta\tau = 0.5$). The protons of a secondary alcohol group ($>\underline{CH}-OH$) absorb near 6.1 τ, and those of the corresponding acetate

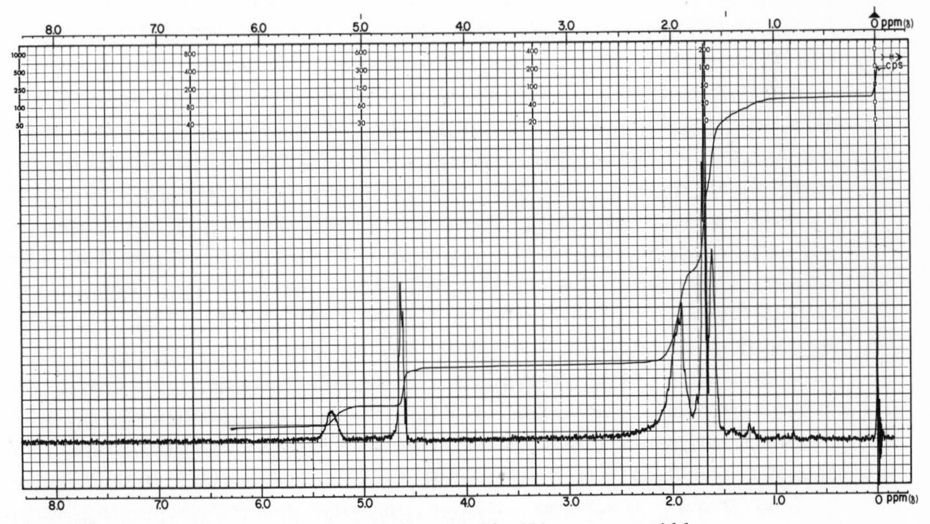

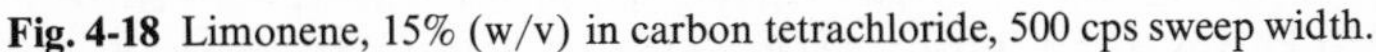
Fig. 4-18 Limonene, 15% (w/v) in carbon tetrachloride, 500 cps sweep width.

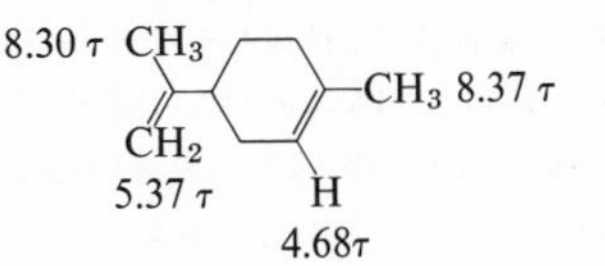

($\rangle$CH—O—$COCH_3$) absorb near 5.0 τ ($\Delta\tau = 1.1$). *N*-Acylation of an amine causes a shift in the absorption position of the protons adjacent to nitrogen of about 0.6 ppm to lower field when compared with the free amine.

O-Methyl groups usually absorb between 6.0 τ and 6.7 τ; *N*-methyl groups absorb between 7.0 τ and 7.9 τ; *S*-methyl groups absorb between 7.2 τ and 7.9 τ. *O*-Methyl and *S*-methyl groups give rise to strong, sharp, three-proton singlets and are usually readily recognizable. *N*-Methyl groups may be singlets or may be coupled to protons attached to the nitrogen. The absorption may be broadened somewhat by interaction with the electric quadrupole moment of nitrogen.

Olefinic protons absorb in the region 3.6–5.4 τ (α-pinene, Fig. 4-14, and limonene, Fig. 4-18). Conjugation of the ethylenic bond with an unsaturated group lowers the τ value for the absorption of the olefinic protons and can, in some cases, exert a paramagnetic deshielding effect (down to about 2 τ). Acetylenic protons absorb near 7.5 τ. The ranges for the absorptions of these protons in a number of different structural environments are given in Fig. 4-16.

Aldehydic protons absorb in the region 0.0–0.6 τ (acetaldehyde, Fig. 4-7, and benzaldehyde, Fig. 4-12). No other common proton group absorbs in this region. Consequently, n.m.r. spectroscopy offers a particularly convenient method of detecting this functional group.

Aromatic protons of substituted benzenes generally absorb in the range 2.0–3.5 τ. Electron-withdrawing groups shift the absorption to lower field, and electron-donating groups shift the absorption to higher field because of the local diamagnetic shielding effect. Limiting cases for benzenoid absorption are 1,3,5-trinitrobenzene (0.53 τ) and 1,3,5-trimethoxybenzene (4.05 τ). There appears to be a good correlation between the ring proton shifts relative to benzene (2.73 τ) and the π electron densities of the carbon atoms to which the protons are attached. A shift of 1 ppm is equivalent to a change in the π electron density of about 0.1 electron. Thus, the π electron density of the 2, 4, and 6 carbon atoms of 1,3,5-trinitrobenzene is about 0.78, and for the corresponding atoms of 1,3,5-trimethoxybenzene, about 1.13. The effect on the ring proton chemical shifts caused by a substituent group is greatest for the *ortho* proton and least for the *meta* proton. Data for nitrobenzene (τ value, π electron density: *ortho,* 1.78, 0.90; *meta,* 2.52, 0.98; *para,* 2.40, 0.97) and aniline (*ortho,* 3.49, 1.08; *meta,* 2.93, 1.02; *para,* 3.35, 1.06) demonstrate this effect. The position of absorption of an aromatic proton depends on at least three factors: the diamagnetic shielding, which is the most important and depends on the electron density at the carbon atom to which the proton is attached, paramagnetic shielding as a result of the ring current, whose magnitude will be greater for electron-releasing substituent groups than for electron-

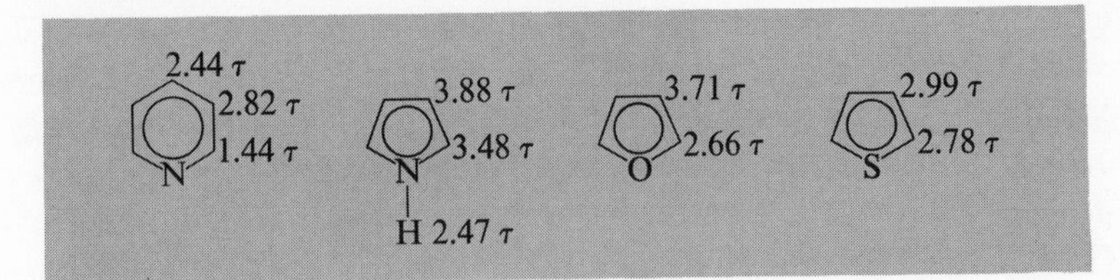

withdrawing substituent groups, and a possible diamagnetic anisotropic effect, which will be greatest at positions *ortho* to the substituent group.

Protons adjacent to a hetero-atom of heterocyclic aromatic compounds absorb at lower τ values than those in other positions. Data (τ values for 10% v/v solutions in carbon tetrachloride) for pyridine, pyrrole, furan, and thiophene are given by their formulas.

4.9 CORRELATIONS: HYDROGEN BOUND TO OTHER NUCLEI

Other than protons attached to carbon, those attached to oxygen, nitrogen, and sulfur are routinely of interest to the organic chemist. Functional groups exemplified by these are alcohols, phenols, carboxylic acids, enols, amines, amides, and sulfhydryl compounds. Protons associated with these functional groups are commonly considered to be active hydrogens. The n.m.r. spectra of such protons depend on the extent of intermolecular hydrogen bonding and the rate of chemical exchange. The absorption positions of the protons depend on concentration, temperature, and the nature of the solvent.

The combined use of carbon tetrachloride (or some other organic solvent) and deuterium oxide, if the compound is soluble in both solvents, is worthy of emphasis. Because of rapid equilibration of exchangeable protons with deuterons in the presence of a large excess of deuterium oxide, the initial protons are replaced by deuterons. The relative number of protons indicated by the water (or HDO) absorption (near 5 τ) that results from this equilibration can sometimes be estimated reasonably accurately. This number is the number of exchangeable protons that were present in the molecule.

Alcohols, under ordinary experimental conditions (0.10–0.90 mole fraction in an inert solvent), absorb in the region 4.5–6 τ (ethanol, Figs. 4-3 and 4-5; methanol, Fig. 4-6). On extensive dilution, the position of absorption of the hydroxyl proton is shifted to higher field and on extrapolation to infinite dilution is near 9.5 τ. For ethyl alcohol in carbon tetrachloride (CH_3— = 8.83 τ; —CH_2— = 6.41 τ) the hydroxyl absorption occurs at 9.24 τ at infinite dilution, which compares favorably with the value (9.29 τ at 220°) determined in the gas phase. The position of hydroxyl absorption is dependent on the temperature if an appreciable enthalpy change is involved in the equilibria of hydrogen-bonded complexes. For ethanol, the change is nearly 0.01 ppm/° to higher field with increasing temperature. Figure 4-6 shows spectra of methanol at different temperatures. It was indicated previously (Sec. 4.5) that the rate of chemical exchange increases with increasing temperature.

When the spectrum of an alcohol is examined when dimethyl sulfoxide is used as the solvent, it is found that, because of strong hydrogen bonding to the solvent, the hydroxyl absorption is shifted downfield somewhat. In addition, the rate of chemical exchange is retarded so spin-coupling of the hydroxyl proton to protons on an adjacent carbon atom may be observed, and separate signals are obtained from different hydroxyl groups. Thus, this technique offers a rapid method for the classification (primary, secondary, or tertiary) of the alcohol groups that a substance contains.

Phenols, at ordinary concentrations, absorb in the range 2.3–4.0 τ. At infinite dilution they absorb in the range 5–6 τ. Figure 4-19 shows the spectrum of phenol and the hydroxyl proton absorption at several concentrations. Some *o*-substituted phenols are intramolecularly hydrogen-bonded so that the change on dilution is not so appreciable. Phenols with very strong intramolecular hydrogen bonds absorb in the region −2.5 to

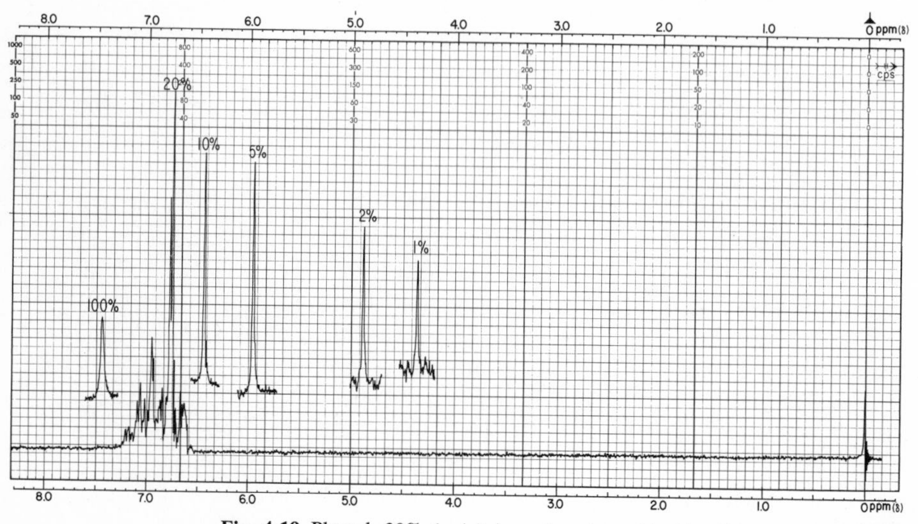

Fig. 4-19 Phenol, 20% (w/v) in carbon tetrachloride, 500 cps sweep width. Hydroxyl absorption also shown neat and 10%, 5%, 2%, and 1% (w/v) in carbon tetrachloride.

Conc., w/v in CCl_4	τ of —OH
100%	2.55
20	3.25
10	3.55
5	4.05
2	5.12
1	5.63

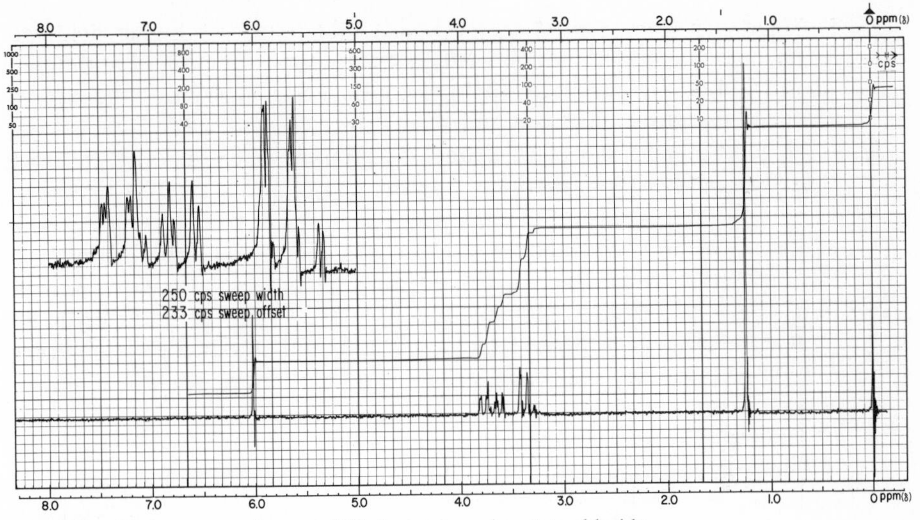

Fig. 4-20 *o*-Hydroxyacetophenone, 15% (w/v) in carbon tetrachloride, 1000 cps sweep width.

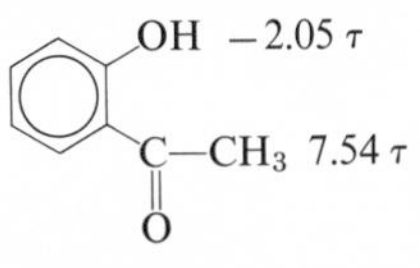

−0.5 τ and do not show a great shift on dilution [for example, methyl salicylate, −0.58 τ, salicylaldehyde, −0.95 τ, *o*-hydroxyacetophenone, −2.05 τ (Fig. 4-20)].

Enols owe their existence to very strong intramolecular hydrogen bonds. The hydroxylic absorption of enols occurs at very low field (−6 to −5 τ) and is usually unaffected by dilution or solvent interaction. In spectra of acetic acid solutions of enols, both hydroxyl and carboxyl absorptions may be observed, which indicates negligible chemical exchange even in this solvent. The hydroxyl group of the enol form of acetylacetone (Fig. 4-21) absorbs at −4.92 τ. The n.m.r. spectra of enols show absorptions of both keto and enol forms. Thus, interchange between these two forms on the n.m.r. time scale (Sec. 4.5) is very slow. Integration of the spectrum of acetylacetone (Fig. 4-21) indicates the presence of 84% of the enol form and 16% of the keto form in the pure liquid at 40°.

Carboxylic acids absorb in the region −2.0 to −0.5 τ. This absorption does not shift appreciably on dilution by inert solvents because of the strong hydrogen-bonded dimer structure of this group. An example of the carboxylic acid absorption is phenylacetic acid (Fig. 4-22). Hydroxyl and carboxyl groups of compounds that contain both groups usually undergo rapid chemical exchange; the average absorption position that results (—CO_2H and —OH) is concentration-dependent.

Amines ordinarily give rise to single, sharp absorption lines, a behavior

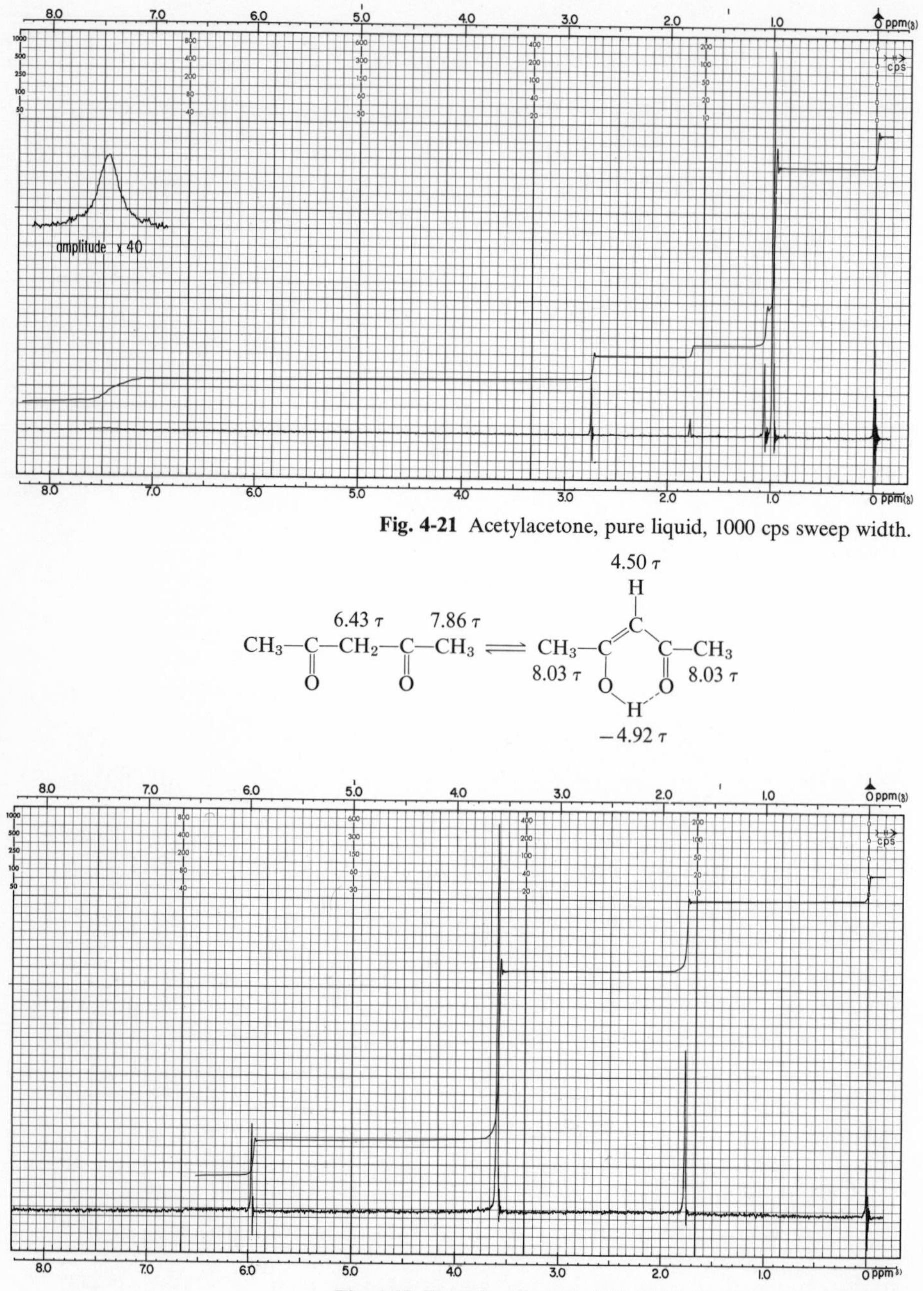

Fig. 4-21 Acetylacetone, pure liquid, 1000 cps sweep width.

CH_3—CO—CH_2—CO—CH_3 ⇌ CH_3—C(OH)=CH—CO—CH_3 (enol, H-bonded O—H···O)

Keto form: CH_2 6.43 τ; CH_3 7.86 τ

Enol form: =CH 4.50 τ; CH_3 8.03 τ, 8.03 τ; O—H···O −4.92 τ

Fig. 4-22 Phenylacetic acid, 15% (w/v) in carbon tetrachloride, 1000 cps sweep width.

C_6H_5—CH_2—CO_2H
2.79 τ 6.47 τ −1.95 τ

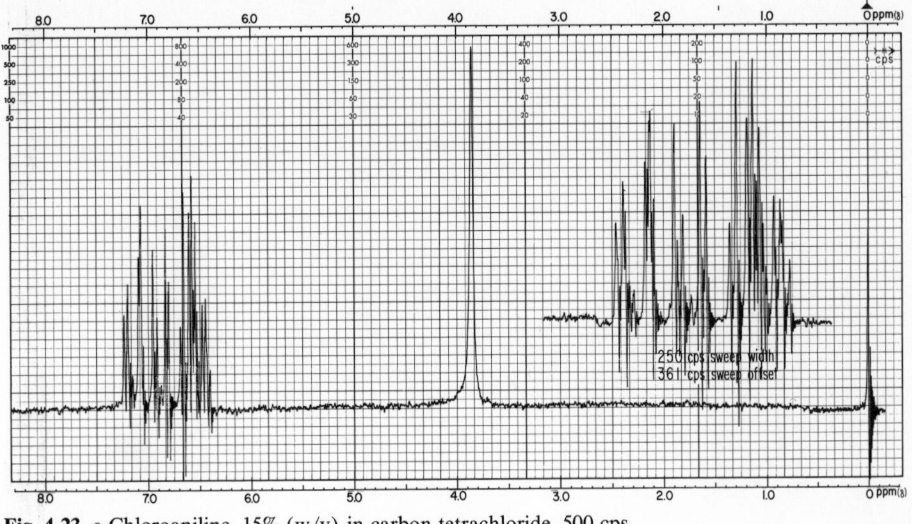

Fig. 4-23 *o*-Chloroaniline, 15% (w/v) in carbon tetrachloride, 500 cps sweep width.

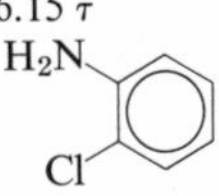

(similar to alcohol groups) that indicates rapid chemical exchange of the amino hydrogen atoms. Aliphatic amines absorb in the region 7.8–9.7 τ, and aromatic amines absorb in the region 5.3–7.4 τ (*o*-chloroaniline, Fig. 4-23). These absorption values are shifted to higher field on dilution with inert solvents. Because the nitrogen nucleus has a spin of unity ($I = 1$), the absorption of a proton attached to nitrogen will in theory be split into a triplet. This behavior is observed for amines in acid solution. Figure 4-24 shows the spectra of methylamine in water at three different *p*H values. At *p*H 10, chemical exchange of —OH and $—NH_2$ protons is very rapid, and only one absorption is observed. The intermolecular exchange of the amino protons must also be very rapid, because the methyl group absorption is a singlet. At *p*H 4.1, chemical exchange is retarded somewhat, and separate absorptions may be observed for the protons of H_2O (5.55 τ) and $—NH_3^+$ (a broad absorption centered at 2.62 τ). The intermolecular exchange of the amino protons is still rapid, however, since the methyl group absorption is a singlet. At *p*H 0.87, the rates of exchange are very slow. The methyl group absorption is a quartet that has $J = 7.4$ cps, which indicates that the rate of intermolecular exchange of the amino protons is much slower than sixteen times a second. The $—NH_3^+$ absorption is a widely spaced triplet that has $J = 52$ cps. The magnitude of the coupling constant (J_{HN}) of this triplet is characteristic of a proton when coupled to nitrogen. Although the components of the triplet are broadened because of the electric quadrupole moment of the

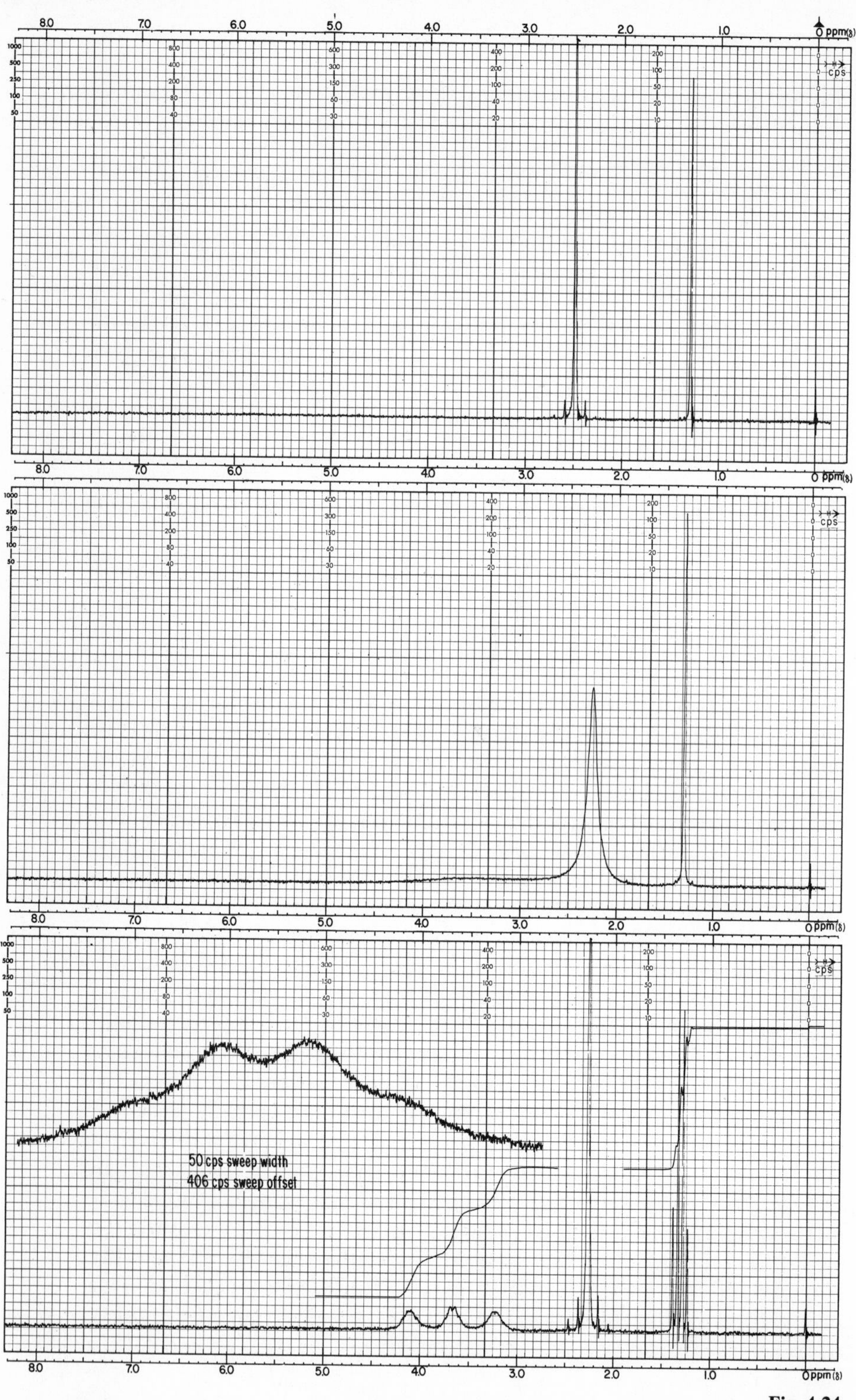

Fig. 4-24

nitrogen nucleus, the spectrum does show that each of the components of the $—NH_3^+$ triplet is a quartet as a result of coupling with the protons of the methyl group.

Trifluoroacetic acid is an excellent solvent for many organic compounds. It contains only one proton, which absorbs at very low field ($-1.2\ \tau$), and consequently does not interfere with most spectra. Trifluoroacetic acid is an especially useful solvent for amines. The protons of substituted aliphatic ammonium ions absorb in the range 2.4–2.9 τ, and the protons of substituted aromatic ammonium ions absorb in the range 0.5–1.5 τ. The absorptions are broad single peaks when insufficient excess acid is present to retard rapid chemical exchange or broad triplets when a large excess of acid is present.

Amide N—H groups give rise to somewhat broad absorption bands in the region 1.5–5.0 τ (*N*-methylacetamide, Fig. 4-25). Protons attached to amide nitrogen do not undergo rapid chemical exchange, because spin-

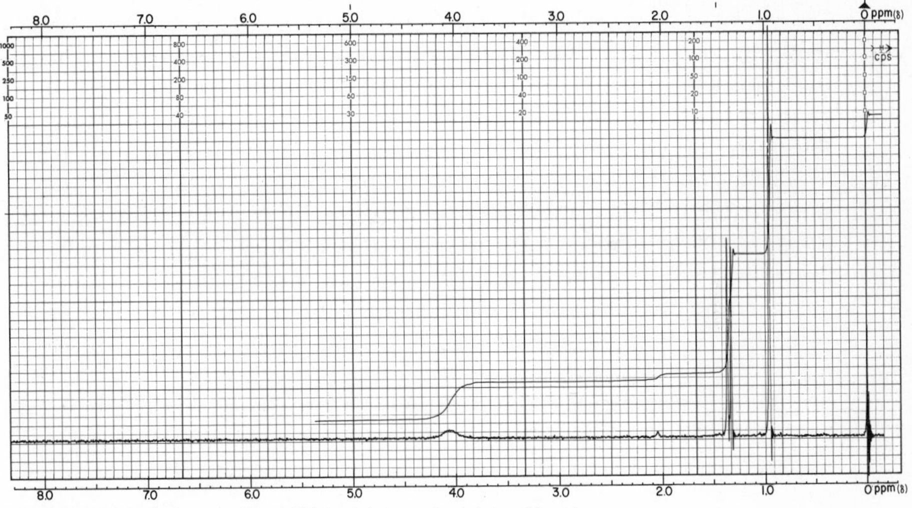

Fig. 4-25 *N*-Methylacetamide, 15% (w/v) in carbon tetrachloride, 1000 cps sweep width.

8.08 τ $CH_3—C(=O)—N—H$ 1.87 τ; N—CH_3 7.30 τ $J = 4.7$ cps

Fig. 4-24 Methylamine in water and hydrochloric acid, 1000 cps sweep width. Top, *p*H 10; middle, *p*H 4.1; bottom, *p*H 0.87.

Top:
H_2O, $H_2N—CH_3$ 7.40 τ
*p*H 10.0

Middle:
$H_2N—CH_3$
*p*H 4.10

Bottom:
2.67 τ $H_3\overset{\oplus}{N}—CH_3$ 7.37 τ
*p*H 0.87
$J_{HN} = 52$ cps
$J_{HH'} = 7.4$ cps

spin coupling with alkyl groups also attached to the same nitrogen can be observed. Because the position of absorption of amide protons is dependent to a small extent on concentration, it is possible that slow chemical exchange does exist.

Sulfhydryl compounds absorb in the range 8.4–8.8 τ if aliphatic and near 6.4 τ if aromatic. The absorption is shifted to higher field on dilution with an inert solvent. Since sulfur (S^{32}) is nonmagnetic, no coupling with this nucleus is observed. When chemical exchange is slow, coupling with adjacent C—H groups may be observed.

Protons attached to other nuclei can sometimes be observed with the ordinary proton magnetic resonance spectrometer (the Varian A-60 instrument can detect protons in the range -23 to $+18$ τ). Absorption positions have been recorded for the following compounds (τ) in the vapor phase: H_2, 5.57; NH_3, 9.82; H_2O, 9.17; SiH_4, 6.77; PH_3, 8.29; H_2S, 9.69; HF, 7.27; HCl, 10.22; HBr, 14.12; HI, 23.02. Protons bonded to transition metals absorb in the region 17–30 τ.

A proton may couple with any nucleus (if $I > 0$) to which it is covalently bonded, but if that nucleus has an appreciable electric quadrupole moment, which is common for nuclei that have $I > \frac{1}{2}$ (*e.g.*, N, Cl, Br, I), coupling will not commonly be observed. Protons couple efficiently with fluorine ($I = \frac{1}{2}$) in organic compounds ($J_{HCF} \sim 60$ cps; $J_{HCCF} \sim 20$ cps). The absorptions of protons coupled to phosphorus (P^{31}, $I = \frac{1}{2}$) are split into doublets; the coupling constant (J_{HP}) is large (200–700 cps) and observable, but diminished, through at least four covalent bonds. The presence of deuterium ($I = 1$) in an organic compound has the anticipated effect on the proton magnetic resonance spectrum. The proton coupling constant for gaseous HD is 43 cps; the coupling constant for a proton with a deuteron in the situation H—C—D is generally about 2 cps and in the situation H—C—C—D, it is less than 1 cps. In general, it has been found that $J_H/J_D \cong 6$–7. Deuteration of an organic compound is frequently a useful technique that can be studied by n.m.r. spectroscopy. Protons α to an enolizible functional group can be equilibrated with deuterons in the presence of a basic catalyst. The change in the n.m.r. spectrum not only shows the presence of such groups but can also serve to demonstrate their number and can be used to study rate processes.

Ordinary carbon (C^{12}) is nonmagnetic ($I = 0$), but the natural abundance (1.11%) of C^{13} ($I = \frac{1}{2}$) gives rise to observable H—C^{13} coupling, especially in spectra recorded at high amplitude. Absorptions resulting from coupling with this nucleus are frequently called C^{13} satellite peaks. The H—C^{13} coupling constant is rather large; $J_{HC^{13}} = ca$ 100–250 cps. The absorptions appear as weak peaks symmetrical on either side of the

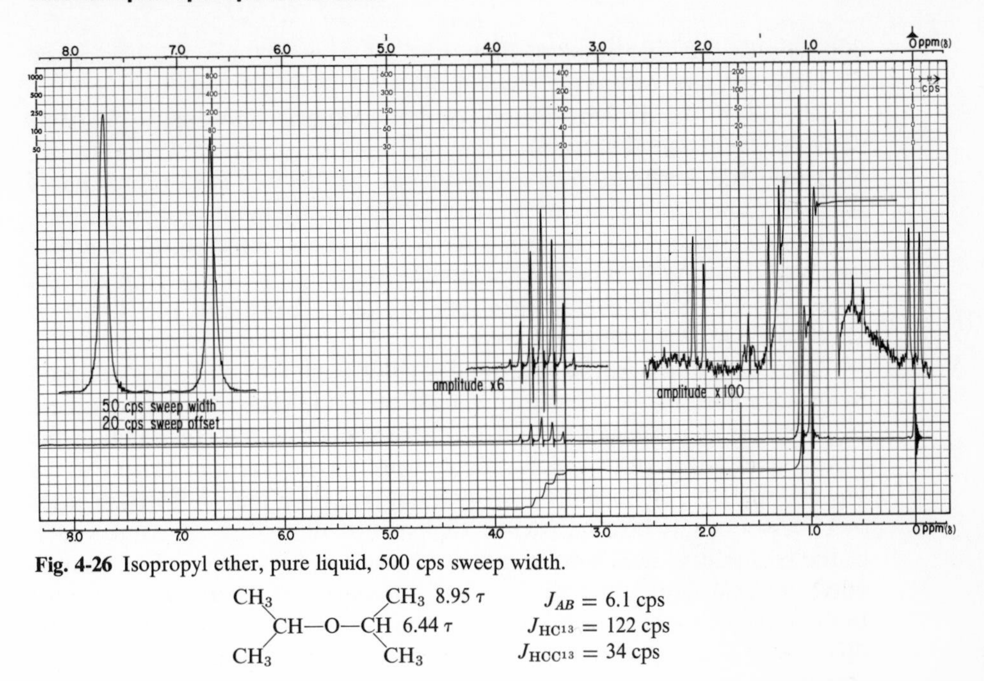

Fig. 4-26 Isopropyl ether, pure liquid, 500 cps sweep width.

$(CH_3)_2CH{-}O{-}CH(CH_3)_2$ — CH_3 8.95 τ; CH 6.44 τ

$J_{AB} = 6.1$ cps
$J_{HC^{13}} = 122$ cps
$J_{HCC^{13}} = 34$ cps

much stronger proton resonance of the H—C^{12} groups. Such peaks resulting from HC^{13} coupling are seen in the high-amplitude spectrum of isopropyl ether (Fig. 4-26). In this spectrum it is seen that the proton spin-spin coupling constant is 6.1 cps. In the high-amplitude trace it is seen that the methyl group doublet is surrounded by two sets of C^{13} satellite doublets—$J_{HC^{13}} = 122$ cps and $J_{HCC^{13}} = 34$ cps. There appears to be a reasonable correlation between the magnitude of $J_{HC^{13}}$ and the hybridization (degree of *s* character) of the carbon atom to which the proton is attached. When the hybridization is sp^3, $J \cong 120$ cps; when it is sp^2, $J \cong 170$ cps; and when it is sp, $J \cong 250$ cps.

4.10 COMPLEX SPIN-SPIN INTERACTIONS

It is rarely possible to deduce a structural formula solely from the nuclear magnetic resonance spectrum of a compound. The more important factors necessary for the exact interpretation of a spectrum are line positions (correlated with values from the literature or known compounds), intensities (available from integration of the spectrum), and the precise nature of spin-spin multiplets. An occasional problem in the interpretation of spectra of complex molecules is the distinction between signals that correspond to transitions of nuclei that are not spin-spin coupled to other nuclei and those signals that are components of spin-spin multiplets. Powerful techniques aiding these interpretations are the determination of the spectrum at different field strengths and the use of the double resonance technique (Sec. 4.13).

Chemically equivalent protons do not ordinarily show spin-spin splitting. Thus, only single proton resonance lines are observed for hydrogen, methane, and benzene. The effect of one proton on the absorption of another proton or group of equivalent protons generally depends in a predictable manner on the number and kind of intervening chemical bonds and on the stereochemical relationships of the interacting groups. Some of the more useful spin-spin coupling constants are listed in Table 4-1.

According to the simple multiplicity rules (Sec. 4.4), the areas enclosed by the components of a multiplet should be in the ratio of whole numbers —for example, a quartet should have the ratio 1:3:3:1. In practice this situation is never observed for proton-proton interactions. Even if the separation of the signals of two interacting groups of nuclei is of the order of 150 cps (as may be the case for ethyl groups at 60 Mc), the components of the multiplets are not quite in the ratio of whole numbers. For such an ethyl group one might observe relative intensities of 0.9:2.9:3.1:1.1 for the methylene quartet and 1.1:2.0:0.9 for the methyl group triplet. This divergence from ideality is quite general and is actually of considerable value in the interpretation of spectra. It is found that the intensities of the spin-spin multiplets are greater on that side *toward* the absorption of the group of protons responsible for the observed multiplicity.

Interacting protons for which the separation of peaks is of approximately the same magnitude as the coupling constant give complicated spectra that are usually unrecognizable in terms of the simple splitting rules given in Sec. 4.4. In these cases mathematical analysis of the spectral data is required to obtain values for the chemical shifts of the protons and the coupling constants. In the analysis of complex spectra, interacting groups of nuclei are by convention labeled A, B, . . . (in order of increasing τ value) if they have approximately the same chemical shift value, and M, N, . . . and/or X, Y, . . . if the chemical shift values are very much different from other interacting nuclei (A, B, . . .). Equivalent nuclei are assigned the same letter. Thus, ethyl bromide is an A_2B_3 system, *p*-nitrobenzonitrile an A_2B_2 system, vinyl bromide an ABC system, and 1,3,5-trifluorobenzene an A_3X_3 system. The frequency separation (in cps) of the positions of absorption of the interacting nuclei is given by the symbol $\Delta\nu$.

Occasionally the splitting observed for a group of equivalent protons can be *approximately* analyzed according to the simple splitting rules stated in Sec. 4.4. Two examples of this are *n*-propyl iodide (Fig. 4-27) and pure ethyl alcohol (Fig. 4-5). The protons of propyl iodide form an $A_2B_2C_3$ system. The A protons (adjacent to iodine) are coupled to the B protons, and the methyl C protons are coupled to the B protons. Examination of an expanded spectrum of propyl iodide reveals that $J_{AB} = 6.8$

Table 4-1

SPIN-SPIN COUPLING CONSTANTS

Type	J, cps	Type	J, cps
H_2†	280	$>C{=}CH{-}CH{=}C<$	9–13
CH_4†	12.4	$H{-}C{\equiv}C{-}H$†	9.1
$>C(H)H$ (geminal)	12–15	$>CH{-}C{\equiv}C{-}H$	2–3
$>CH{-}CH<$	2–9	$>CH{-}C(H){=}O$	1–3
$-C(H){-}(-C-)_n{-}C(H)-$	~0	$>C{=}C(H){-}C(H){=}O$	6–8
$CH_3{-}CH_2{-}X$	6.5–7.5	benzene	*o*- 6–9 *m*- 1–3 *p*- 0–1
$(CH_3)_2CH{-}X$	5.5–7.0	furan	$\alpha\beta$ 1.6–2.0 $\alpha\beta'$ 0.6–1.0 $\alpha\alpha'$ 1.3–1.8 $\beta\beta'$ 3.2–3.8
cyclohexane $H{-}C(X){-}C(Y){-}H$	a,a 5–10 a,e 2–4 e,e 2–4	pyrrole (N–H)	$\alpha\beta$ 2.0–2.6 $\alpha\beta'$ 1.5–2.2 $\alpha\alpha'$ 1.8–2.3 $\beta\beta'$ 2.8–4.0
$>C{=}C(H)H$	0.5–3	thiophene	$\alpha\beta$ 4.6–5.8 $\alpha\beta'$ 1.0–1.8 $\alpha\alpha'$ 2.1–3.3 $\beta\beta'$ 3.0–4.2
$H(C{=}C)H$ (cis)	7–12	pyridine	$\alpha\beta$ 4.9–5.7 $\alpha\gamma$ 1.6–2.6 $\alpha\beta'$ 0.7–1.1 $\alpha\alpha'$ 0.2–0.5 $\beta\gamma$ 7.2–8.5 $\beta\beta'$ 1.4–1.9
$H(C{=}C)H$ (trans)	13–18		
$>C{=}C(H){-}C{-}H$	4–10		
$H{-}C{=}C{-}C{-}H$ (transoid)	0.5–2.5		
$H{-}C{=}C{-}C{-}H$ (cisoid)	~0		

† The coupling constant for these molecules, which contain only equivalent protons, has been determined from the spectra of the partially deuterated substances.

cps and $J_{BC} = 7.3$ cps. If these values for the coupling constants are used, the appearance of the pattern of the B protons may be calculated‡ (Fig. 4-28). In Fig. 4-28, the unperturbed line for the B protons (a) is split into a quartet ($J_{BC} = 7.3$ cps) by the methyl C protons (b). Each

‡ For the sake of simplicity, symmetrical multiplets are assumed in these calculated spectra. This would actually be the case only if the protons of propyl iodide formed an $A_2M_2X_3$ system.

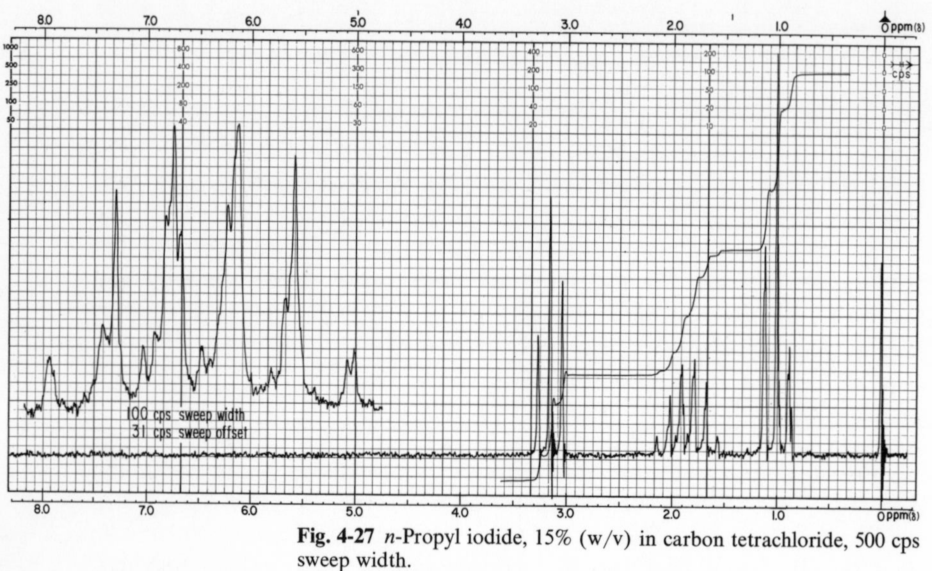

Fig. 4-27 *n*-Propyl iodide, 15% (w/v) in carbon tetrachloride, 500 cps sweep width.

CH_3—CH_2—CH_2—I	$J_{AB} = 6.8$ cps
8.98 τ 8.14 τ 6.83 τ	$J_{BC} = 7.3$ cps

component of this quartet is then split into a triplet ($J_{AB} = 6.8$ cps) by the methylene *A* protons (c). It can be seen that the analysis compares favorably with the expanded spectrum of the *B* protons (Fig. 4-27). If J_{AB} were exactly equal to J_{BC}, a symmetrical sextet would in theory result. As the values for J_{AB} and J_{BC} are very nearly the same in this example, the *B* methylene group multiplet resembles a sextet.

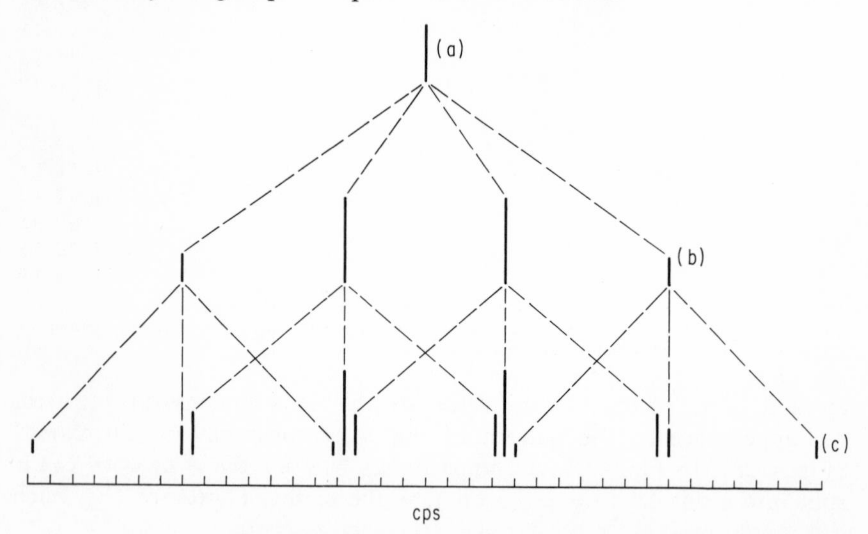

Fig. 4-28 Analysis of the *B* protons of *n*-propyl iodide; $J_{AB} = 6.8$ cps, $J_{BC} = 7.3$ cps.

If the coupling constants of a system such as that described above do not have nearly the same value, a pattern resembling that predicted by the simple multiplicity rules does not result. Such is the case with pure ethyl alcohol (Fig. 4-5), which may be treated as an AB_2C_3 case. Examination of an expanded spectrum of pure ethyl alcohol reveals that $J_{AB} = 5.0$ cps and $J_{BC} = 7.2$ cps. When these values are used (and if symmetry of the multiplets is assumed), the appearance of the absorption due to the methylene group may be calculated (Fig. 4-29). In Fig. 4-29, the unperturbed line for the methylene protons (a) is split into a quartet ($J_{BC} = 7.2$ cps) by the methyl protons (b), each component of which is split into a doublet ($J_{AB} = 5.0$ cps) by the hydroxyl proton (c). Because symmetry of the multiplets was assumed for the calculated spectrum, it agrees quite well with the experimental result (Fig. 4-5). The multiplet does not, however, much resemble a quintet, which would result if $J_{AB} = J_{BC}$. If the values for the coupling constants are much more different, larger deviations from the simple multiplicity rules (Sec. 4.4) result.

Greater divergence from the symmetrical nature of a multiplet results when the absorption positions of the interacting groups are closer together. It is readily seen that the methyl group triplet of *n*-propyl iodide (Fig. 4-27), in which $\Delta\nu$ ($CH_3 - CH_2$) = 50 cps is less symmetrical than that of ethyl alcohol (Fig. 4-5), in which $\Delta\nu$ ($CH_3 - CH_2$) = 147 cps. The

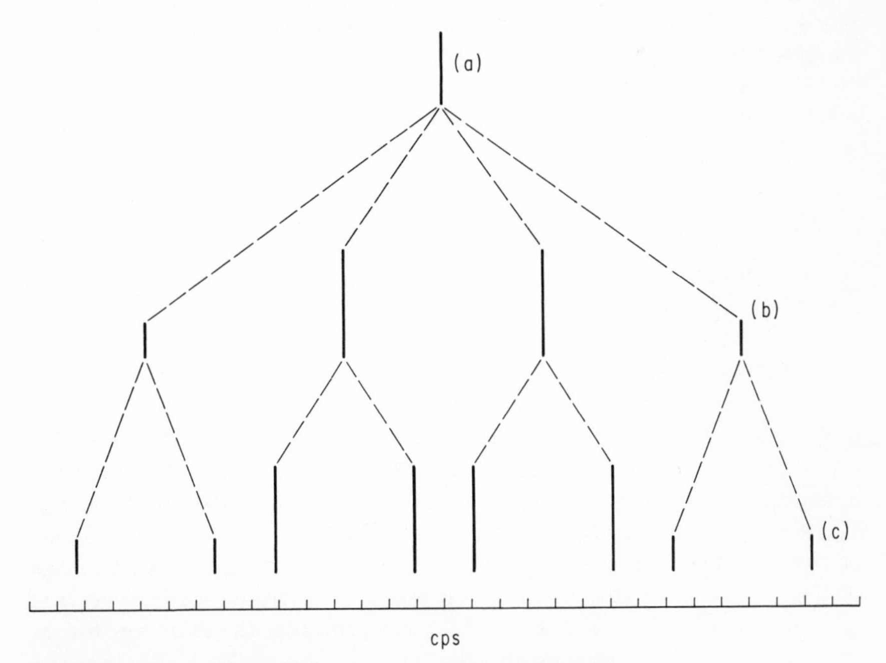

Fig. 4-29 Analysis of the methylene protons of pure ethyl alcohol; $J_{AB} = 5.0$ cps, $J_{BC} = 7.2$ cps.

following parts of this section are devoted to a brief examination of the types of spectral patterns to be anticipated for various types of interactions for which $J \cong \Delta\nu$.

Two Interacting Nuclei: A_2, AB, AX. Interaction between the magnetically equivalent protons A_2 is not observable, and hence this system gives rise to a single absorption line. The AX system results in a pair of doublets of relative intensity 1:1; J and $\Delta\nu$ can be determined directly from the spectrum. The A_2 and AX cases are extreme examples of the interactions possible for two nuclei. Spectra of AB cases consist of two doublets, or four lines, which are symmetric about the mid-point of the spectrum. As $J_{AB}/\Delta\nu_{AB}$ increases, the intensity of the inner pair of lines increases at the expense of the outer pair. Calculated AB spectra for which $J_{AB}/\Delta\nu_{AB} = \frac{1}{6}, \frac{1}{2}$, and $1\frac{1}{3}$ are shown in Fig. 4-30. The coupling constant for the interacting groups can be read directly from the spectrum. If the peaks are numbered from left to right and the positions are measured in cps, $J_{AB} = |1 - 2| = |3 - 4|$. The peak position for the A proton (lines 1 and 2) and the B proton (lines 3 and 4) cannot be read directly from the spectrum. The relative positions ($\Delta\nu_{AB}$) are obtained from the expression

$$|1 - 3| = |2 - 4| = \sqrt{\Delta\nu_{AB}^2 + J_{AB}^2}$$

The absorption positions (in cps) for the A and B protons are $\pm\frac{1}{2}\Delta\nu$ from the mid-point of the spectrum. The relative intensities i of the lines are given by the expressions

$$i_1 = i_4 = 1 - \frac{J_{AB}}{\sqrt{\Delta\nu_{AB}^2 + J_{AB}^2}}$$

$$i_2 = i_3 = 1 + \frac{J_{AB}}{\sqrt{\Delta\nu_{AB}^2 + J_{AB}^2}}$$

An example of an AB spectrum is shown by the aromatic protons of 2-methyl-3-hydroxymethylfuran (Fig. 4-31), in which $J = 1.9$ cps and $\Delta\nu = 52.6$ cps ($J/\Delta\nu = 0.036$).

Three Interacting Nuclei: A_3, AB_2, ABC, AX_2, ABX, AMX. The A_3 system gives rise to a single absorption peak. The AX_2 system gives rise to two absorptions: a 1:2:1 triplet for the A proton and a 1:1 doublet for the X protons; J and $\Delta\nu$ can be obtained directly from the spectrum. Spectra of AMX systems consist of three quartets, or twelve lines; J_{AM}, J_{AX}, J_{MX}, and the positions of absorption of the A, M, and X nuclei may be obtained by a simple analysis of the spectrum. An example of an AMX system is given by the aromatic protons of pyrrole-2-carboxylic acid (Fig. 4-32). The A_3, AX_2, and AMX types represent the extremes for the other cases of three interacting nuclei.

Spectra of AB_2 systems show similarity to AX_2 spectra only if

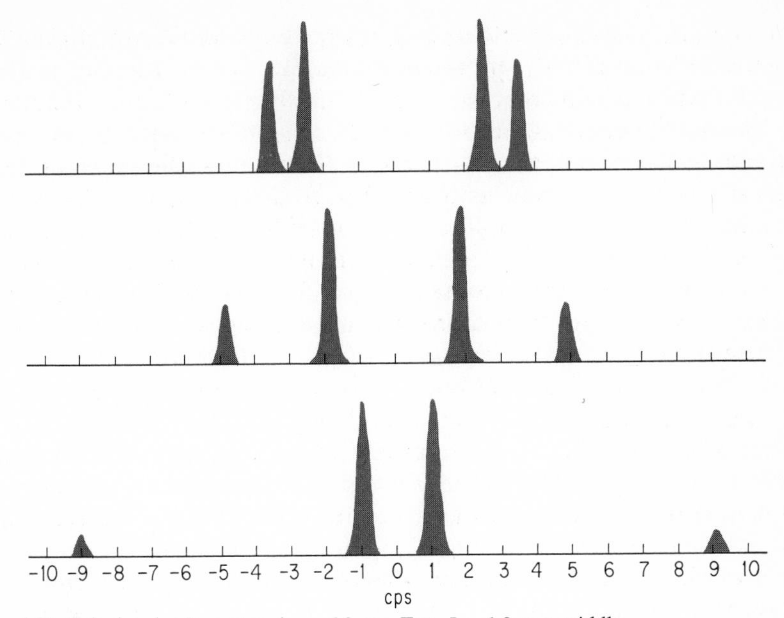

Fig. 4-30 Calculated AB spectra. $\Delta\nu = 6.0$ cps. Top, $J = 1.0$ cps; middle, $J = 3.0$ cps; bottom, $J = 8.0$ cps.

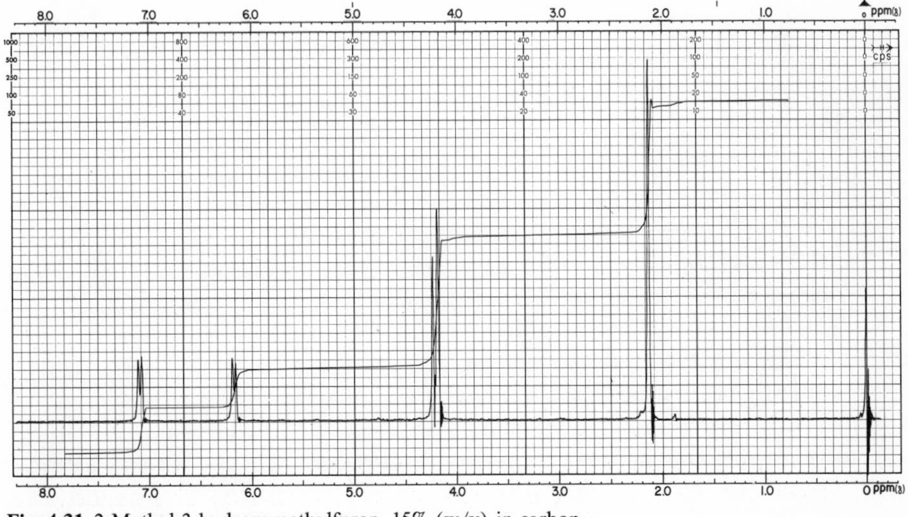

Fig. 4-31 2-Methyl-3-hydroxymethylfuran, 15% (w/v) in carbon tetrachloride, 500 cps sweep width.

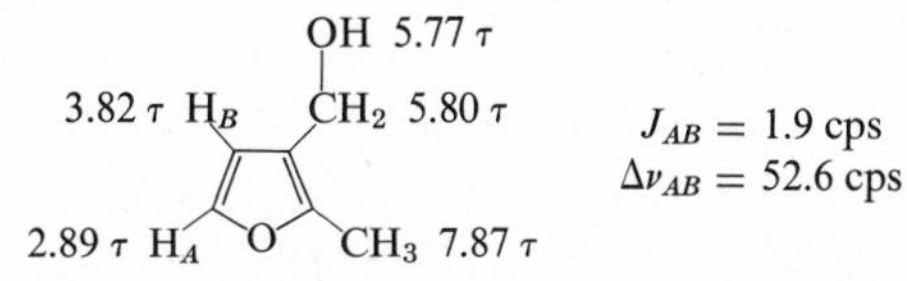

$J_{AB} = 1.9$ cps
$\Delta\nu_{AB} = 52.6$ cps

$\Delta\nu_{AB} \gg J_{AB}$. Because $J_{AB} = J_{AB'}$, $J_{BB'}$ has no effect on the spectrum. Examples of theoretical AB_2 spectra in which $J_{AB}/\Delta\nu_{AB} = \frac{1}{6}, \frac{1}{2}$, and 1.0 are shown in Fig. 4-33. AB_2 spectra consist of nine lines; four for the A proton, four for the B protons, and a weak combination line that is usually not observed. If the peaks are numbered from left to right, the chemical shift of the A proton is always given by line 3; the chemical shift of the B protons is given by the average of the positions of lines 5 and 7. Because the positions of absorption of the A and B protons can be read directly from the spectrum, the coupling constant J_{AB} is obtained by relatively simple mathematical analysis. An example of an AB_2 spectrum is given by the aromatic protons of pyrogallol (Fig. 4-34), in which $\Delta\nu = 8.6$ cps and $J = 8.4$ cps ($J/\Delta\nu = 0.98$). The similarity of the spectrum of pyrogallol and that calculated for $J_{AB} = \Delta\nu_{AB}$ is to be expected.

Coupling between three nonequivalent protons gives rise (in addition to the AMX case) to ABC and ABX spectra, which consist in theory of 15 lines. Three coupling constants are involved in these spectra: J_{AB}, $J_{AX(C)}$, and $J_{BX(C)}$. Only if $J_{AB} = J_{AX(C)}$ is a relatively simple spectrum obtained, which consists of an unsymmetrical triplet for the $X(C)$ nucleus and unsymmetrical doublets for the A and B protons. When one of the three protons has a chemical shift very much different from the other two (the ABX case), the spectrum consists of two quartets (that sometimes overlap) for the A and B protons, four lines for the X proton, and three

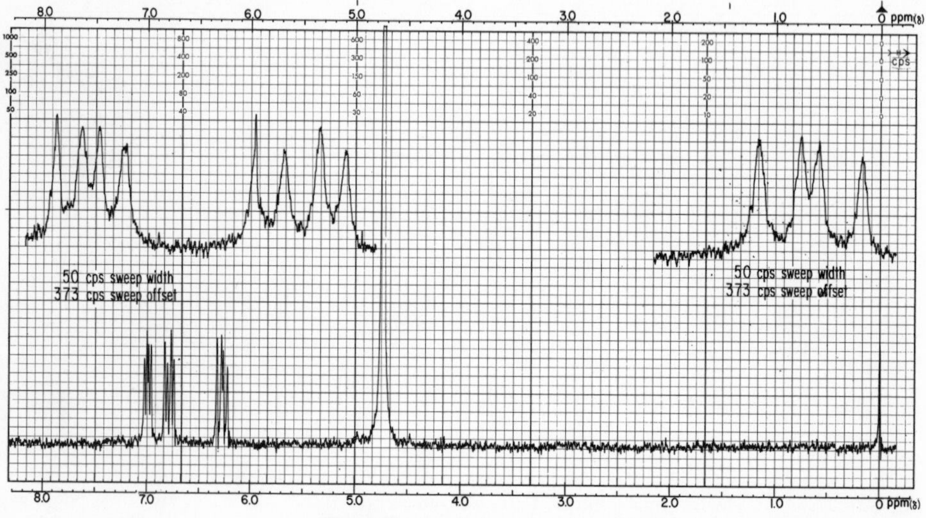

Fig. 4-32 Pyrrole-2-carboxylic acid, 20% (w/v) in deuterium oxide, 500 cps sweep width.

3.74 τ H_X — H_M 3.21 τ

3.01 τ H_A — N — CO_2H

H

$J_{AM} = 1.6$ cps
$J_{AX} = 2.6$ cps
$J_{MX} = 3.7$ cps

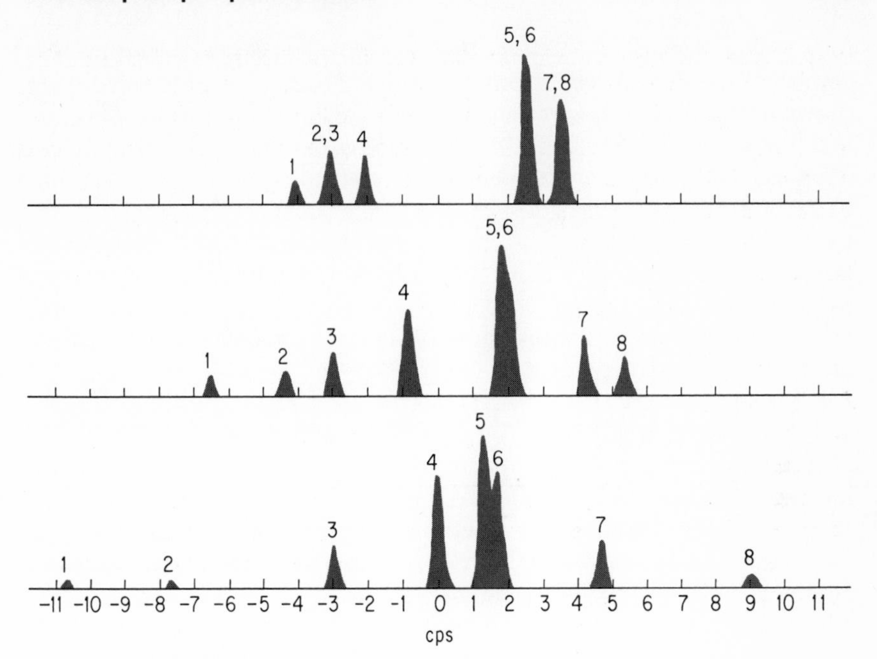

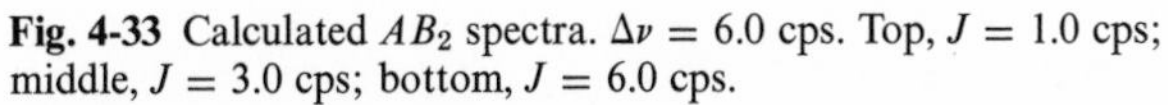
Fig. 4-33 Calculated AB_2 spectra. $\Delta\nu = 6.0$ cps. Top, $J = 1.0$ cps; middle, $J = 3.0$ cps; bottom, $J = 6.0$ cps.

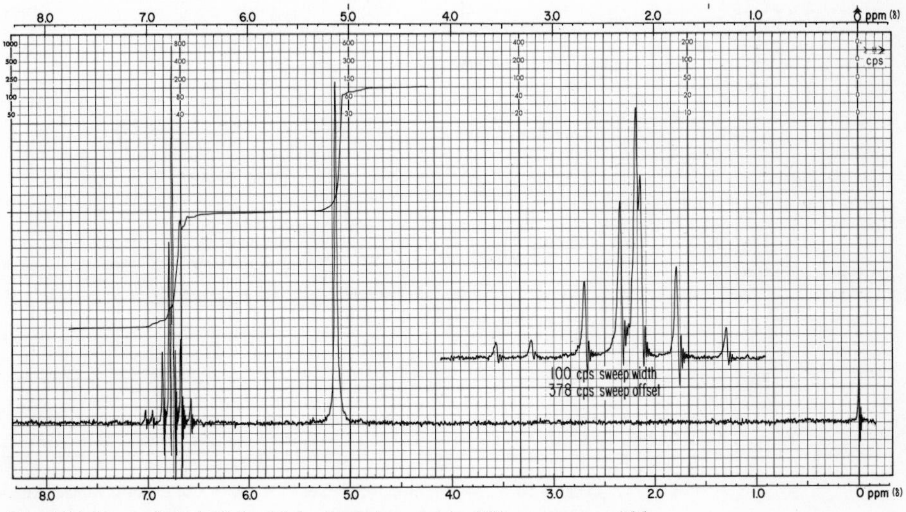

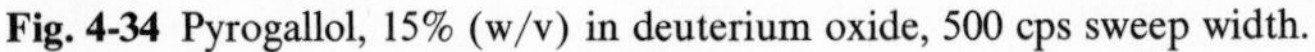
Fig. 4-34 Pyrogallol, 15% (w/v) in deuterium oxide, 500 cps sweep width.

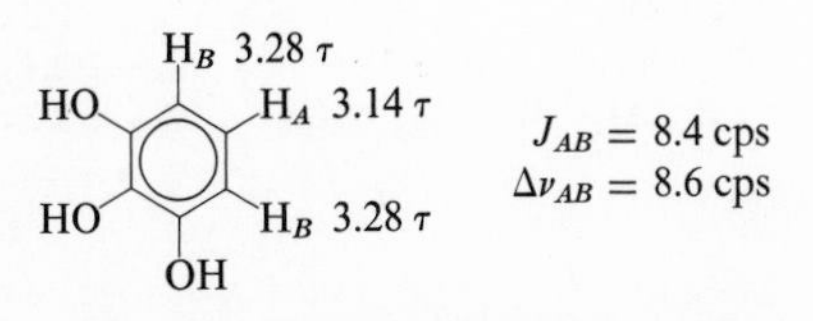

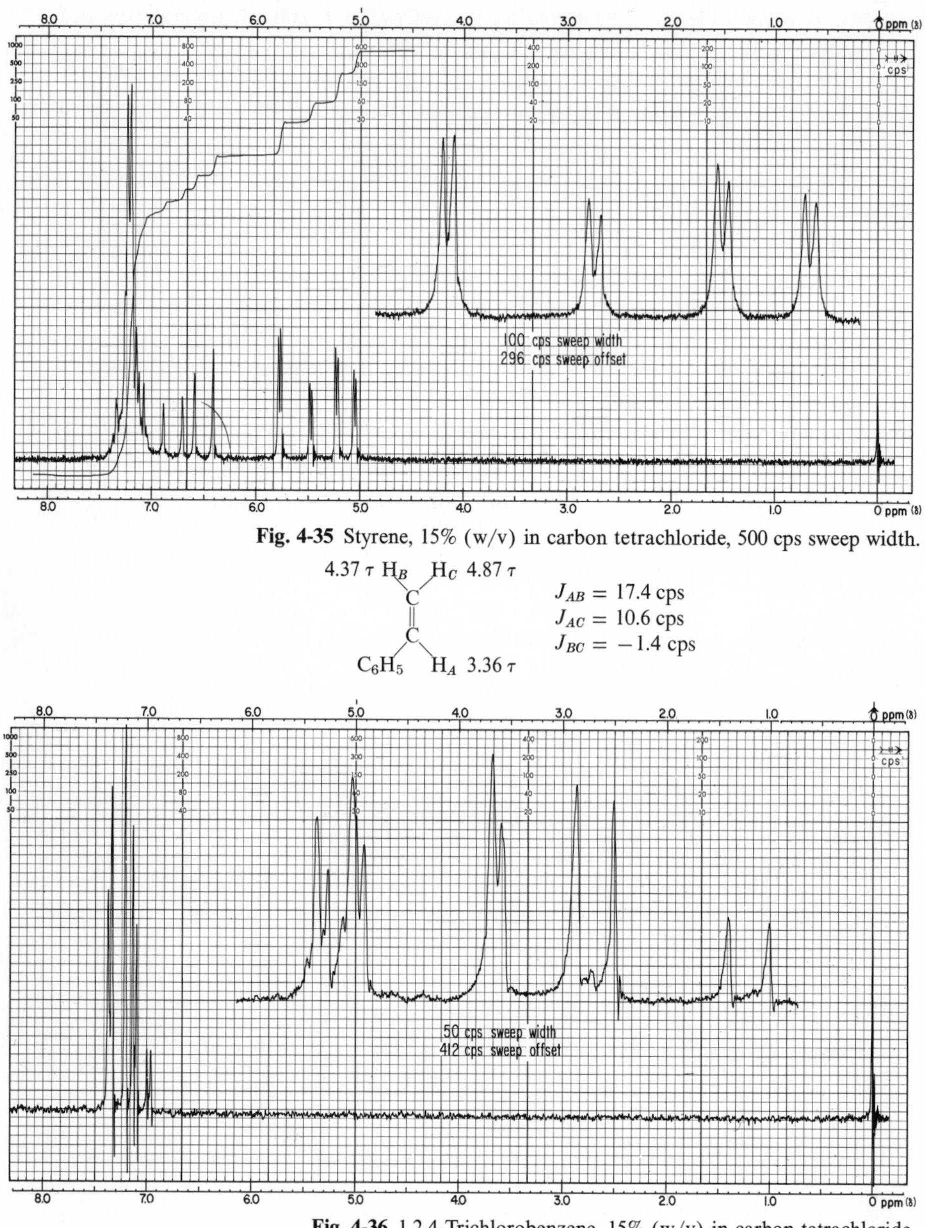

Fig. 4-35 Styrene, 15% (w/v) in carbon tetrachloride, 500 cps sweep width.

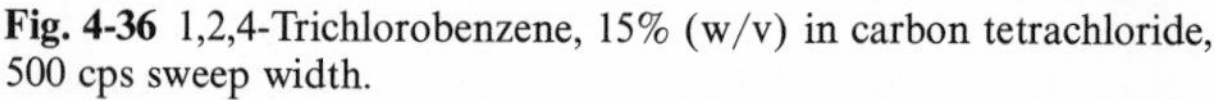

Fig. 4-36 1,2,4-Trichlorobenzene, 15% (w/v) in carbon tetrachloride, 500 cps sweep width.

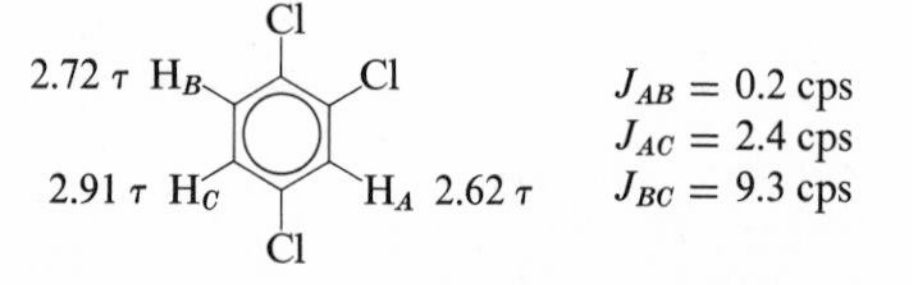

weak combination lines. The two quartets of the AB part of the spectrum are each a typical AB spectrum. If all of the lines of the spectrum are observed, the three coupling constants can be measured directly from the spectrum. Little additional information can be derived directly from the spectrum in ordinary cases; mathematical analysis or comparison with calculated spectra is required. An example of an ABX spectrum is styrene (Fig. 4-35).

Relatively complicated spectra result from an ABC system. This system is of common occurrence in organic molecules; examples are certain trisubstituted aromatic compounds (1,2,4-trichlorobenzene, Fig. 4-36) and some monosubstituted olefins (ethyl acrylate, Fig. 4-37), among others. There is no over-all element of symmetry to be expected from ABC or ABX spectra.

Four Interacting Nuclei: Of the many possible combinations of four interacting nuclei, those most easily analyzed and of most interest to the organic chemist are AB_3 systems (and those approaching AX_3) and A_2B_2 systems (and those approaching A_2X_2). The limiting cases are AX_3, which consists of a quartet for the A nucleus and a doublet for the X nuclei

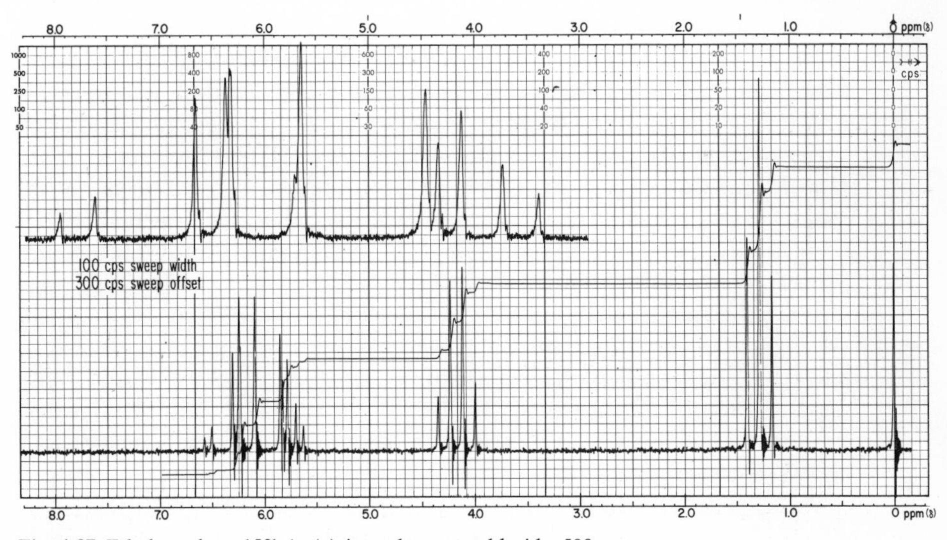

Fig. 4-37 Ethyl acrylate, 15% (w/v) in carbon tetrachloride, 500 cps sweep width.

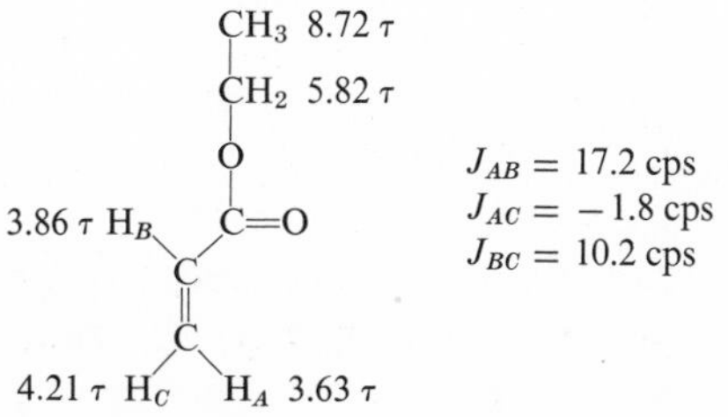

(acetaldehyde, Fig. 4-7), and the A_2X_2 case, which consists of two triplets. In theory, 56 lines are present in spectra of four interacting nuclei. Many of these lines may have zero intensity, may be so weak as to be unobservable, or may be nearly superimposed on other lines.

The most common example of an AB_3 case is the group CH_3—C—H (with single bonds drawn above and below the C).

Since free rotation about the carbon-carbon bond may be assumed, the three coupling constants have an average value, and the spectrum is described by only the two quantities J_{AB} and $\Delta\nu_{AB}$. If $J_{AB}/\Delta\nu_{AB} = 0.1$, the similarity to the AX_3 spectrum is still recognizable, but the doublet and quartet are distorted, and both absorption bands are broadened. As the ratio $J/\Delta\nu$ increases, the changes become severe; the A and B bands overlap, and additional peaks are observed.

The commanding feature for the identification of A_2X_2 and A_2B_2 spectra is the fact that they are symmetrical about the mid-point of the spectrum. That is, the spectrum due to the A nuclei is the mirror image of the spectrum due to the B (or X) nuclei. Spectra of A_2X_2 systems have the additional element of symmetry in that the A and X portions are themselves symmetrical about mid-points. The symmetry of these spectra render them easily recognizable. With the exception of AB (and AX) spectra, these groups of interacting nuclei are the only ones that give rise to symmetrical spectra. Four coupling constants, $J_{AA'}$, J_{AB}, $J_{AB'}$, and $J_{BB'}$ ($J_{A'B'} = J_{AB}$ and $J_{AB'} = J_{A'B}$ because of symmetry) are involved in these cases, and usually $J_{AB} \neq J_{AB'}$. It has been indicated previously that, in certain cases, coupling between equivalent nuclei is not observable (A_2, A_3, and AB_2 cases). The values for $J_{AA'}$ and $J_{BB'}$ in the A_2B_2 case are observable and affect the spectrum *because* $J_{AB} \neq J_{AB'}$. In the AB_2 case, $J_{AB} = J_{AB'}$, and hence $J_{BB'}$ is not observed to have an effect on the spectrum. *If all the coupling constants between two sets of equivalent nuclei are equal, the coupling of equivalent nuclei has no effect on the spectrum.* A_2B_2 spectra are not easily analyzed; values for $\Delta\nu$ and J are best obtained by mathematical treatment of the spectral data or by comparison with calculated spectra.

If $J_{AB} = J_{AB'}$ and $\Delta\nu_{AB} \gg J_{AB}$, the spectrum is independent of $J_{AA'}$ and $J_{BB'}$. Two triplets result which resemble the A_2X_2 case. An example is β-alanine (Fig. 4-38), for which the values for J_{AB} and $J_{AB'}$ are very nearly the same. In all 1,2-disubstituted ethanes, $J_{AA'} \cong J_{BB'}$. If $\Delta\nu_{AB} \cong J_{AB}$, a very complicated spectral pattern results. An example is 1-bromo-2-chloroethane (Fig. 4-39), in which $\Delta\nu_{AB} = 12.60$ cps, $J_{AB} = 5.97$ cps, $J_{AB'} = 9.03$ cps, and $J_{AA'} - J_{BB'} = 0.95$ cps.

Other common examples of A_2B_2 systems in organic compounds are p-disubstituted benzenes and symmetrically o-disubstituted benzenes. In p-disubstituted benzenes, the A protons and the B protons are, respec-

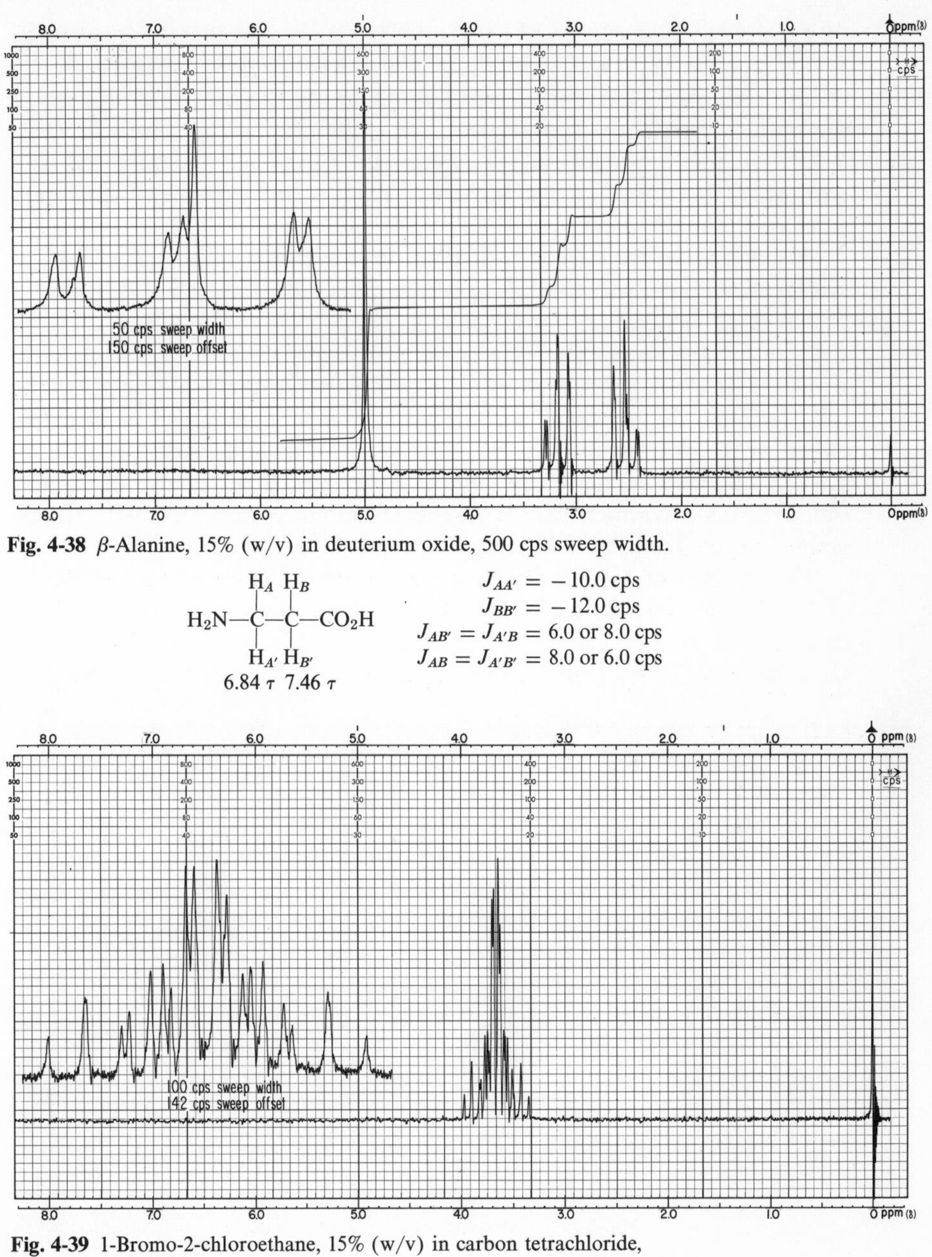

Fig. 4-38 β-Alanine, 15% (w/v) in deuterium oxide, 500 cps sweep width.

H_2N—C(H_A)($H_{A'}$)—C(H_B)($H_{B'}$)—CO_2H

6.84 τ 7.46 τ

$$J_{AA'} = -10.0 \text{ cps}$$
$$J_{BB'} = -12.0 \text{ cps}$$
$$J_{AB'} = J_{A'B} = 6.0 \text{ or } 8.0 \text{ cps}$$
$$J_{AB} = J_{A'B'} = 8.0 \text{ or } 6.0 \text{ cps}$$

Fig. 4-39 1-Bromo-2-chloroethane, 15% (w/v) in carbon tetrachloride, 500 cps sweep width.

Cl—C(H_A)($H_{A'}$)—C(H_B)($H_{B'}$)—Br

6.23 τ 6.43 τ

$$J_{AB'} = J_{A'B} = 6.0 \text{ or } 9.0 \text{ cps}$$
$$J_{AB} = J_{A'B'} = 9.0 \text{ or } 6.0 \text{ cps}$$

tively, *meta* to themselves and *ortho* and *para* to one another; consequently, $J_{AA'} \cong J_{BB'}$. If $\Delta\nu_{AB} \gg J_{AA'}$ or $J_{BB'}$, as is frequently the case if the groups on the ring have different electron-withdrawing or -releasing properties, the pattern resembles four triplets. An example is *p*-chloroanisole (Fig. 4-40). As $\Delta\nu_{AB}$ approaches $J_{AA'}$ or $J_{BB'}$, the peaks become distorted, and the intensities of the inner members increase at the expense of the intensities of the outer members.

In contrast to the case of *p*-disubstituted benzenes, where $J_{AA'} \cong J_{BB'}$, symmetrically *o*-disubstituted benzenes generally have $J_{BB'} \gg J_{AA'}$ (or $J_{AA'} \gg J_{BB'}$, depending on labeling), $J_{AB} \cong J_{BB'}$ (or $J_{AB} \cong J_{AA'}$), and $\Delta\nu_{AB} \cong J$, because protons A and B have approximately the same electronic environment (each is *meta* to one group and *ortho* or *para* to the other) unless the group is one that can have a diamagnetic anisotropic effect on the protons *ortho* to it. As a result of these factors, the spectral pattern obtained for symmetrically *o*-disubstituted benzenes is compact, but, of course, symmetrical about the mid-point of the spectrum. An example is catechol (Fig. 4-41).

Other cases of four interacting nuclei are usually not easy to detect and ordinarily can be analyzed only by mathematical treatment of the data. The aromatic protons of *o*-chloroaniline (Fig. 4-23), an *ABCD* case, show the complexity possible from interaction of four nonequivalent pro-

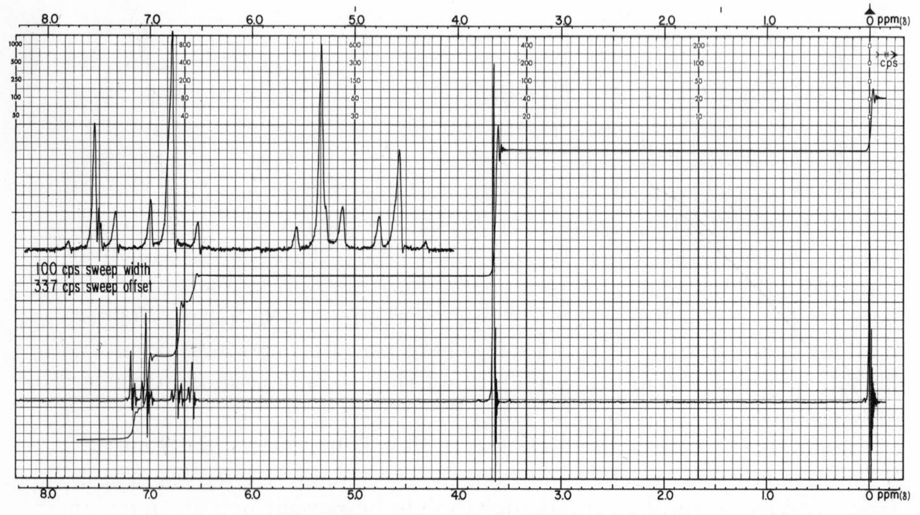

Fig. 4-40 *p*-Chloroanisole, 15% (w/v) in carbon tetrachloride, 500 cps sweep width.

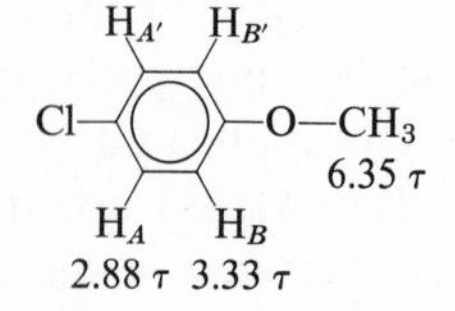

$J_{AB} = J_{A'B'} = 8.8$ cps
$J_{AA'} = 2.5$ or 3.1 cps
$J_{BB'} = 3.1$ or 2.5 cps
$J_{AB'} = J_{A'B} = 0.3$ cps

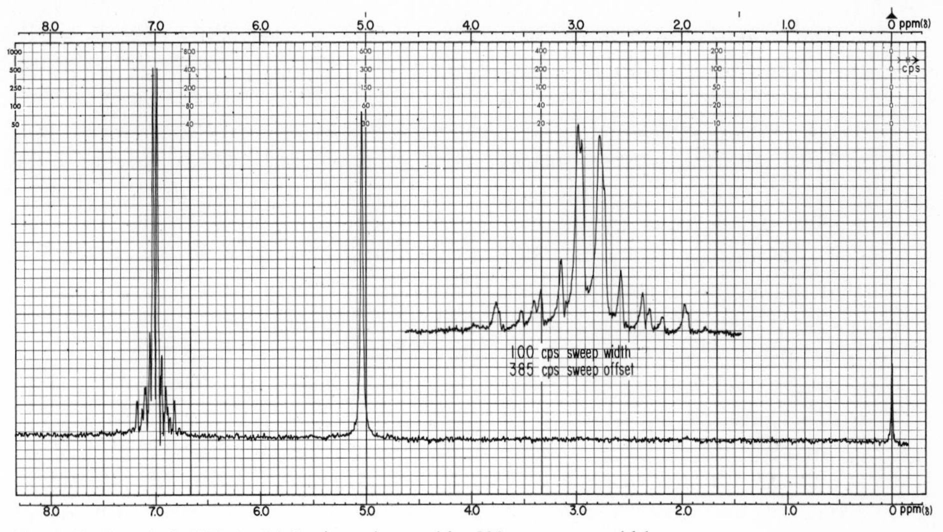

Fig. 4-41 Catechol, 15% (w/v) in deuterium oxide, 500 cps sweep width.

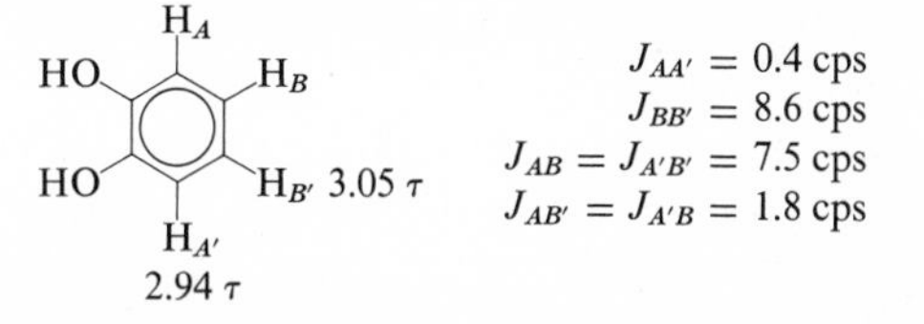

tons. Occasionally, however, when the absorptions of the different nuclei are well separated from one another ($\Delta\nu > J$), the spectrum can be analyzed easily. Such is the case with nicotinamide (Fig. 4-42).

Five Interacting Nuclei: Common examples of A_2B_3 spectra are found in ethyl groups. The protons of the group CH_3—CH_2—X, when X is not carbon, generally have $J_{AB}/\Delta\nu_{AB}$ *ca* 0.05; consequently, the A_2X_3 pattern is easily recognizable. As the ratio $J/\Delta\nu$ increases, the expected complications arise: the multiplets overlap and additional peaks and added distortions appear. In theory, spectra of five interacting nuclei have 240 lines. Most of these cannot be observed. The absorption resulting from the methylene group of acidified ethyl alcohol (Fig. 4-3) does show some fine structure in each of the components of the quartet.

Summary—Complex Interactions: It should be understood that it is not always possible to determine from the spectrum of a complex organic compound which types of interactions might be present in a given region of the spectrum. It is to be noted that many systems of interacting nuclei will not have as well-defined patterns as do most of the examples shown in this section. A gradual transition is to be anticipated from the simple AMX system, through ABX, to the very complicated ABC system. Elements of symmetry (indicating AB or A_2B_2 types) are frequently easily recognized. When chemical information becomes available for a given

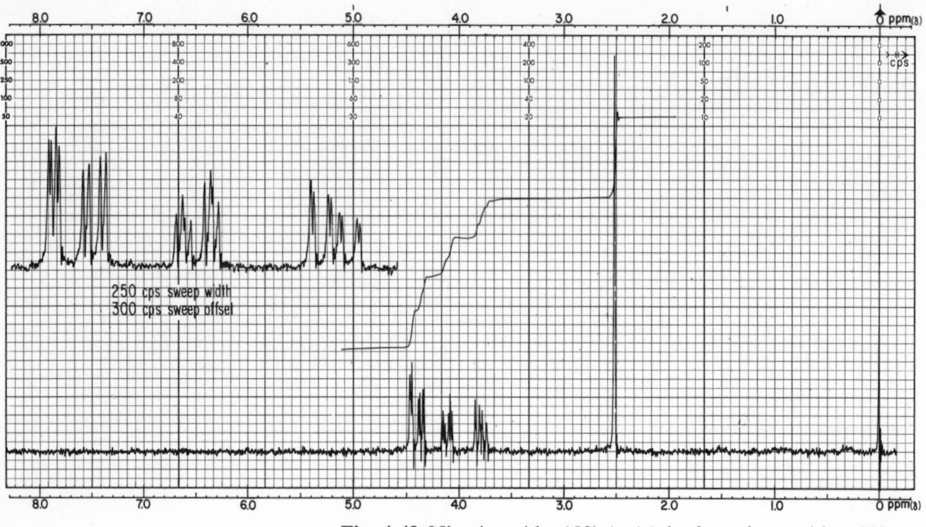

Fig. 4-42 Nicotinamide, 15% (w/v) in deuterium oxide, 1000 cps sweep width.

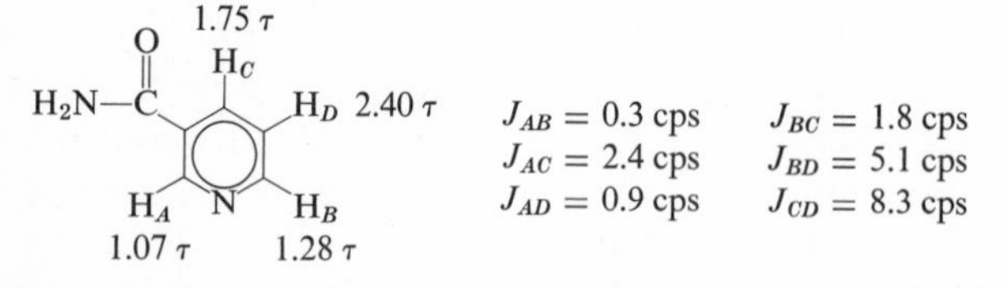

compound, the spectrum should be examined in the light of suggested possible structural formulas. The advantage of determining the spectrum at several field strengths cannot be overemphasized. It must be remembered that the separation of peaks ($\Delta\nu$) is greater with increasing field strength, whereas J, the coupling constant, is independent of field strength. Spectra will usually have quite a different appearance when determined at different field strengths.

Where possible, the analysis of a spectrum is always desirable and will usually yield useful information. For example, simple analysis of a three-proton system will readily indicate if the system is an ABC or AB_2 type. Frequently, analysis of the splitting pattern observed will enable the assignment of the absorption positions for the protons observed in the spectrum (see, for example, nicotinamide, Fig. 4-42).

There is at present no simple experimental method of assigning the absolute *sign* (positive or negative) to the spin-spin coupling constant J. In a simple system of two interacting nuclei (an AB case), each proton absorption is split into a doublet. This corresponds to transitions between aligned and nonaligned spin orientations, respectively. As it cannot be known which alignment orientation is of higher energy, the sign of the coupling constant is not known. For example, if the aligned spin orientations were of higher energy for a particular case, J might be positive. On the other hand, if the nonaligned spin orientations in such a system were of higher energy, J might be negative. In any case, the absolute *magnitude* of J is the same. By mathematical treatment of data derived from complex spectra, it is possible to assign relative signs to coupling constants. It is generally assumed that most *vicinal* coupling constants are positive, and most *geminal* coupling constants are negative.

Analysis of the C^{13}-satellite peaks of 1,1-dimethylcyclopropane shows that J_{gem} has a different sign from J_{cis} and J_{trans} (the values obtained are: J_{gem}, -4.5 cps; J_{cis}, $+9.2$ cps; J_{trans}, $+5.4$ cps). It is interesting that the $J_{HC^{13}}$ coupling constants for cyclopropane compounds are near 160 cps. This indicates that the hybridization of the C—H bonding orbital is close to sp^2.

4.11 HINDERED ROTATION

Rotation about single bonds at room temperature is, in general, so rapid that rotational isomers cannot be isolated. Their presence in solution cannot usually be detected by n.m.r. spectroscopy. The coupling constant(s) for a group of protons on adjacent carbon atoms separated by only a single bond will have an average value if rapid rotation exists. At temperatures much below room temperature, the rate of rotation is frequently diminished so that n.m.r. absorptions resulting from each isomer may be observed. In this way, it has been possible to estimate that, for cyclohexane, the rate of chair-chair interconversion is about 130 times per second at $-66.7°$ and about 160,000 times per second at $25°$.

When the barrier hindering rotation is a formal covalent double bond, the isomers can be isolated (as *cis* and *trans* isomers of olefins) and have different n. m.r. spectra.

When the rate of rotation about a given bond is intermediate between free rotation about unhindered bonds and the severely hindered rotation about formal double bonds, the n.m.r. spectrum usually consists of a superposition of spectra resulting from the two (or more) rotational isomers that are present in equilibrium. One of the most thoroughly investigated examples of this phenomenon is the hindered rotation that exists about the C—N bond in simple amides. Resonance theory predicts that this bond has considerable double bond character:

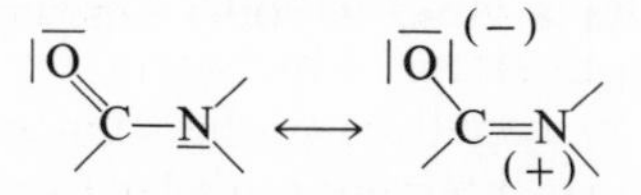

The n.m.r. spectra of simple amides quite generally indicate the magnetic nonequivalence of alkyl groups attached to nitrogen—that is, one group can be *cis* to the oxygen and the other group can be *trans*. The spectrum of *N,N*-dimethylformamide at room temperature (Fig. 4-43) shows the

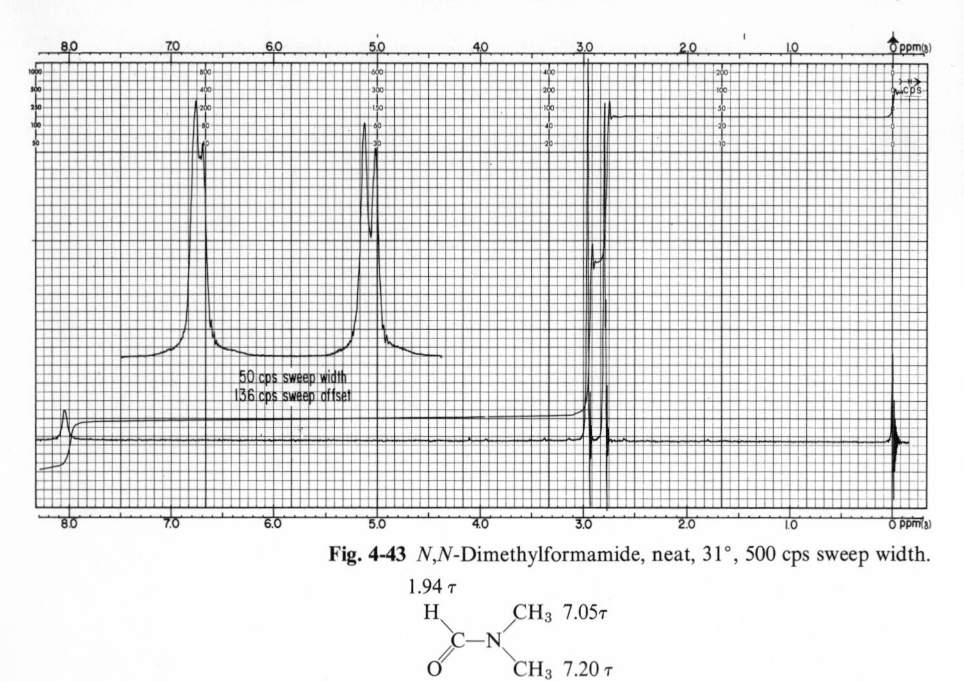

Fig. 4-43 *N,N*-Dimethylformamide, neat, 31°, 500 cps sweep width.

two different kinds of methyl groups. That the two peaks observed are not the result of spin-spin interaction is shown by the fact that the components are separated by 10 cps at 60 Mc and by 5 cps at 30 Mc. The absorption of each methyl group is seen to be a doublet resulting from coupling (through four covalent bonds) with the formyl proton. For the methyl group that absorbs at higher field (7.21 τ), J = 0.6 cps, and for the methyl group that absorbs at lower field (7.06 τ), J = 0.3 cps. Since *trans* coupling constants are quite generally larger than *cis* coupling constants (Sec. 4.12), the methyl group that absorbs at higher field is assumed to be *trans* to the formyl proton.

Figure 4-44 shows the absorptions of the methyl groups of *N,N*-dimethylformamide at higher temperatures. The peaks coalesce at 111° to a single absorption signal. At elevated temperatures the methyl groups become magnetically equivalent because of rapid rotation about the C—N bond.

In addition to amides, other types of compounds that usually exhibit restricted rotation about a bond at room temperature are alkyl nitrites, oximes, and nitrosamines.

4.12 STEREOCHEMISTRY

The magnitude of the coupling constant J depends in part on the number of covalent bonds through which protons may interact and also on the geometrical orientation of the interacting protons. There is a nodal

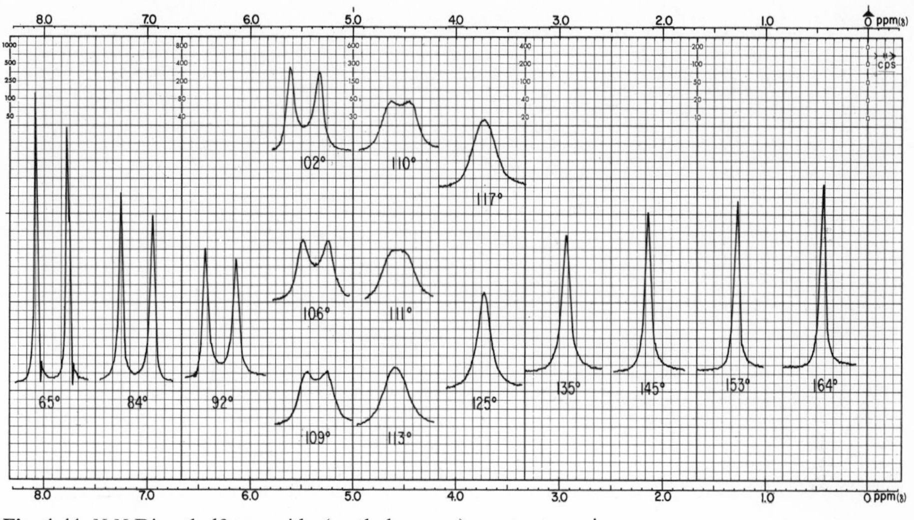

Fig. 4-44 *N,N* Dimethylformamide (methyl groups), neat, at varying temperatures, 250 cps sweep width.

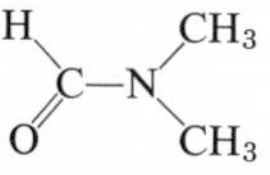

plane perpendicular to the axis of all σ bonds composed of *s*, *sp*, sp^2, or sp^3 atomic orbitals. The probability of an electron being in a position described by this nodal plane is effectively zero. For protons attached to sp^2 or sp^3 hybridized carbon atoms, it is generally found that if a nodal plane associated with the σ bond of one proton passes close to another proton, the coupling constant for that interaction will be small. This situation is shown below for a monosubstituted olefin (all atoms are in the plane of the paper). The nodal plane of the σ bond orbital of C—H′ passes quite close to H; *geminal* coupling constants for olefins are quite small.

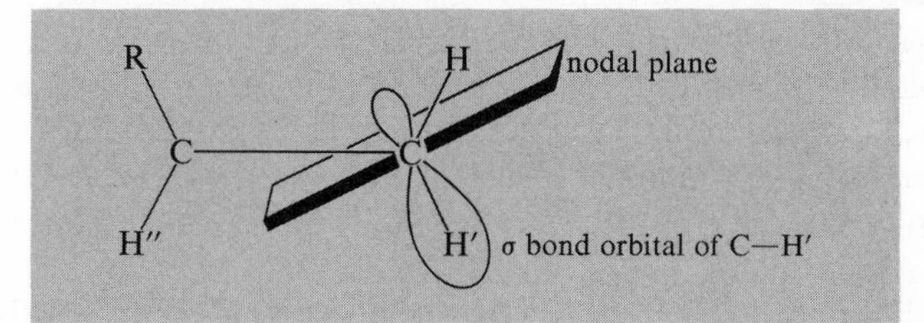

The nodal plane passes close (but at a larger distance) to H″; J_{cis} is always smaller than J_{trans}. For monosubstituted olefins, $J_{trans} > J_{cis} > J_{gem}$. Experimental data for styrene and *t*-butylethylene illustrate this fact. Among isomeric olefins it is usually observed that $J_{cis} \cong \frac{2}{3} J_{trans}$. It is thus

H(C$_6$H$_5$)C=CH′H″		H(*t*-Bu)C=CH′H″	
$J_{H,H'}$	= 10.6 cps	$J_{H,H'}$	= 10.8 cps
$J_{H,H''}$	= 17.4 cps	$J_{H,H''}$	= 17.5 cps
$J_{H',H''}$	= −1.4 cps	$J_{H',H''}$	= −1.4 cps

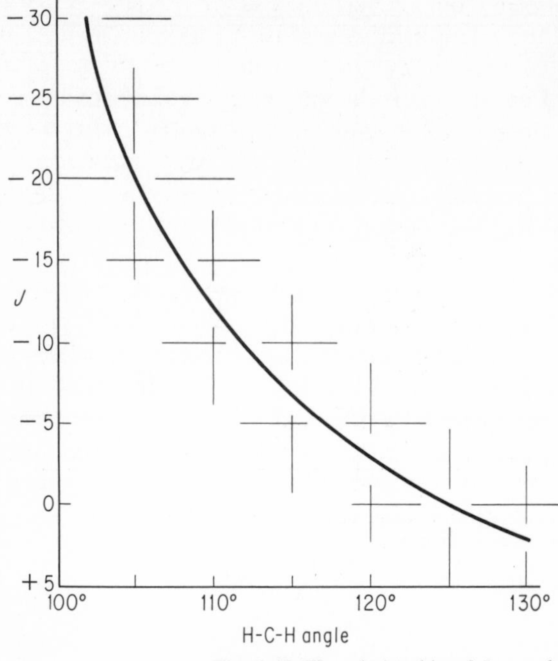

Fig. 4-45 The relationship of J_{gem} and H—C—H angle.

frequently possible (if the spectrum obtained can be analyzed) to determine the geometrical configuration of a particular disubstituted olefin capable of *cis-trans* isomerism.

The magnitudes of *geminal* coupling constants for a system such as —N=CH_2 are much larger than for a normal olefin. Substituent effects appear to be important, as well as the bond angles, in determining the magnitude of J for this particular interaction.

The coupling constant for the protons of a methylene group of a saturated compound (J_{gem}) is dependent on the bond angle. When the bond angle is about 105°, $J \cong -20$ cps; when the bond angle is about 109°, $J \cong -12$ cps. The coupling constant increases to zero when the bond angle is widened to about 125°. Bond angles wider than 125° give rise to small positive values for the coupling constant. The theoretical relationship, which has received considerable experimental support, for the magnitude of J as a function of the H—C—H angle, is shown in Fig. 4-45.

The coupling constant for two vicinal protons in a substituted ethane H_1—C_2—C_3—H_4 has been shown to depend on the dihedral angle (ϕ) formed between the planes that contain H_1—C_2—C_3 and C_2—C_3—H_4. The relationship

$$J = 4.22 - 0.5 \cos \phi + 4.5 \cos 2\phi$$

has been calculated from valence bond theory for substituted ethanes. The coefficients in the relationship are sensitive to bond lengths and the presence of more electronegative substituent groups. A plot of J versus ϕ is given as Fig. 4-46. It is seen that the largest values for the coupling constants are obtained when the angle ϕ is 0° or 180°; near 90° the coupling constant is slightly negative. Because the exact coefficients in this relationship for a particular compound are not known with accuracy, the main utility of the relationship is to provide an *approximate* value for the dihedral angle.

The relationship appears to hold reasonably well for substituted cyclopentanes and cyclohexanes. For cyclopentanes, $\phi_{cis} \cong 0°$, and J would be expected to be about 8 cps, whereas $\phi_{trans} \cong 90°$, and J would be expected to be near 0 cps. It has been indicated that axial and equatorial protons of cyclohexanes absorb differently (Sec. 4.7). For axial-axial interactions ($\phi_{aa} \cong 180°$, $J \cong 8$ cps, whereas for axial-equa-

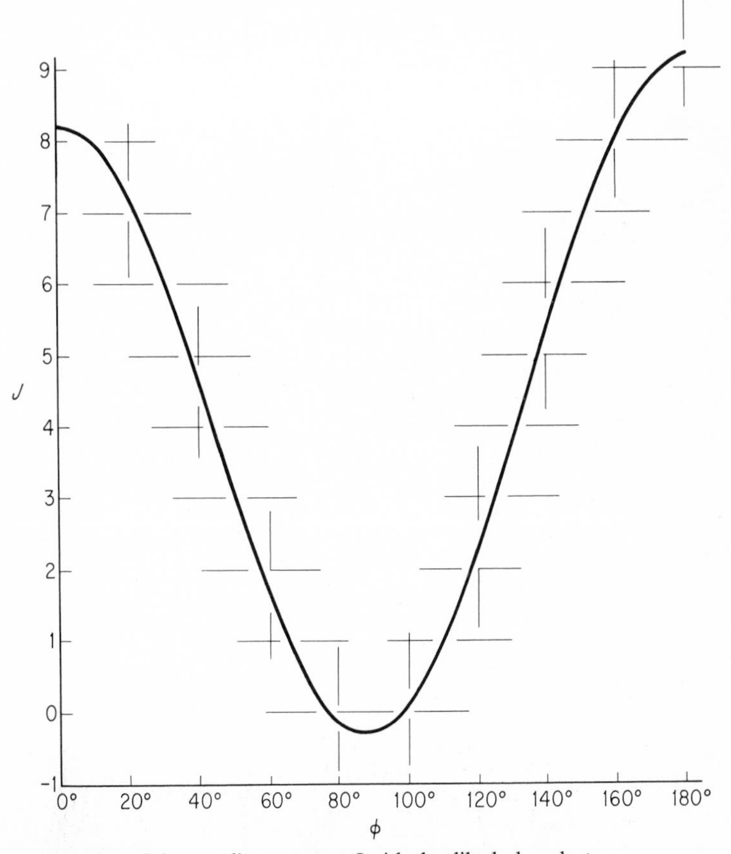

Fig. 4-46 Variation of the coupling constant J with the dihedral angle ϕ for substituted ethanes.

torial and equatorial-equatorial interactions ($\phi_{ae} \cong \phi_{ee} \cong 60°$), $J \cong 2$ cps. Thus it is possible that relative configurations for a particular system can be determined.

The coupling constant for a *vicinal* interaction is the weighted average of the coupling constants for all conformations of a molecule. The average coupling constant (J_{av}) for *vicinal* interactions in molecules capable of free rotation has been found to be related to the sum of the (Pauling) electronegativities (E) of the six groups attached to the C—C bond:

$$J_{av} = 17.97 - 0.80 \sum_{1}^{6} E$$

Geminal coupling constants have been found to be much more sensitive to changes in the electronegativity of the environment than *vicinal* coupling constants.

Occasionally, a reasonably detailed conformational structure for a substance can be derived. A particularly fine example is shown in the spectrum of 1,2-*O*-isopropylidene-3-*O*-benzoyl-5-deoxy-β-*L*-arabinose

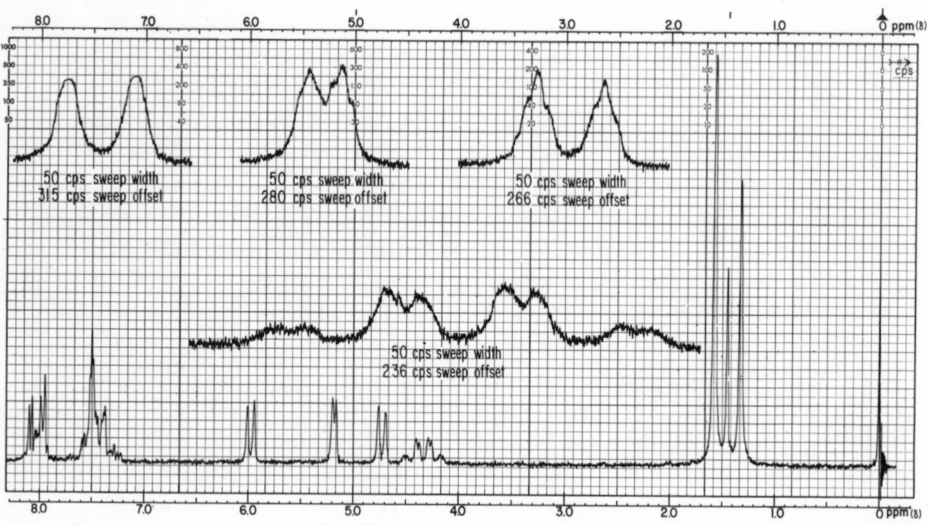

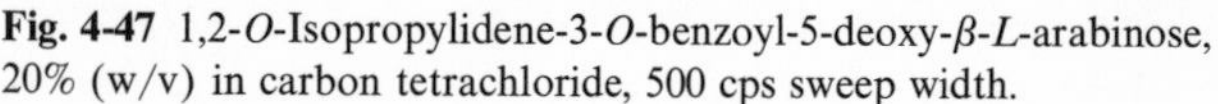
Fig. 4-47 1,2-*O*-Isopropylidene-3-*O*-benzoyl-5-deoxy-β-*L*-arabinose, 20% (w/v) in carbon tetrachloride, 500 cps sweep width.

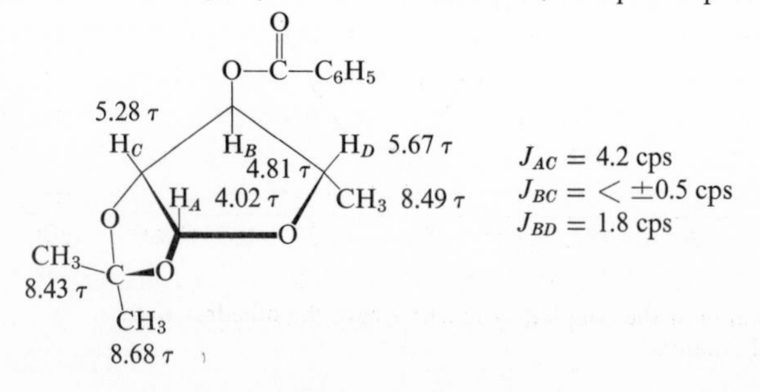

(Fig. 4-47). The complete analysis of this spectrum is simplified by the fact that the four ring protons all have reasonably different chemical shift values. The spectrum can be analyzed as follows. The aromatic protons of the benzoyl group absorb in the region 1.9–2.7 τ (*ortho-*, 1.98 τ; *meta-* and *para-*, 2.57 τ). The proton at C_1 (4.02 τ) absorbs at lower field than any other aliphatic proton, because C_1 is attached to two electronegative oxygen atoms. This absorption is split into a doublet (J = 4.2 cps) by the proton at C_2. The magnitude of this coupling constant indicates that the planes formed by $H_A—C_1—C_2$ and $C_1—C_2—H_C$ intersect at an angle of about 45° or about 132°. The absorption of the proton at C_2 (5.28 τ) is likewise split into a doublet (J = 4.2 cps) by the proton at C_1. The absence of observed interaction of the proton at C_2 with the proton at C_3 leads to the conclusion that the planes formed by $H_C—C_2—C_3$ and $C_2—C_3—H_B$ intersect at some angle between 73° and 106° ($J = 0.0 \pm 0.5$ cps). The absorption of the proton at C_3 (4.81 τ) is split into a doublet (J = 1.8 cps) by the proton at C_4. This indicates that the angle formed by the intersection of the planes formed by $H_B—C_3—C_4$ and $C_3—C_4—H_D$ is about 62° or about 117°. In confirmation of this, the absorption of the proton at C_4 (5.67 τ) is split into a quartet (J = 7.0 cps), each component of which is split into a doublet (J = 1.8 cps). The absorption of the methyl protons at C_5 (8.49 τ) is split into a doublet (J = 7.0 cps) by the proton at C_4; the two magnetically nonequivalent methyl groups of the isopropylidene residue absorb at 8.43 τ and 8.68 τ. Thus the $H_A—H_C$ dihedral angle is about 45°, the $H_B—H_D$ dihedral angle is about 117°, and the $H_C—H_B$ dihedral angle is near 106° (the alternative values for the $H_A—H_C$ and $H_B—H_D$ dihedral angles are excluded by the known absolute stereochemistry of the molecule; such a molecule cannot be constructed). These data show that C_2 is bent out of the plane of the other four atoms of the furanose ring by approximately 40°. Calculations such as these can be used to determine a very reasonable conformational structure of carbohydrate materials and similar molecules in solution.

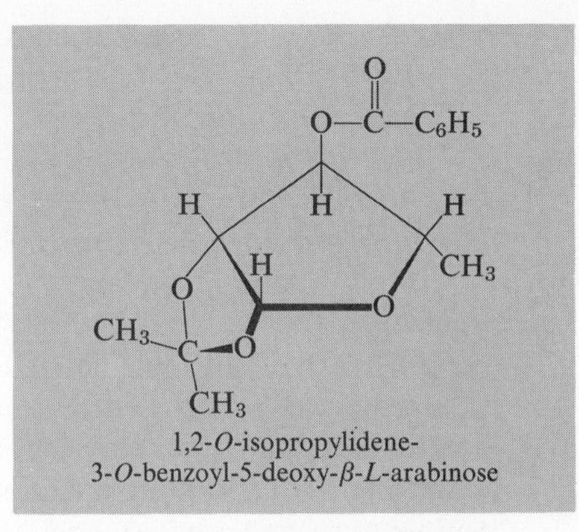

1,2-*O*-isopropylidene-3-*O*-benzoyl-5-deoxy-β-*L*-arabinose

It is found experimentally that the protons in a compound of the type $X—CH_2—CRST$ are not magnetically equivalent and, in fact, give rise to typical AB spectra. An explanation for this fact is obtained by inspection of the three possible noneclipsed conformations for such a molecule. The environments of H_a in Ia and H_b in Ib are not identical, because the nonbonding interactions of the X group are different in the two conformations (Ia: $S—X—T$; Ib: $T—X—R$). Thus in no conformation will

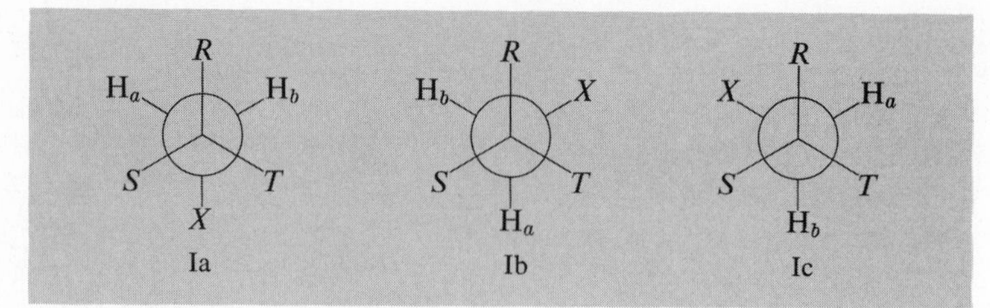

$H_a = H_b$; they are magnetically (and chemically) nonequivalent. It should be recognized that they *may* have the same chemical shift value accidentally, and thus may *appear* to be equivalent. When the rotation about the C—C bond in such a system is rapid (as for example at room temperature and above) and all conformations are essentially equally populated, a simple *AB* pattern will result. At much lower temperatures, the rate of interconversion of conformational isomers may be so slow that the spectrum of each isomer may be observed. In this case three *AB* spectra, or twelve lines, result. This will be the result if each conformation has a significant population at lower temperatures. It is to be anticipated that one or possibly two of the conformational isomers will be present in larger amount. Thus, a simpler spectral pattern may result.

If *R*, *S*, or *T* is a proton in such cases, a more complicated spectral pattern results because the proton will be coupled with the protons of the *X*—CH_2— group. If very rapid rotation about the C—C bond is assumed, a single *ABC* pattern is present. Examples of this are seen (Fig. 4-48) in the spectra of malic acid, potassium malate, and dipotassium malate. For

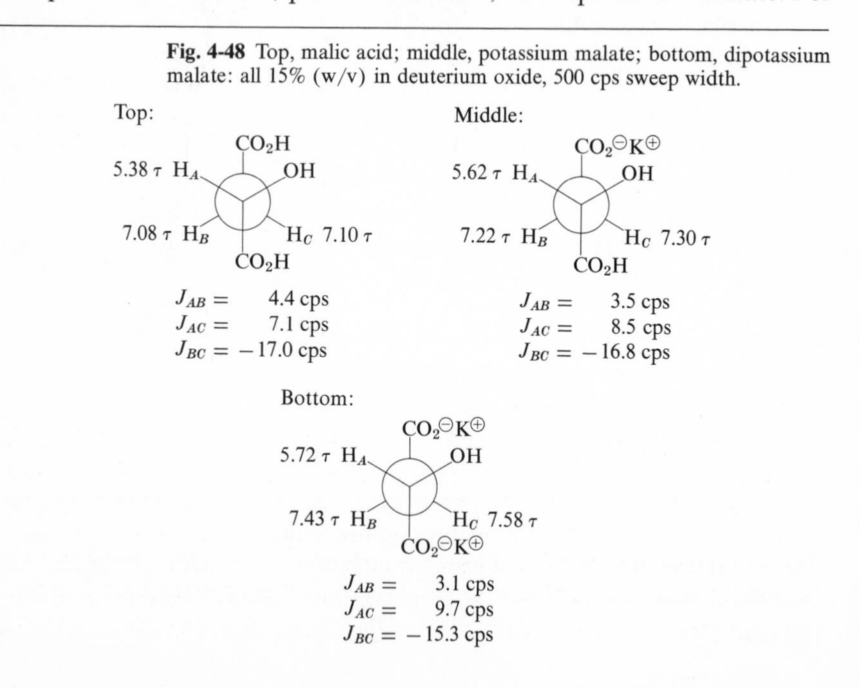

Fig. 4-48 Top, malic acid; middle, potassium malate; bottom, dipotassium malate: all 15% (w/v) in deuterium oxide, 500 cps sweep width.

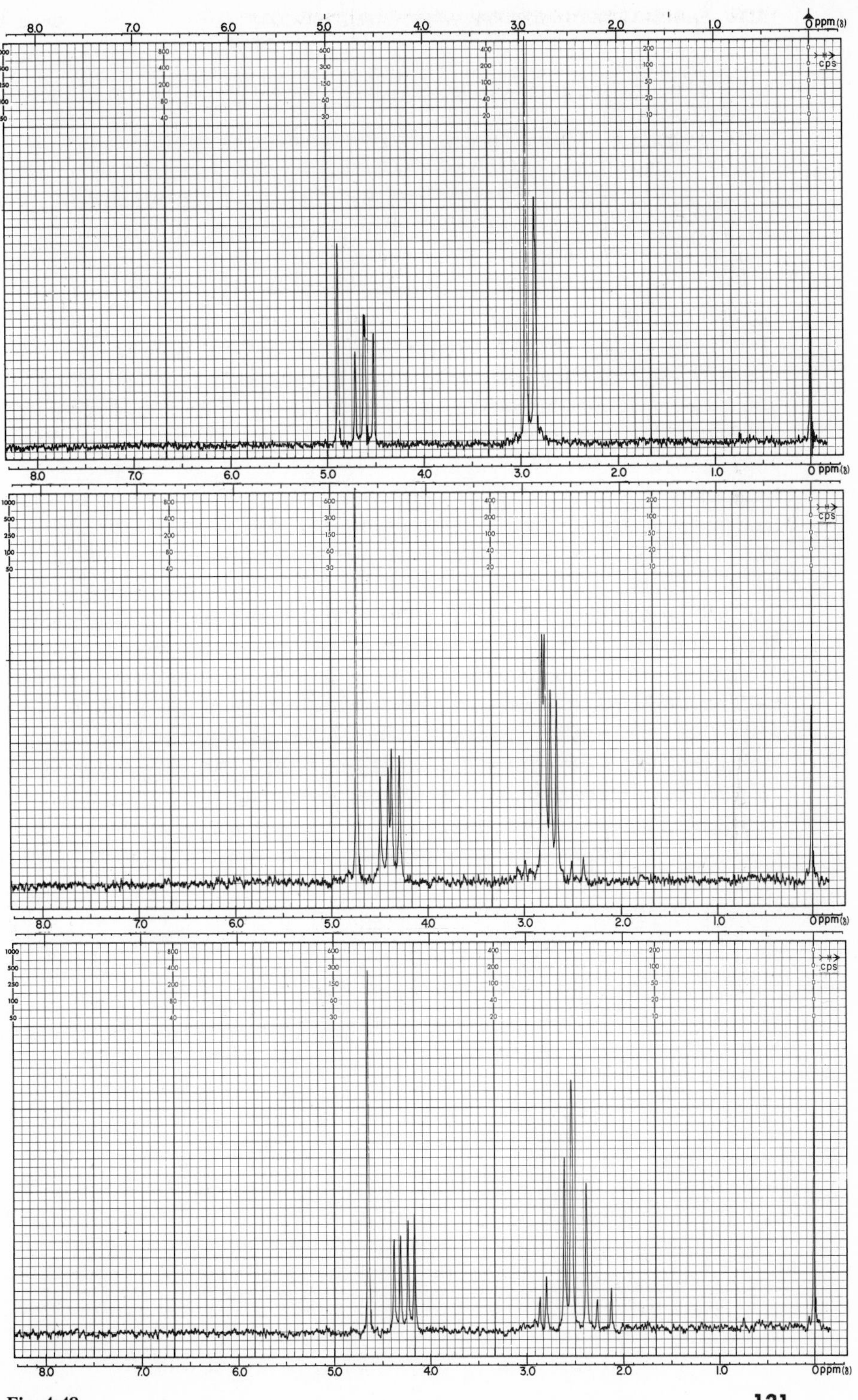

Fig. 4-48

these compounds, the protons of the group $—CH_2—\overset{|}{C}H$ have different coupling constants and chemical shifts at different *p*H values.

The magnetic nonequivalence of two groups attached to carbon adjacent to an asymmetric carbon atom is not limited to protons. The methyl groups of valine, $(CH_3)_2CH—CHNH_2—CO_2H$ are magnetically nonequivalent. In deuterium oxide solution, the methyl groups of valine absorb as two doublets (each coupled with C—H), at 8.95 and 9.02 τ, $J = 7.0$ cps.

It is to be noted that an asymmetric carbon atom is not required for the nonequivalence of the protons of an attached methylene group. In other words, for a compound of the type $X—CH_2—CRST$, R, S, or T may be $X—CH_2—$. The protons of the $X—CH_2—$ group are still nonequivalent. The protons of citric acid form an AB spectrum in which $J_{AB} = -16.3$ cps and $\Delta\nu_{AB} = 9.8$ cps.

4.13 NUCLEAR MAGNETIC DOUBLE RESONANCE

The phenomenon of double resonance is very similar to spin decoupling through rapid chemical exchange. The methylene protons of acidified ethyl alcohol (Fig. 4-3) absorb as a quartet, because they experience the instantaneous spin orientations of the protons of the methyl group. These methylene protons are not spin-spin coupled to the hydroxyl proton because of rapid chemical exchange of the hydroxyl proton. If the protons of the methyl group could be made to undergo very frequent spin transitions, the protons of the methylene group would experience only an average of the possible spin orientations of the methyl protons. Hence, the absorption of the methylene protons would be a singlet. This can be done by applying a very strong, stationary radio-frequency field at the resonance frequency of the protons of the methyl group. The protons of the methyl group are then saturated (See Sec. 4.2). As the field is then swept, one observes a singlet for the hydroxyl proton and a singlet for the methylene protons. Because an additional field is used, this experiment is called *double resonance, double irradiation,* or *spin decoupling.*

Figure 4-49 shows the anticipated result when the three different kinds of protons of pure ethyl alcohol (Fig. 4-5) are subjected to double resonance. When the protons of the methyl group are irradiated, the absorption caused by methylene protons collapses to a doublet because they are coupled only with the hydroxyl proton. Similarly, when the protons of the methylene group are irradiated, the absorptions resulting from the hydroxyl and methyl protons both collapse to singlets.

The principal application of the double resonance technique is as an aid in the interpretation of spectra. A simpler spectrum always results. In a complicated spectrum it is possible to determine which multiplet is

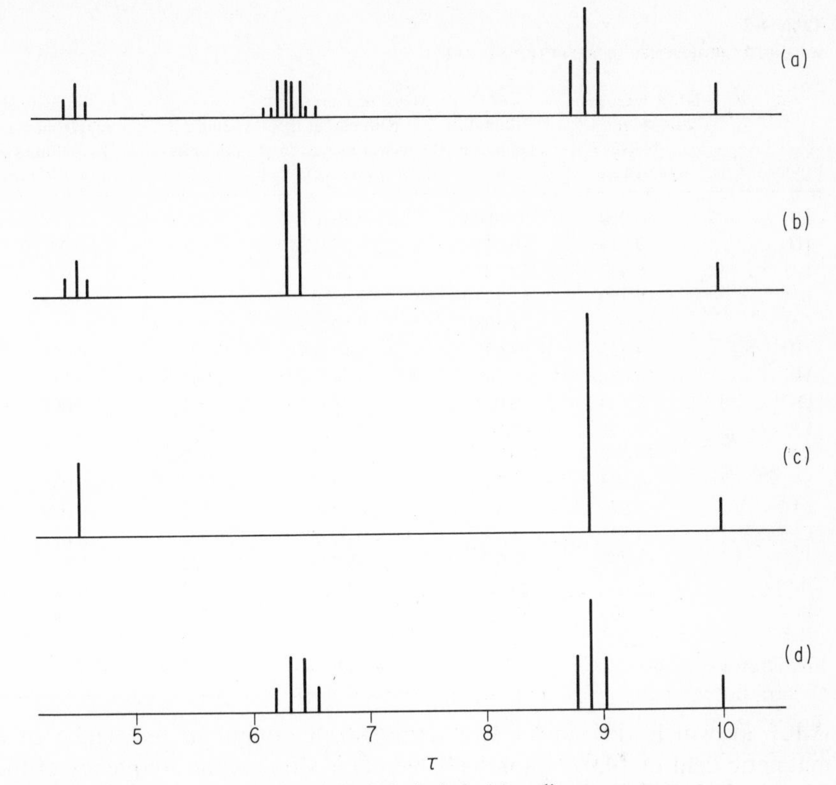

Fig. 4-49 Double resonance with pure ethyl alcohol: (**a**) ordinary spectrum; (**b**) methyl group irradiated; (**c**) methylene group irradiated; (**d**) hydroxyl group irradiated.

coupled with another. The technique can aid in the analysis of spectral data as well. For example, in an ABX spectrum, where it is frequently difficult to extract coupling constants, if the X nucleus is irradiated, the result is a simple AB system, from which coupling constants can easily be obtained.

Although not widely used, the technique of triple resonance has been shown to be applicable as an aid in the interpretation of spectra. Here, *two* additional stable radio-frequency fields are imposed on selected parts of the spectrum. This technique is ordinarily not required for an adequate interpretation of spectral data.

4.14 RESONANCE OF OTHER NUCLEI

Any nucleus that has $I > 0$ is capable of exhibiting a nuclear magnetic resonance spectrum. Table 4-2 lists some nuclear properties for elements that are occasionally of interest to organic chemists. The frequency

Table 4-2

MAGNETIC PROPERTIES OF SELECTED NUCLEI

Isotope	NMR frequency in Mc for a 14,092 gauss field	Natural abundance, %	Magnetic moment μ, in multiples of the nuclear magneton ($eh/4\pi Mc$)	Spin I, in multiples of $h/2\pi$	Electric quadrupole moment, in multiples of $e \times 10^{-24}$ cm^2
H^1	60.000	99.9844	2.79268	1/2	
H^2	9.211	0.0156	0.857386	1	0.00277
B^{10}	6.447	18.83	1.8005	3	0.074
B^{11}	19.250	81.17	2.6880	3/2	0.0355
C^{13}	15.085	1.108	0.70220	1/2	
N^{14}	4.335	99.635	0.40358	1	0.071
N^{15}	6.081	0.365	−0.28304	1/2	
O^{17}	8.134	0.037	−1.8930	5/2	−0.004
F^{19}	56.446	100.0	2.6273	1/2	
P^{31}	24.288	100.0	1.1305	1/2	
S^{33}	4.602	0.74	0.64274	3/2	−0.053
Cl^{35}	5.879	75.4	0.82091	3/2	−0.079
Cl^{37}	4.893	24.6	0.68330	3/2	−0.0621
Co^{59}	14.237	100.0	4.6388	7/2	0.5
Br^{79}	15.032	50.57	2.0990	3/2	0.34
Br^{81}	16.203	49.43	2.2626	3/2	0.28
I^{127}	12.005	100.0	2.7937	5/2	−0.75
Free electron	39,449.0	...	−1836.0	1/2	

(Mc) at which the nuclei will demonstrate magnetic resonance in a magnetic field of 14,092 gauss is listed. This value is the frequency of the oscillator required. Clearly, several oscillators are required for the study of the magnetic resonance spectra of other nuclei. The magnitude of the nuclear magnetic moment μ determines the energies of the nuclear transitions at resonance. The spin number I indicates the number $(2I + 1)$ of orientations that a nucleus may assume in a magnetic field.

It was previously indicated that an electric quadrupole moment was associated with nuclei that have $I > \frac{1}{2}$ and that the magnitude of this moment was a measure of the nonspherical nature of the electric charge distribution within a nucleus. Spin-lattice relaxation of nuclei that possess an electric quadrupole moment arises at least in part through interaction of the quadrupole moment with the fluctuating electric field gradients. Thus, these nuclei have short relaxation times and may, depending on the *magnitude* of the electric quadrupole moment, broaden signals of nuclei that are coupled to them or be completely decoupled from adjacent nuclei. The absorptions of protons coupled with deuterons, which have only a small electric quadrupole moment, are not appreciably broadened. The absorptions of protons coupled with a nitrogen nucleus are nearly always broadened because of the intermediate value for the quadrupole moment of the nitrogen nucleus. Protons do not couple with halogen atoms (except fluorine) on adjacent atoms or on the same atom, because the very large electric quadrupole moments of the halogen atoms effectively cause spin-decoupling of adjacent protons. Magnetic resonance spectra of nuclei that have large electric quadrupole moments have very broad bands, rather than sharp peaks, as is the case with proton spectra.

The spread in resonance frequencies of other nuclei and the magnitude of the coupling constants are frequently very large when compared with the corresponding values for proton spectra. For example, the resonance frequency of lead (II) chloride at 6.3208 Mc is 12,000 ppm (compared to lead metal at 0 ppm), which amounts to 1.2% of the field (a spread of proton resonance frequencies of 15 ppm at 60 Mc amounts to only 0.0015% of the field). The fluorine resonance spectrum of PF_3 exhibits a doublet for which $J = 1400$ cps, whereas the proton resonance spectrum of PH_3 exhibits a doublet for which $J = 183$ cps.

Spectra of other nuclei provide structural information about compounds just as proton magnetic resonance spectroscopy does. For example, C^{13} spectra can be obtained by utilizing only the natural abundance of this isotope. The C^{13} spectrum of acetic acid shows a quartet ($J_{HCC^{13}} = 26$ cps) for the carboxyl carbon and a quartet ($J_{HC^{13}} = 132$ cps) for the methyl carbon. The fluorine resonance spectrum of ClF_3 at $-60°$ exhibits an AX_2 pattern: a 2F doublet, $J = 400$ cps, and a 1F triplet, $J = 412$ cps. The spectrum shows that two fluorine atoms are equivalent and the other distinct and confirms the "T" structure of ClF_3 that was determined in other ways. The B^{11} spectrum of aqueous sodium borohydride exhibits a 1:4:6:4:1 quintet, which indicates that the borohydride anion is symmetrical and all hydrogens are equivalent.

The double resonance technique may be used to remove broadening of nuclei attached to an element that has an electric quadrupole moment. It was seen that the amide proton absorption of *N*-methylacetamide was broad (Fig. 4-25). If the sample were subjected to the action of a second, stable radio-frequency oscillator (4.335 Mc at 14,092 gauss for N^{14}), the amide proton absorption of *N*-methylacetamide would appear as a quartet ($J = 4.7$ cps) because of spin-spin coupling with the protons of the N—CH_3 group. The broadening of the absorption caused by interaction with the electric quadrupole moment of nitrogen has been removed.

4.15 PROBLEMS

Occasionally the structural formula of an organic compound can be derived from its formula and nuclear magnetic resonance spectrum. When a provisional structure has been derived from the formula, intensities, and spin-spin coupled interactions observed in the spectrum, the absorption positions of the groups should be checked with correlation tables. Where complicated spin-spin interactions are present, they should be analyzed if possible.

1. Compound **1** contains C, H, and O. Analytical data were obtained (62.2% C, 10.3% H) and the n.m.r. spectrum was determined (Fig. 4-50). Deduce the structure of the compound.

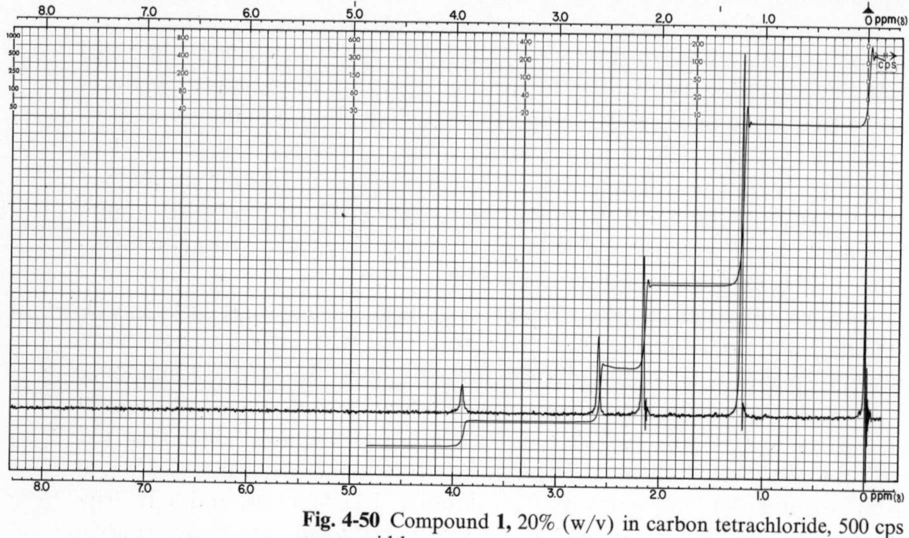

Fig. 4-50 Compound **1,** 20% (w/v) in carbon tetrachloride, 500 cps sweep width.

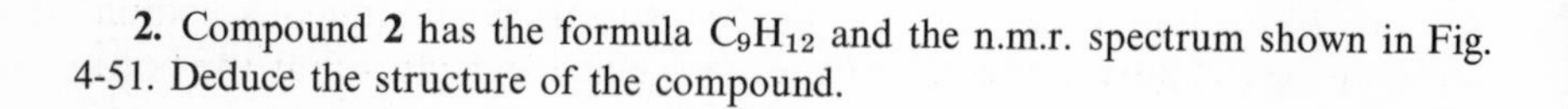

2. Compound **2** has the formula C_9H_{12} and the n.m.r. spectrum shown in Fig. 4-51. Deduce the structure of the compound.

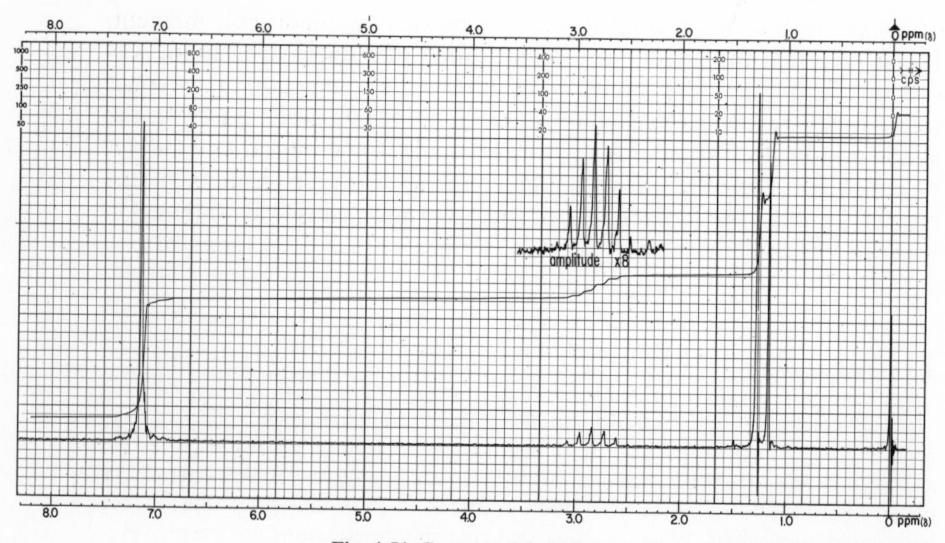

Fig. 4-51 Compound **2,** 20% (w/v) in carbon tetrachloride, 500 cps sweep width.

3. Compound **3** contains C, H, and O. Analytical data were obtained (57.3% C, 8.7% H) and the n.m.r. spectrum was determined (Fig. 4-52). Deduce the structure of the compound.

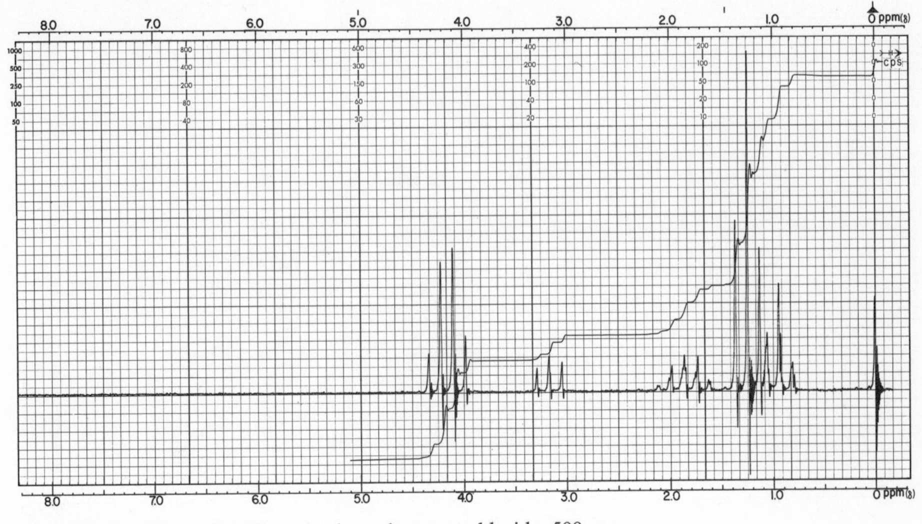

Fig. 4-52 Compound **3,** 20% (w/v) in carbon tetrachloride, 500 cps sweep width.

4. Compound **4** contains C, H, and O. Analytical data were obtained (55.5% C, 7.6% H) and the n.m.r. spectrum was determined (Fig. 4-53). Deduce the structure of the compound.

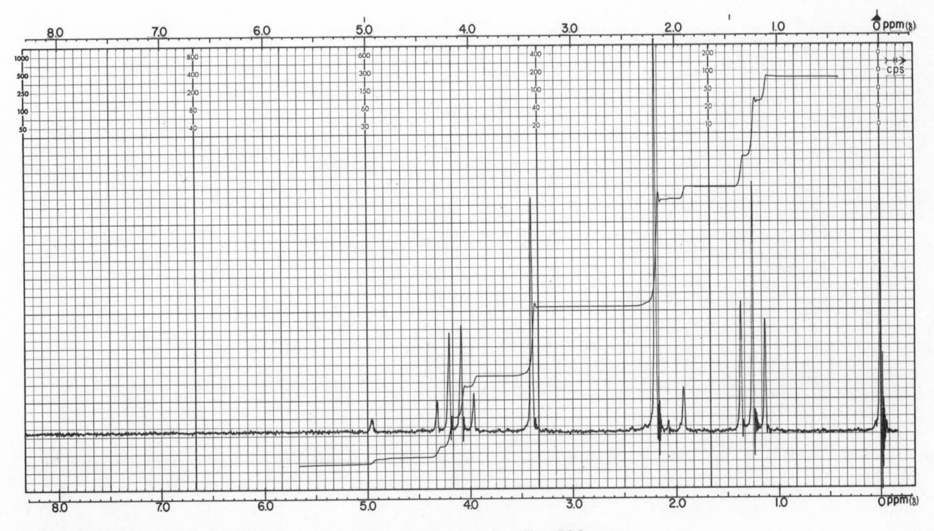

Fig. 4-53 Compound **4,** 20% (w/v) in carbon tetrachloride, 500 cps sweep width.

5. Compound **5** has the formula $C_8H_7O_2Cl$, gives a positive ferric chloride test, and has the n.m.r. spectrum shown in Fig. 4-54. Deduce the structure of the compound.

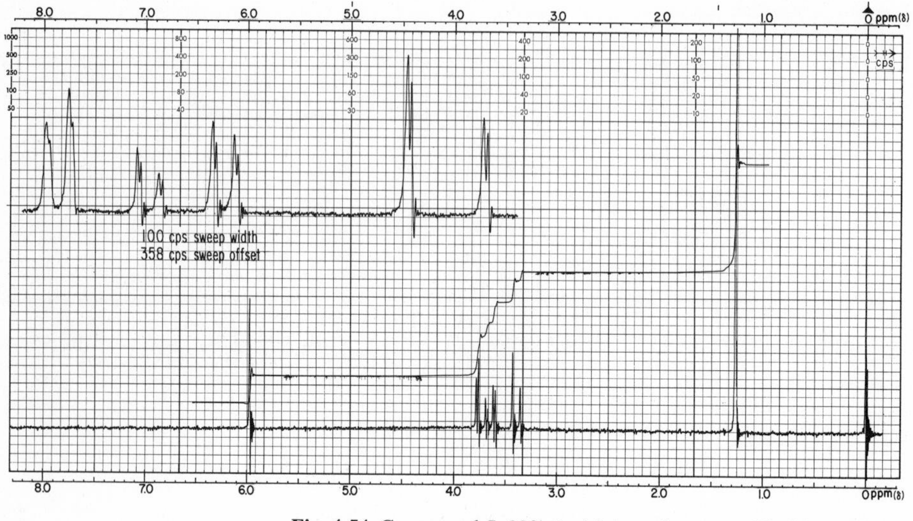

Fig. 4-54 Compound **5**, 20% (w/v) in carbon tetrachloride, 1000 cps sweep width.

6. Compound **6,** a hydrocarbon, has the n.m.r. spectrum shown in Fig. 4-55 and on vigorous oxidation gives phthalic acid. What is the structure of the hydrocarbon?

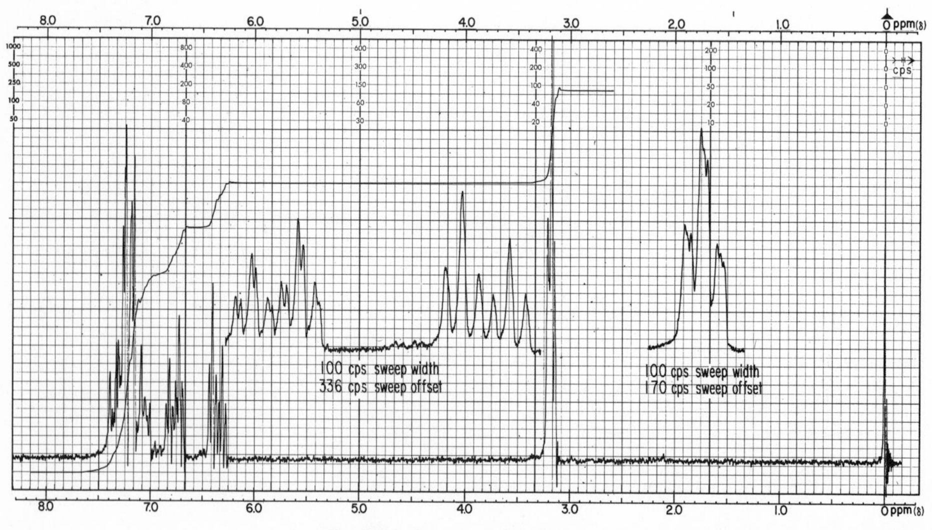

Fig. 4-55 Compound **6,** 20% (w/v) in carbon tetrachloride, 500 cps sweep width.

7. Compound 7 has the formula $C_9H_{14}O$, the *IR* spectrum shown in Fig. 4-56, and the n.m.r. spectrum shown in Fig. 4-57. The compound shows λ_{max}^{EtOH} 236 mμ, ε 8,400. What is the structure of the compound?

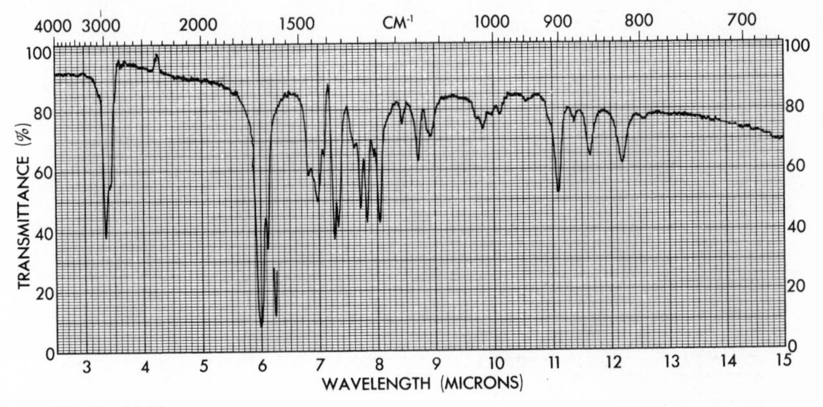

Fig. 4-56 Compound 7, liquid film.

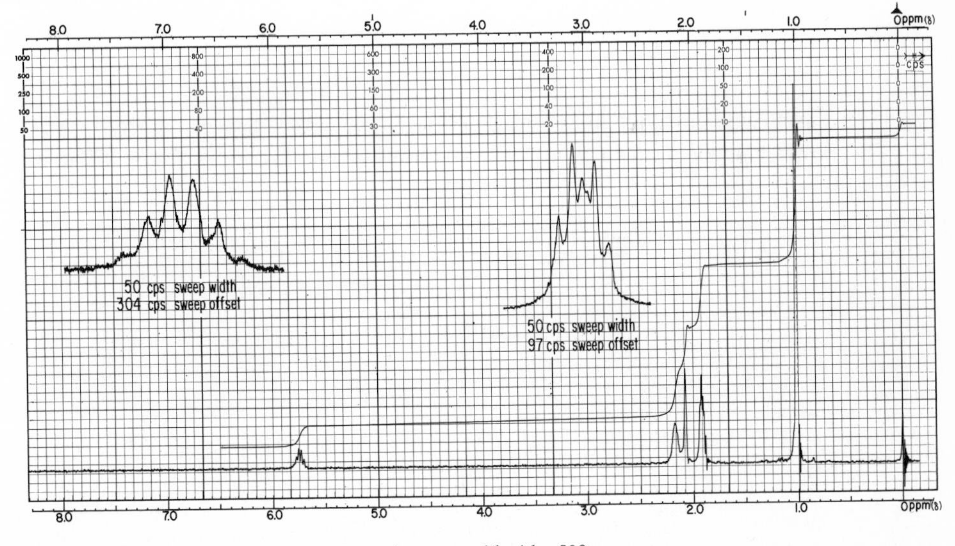

Fig. 4-57 Compound 7, 20% (w/v) in carbon tetrachloride, 500 cps sweep width.

8. Compound **8** contains C, H, Br, and S. Analytical data were obtained (19.6% S, 49.0% Br; mol. wt., 160 ± 4) and the n.m.r. spectrum was determined (Fig. 4-58). Deduce the structure of the compound.

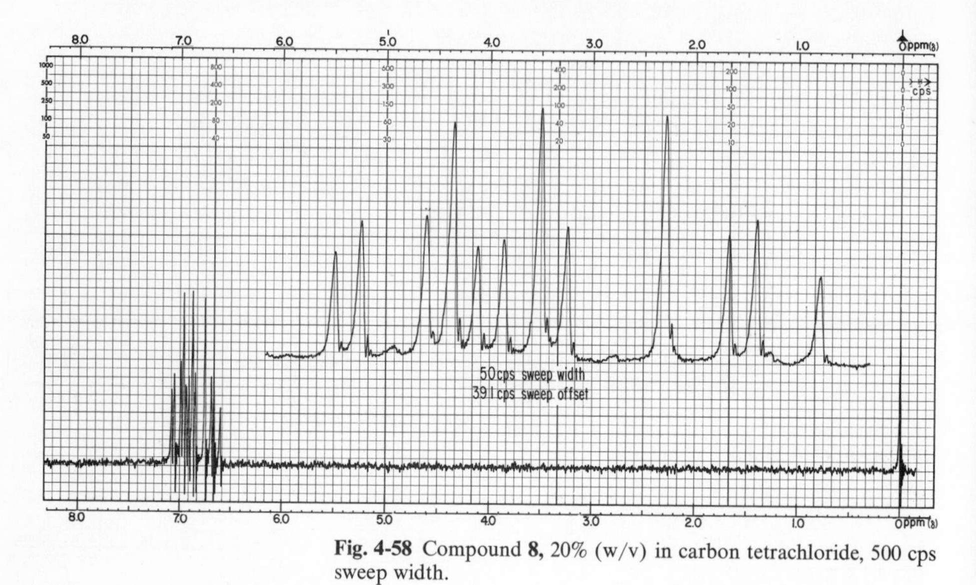

Fig. 4-58 Compound **8,** 20% (w/v) in carbon tetrachloride, 500 cps sweep width.

9. Compound **9** contains only C, H, and N and was found to be a primary aromatic amine. Using its n.m.r. spectrum (Fig. 4-59), suggest a structural formula for the compound.

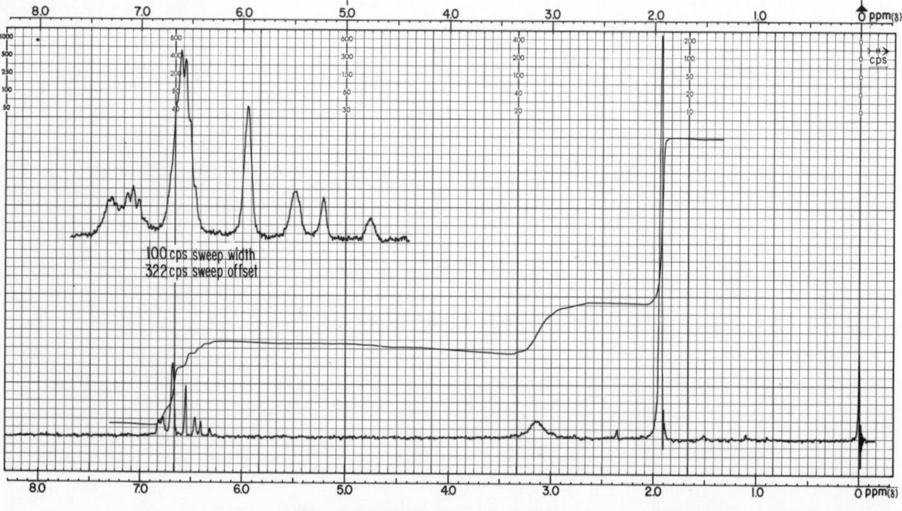

Fig. 4-59 Compound **9,** 20% (w/v) in carbon tetrachloride, 500 cps sweep width.

10. Compound **10a,** $C_{13}H_{20}O$, is an optically inactive substance that has a penetrating, pleasant odor. An n.m.r. spectrum (Fig. 4-60), an infrared spectrum (Fig. 4-61), and an ultraviolet spectrum (λ_{max}^{EtOH} 295 mμ, ε 10,000) were obtained. The compound gave a positive iodoform test, and on oxidation by excess potassium permanganate solution kept neutral by magnesium sulfate, it was converted into a ketoacid, compound **10b,** $C_9H_{16}O_3$. Compound **10b,** when allowed to stand with excess deuterium oxide and sodium deuteroxide, incorporated nearly five carbon-bound deuterium atoms per molecule, and when allowed to react with a solution of iodine and sodium hydroxide, was converted into a dicarboxylic acid, compound **10c,** $C_8H_{14}O_4$. When a mixture of **10c** and barium oxide was heated to 300°, **10c** was converted into **10d,** $C_7H_{12}O$, whose infrared spectrum showed λ_{max} 5.73 μ (1745 cm^{-1}). When compound **10c** was heated with methanolic hydrogen chloride, it was

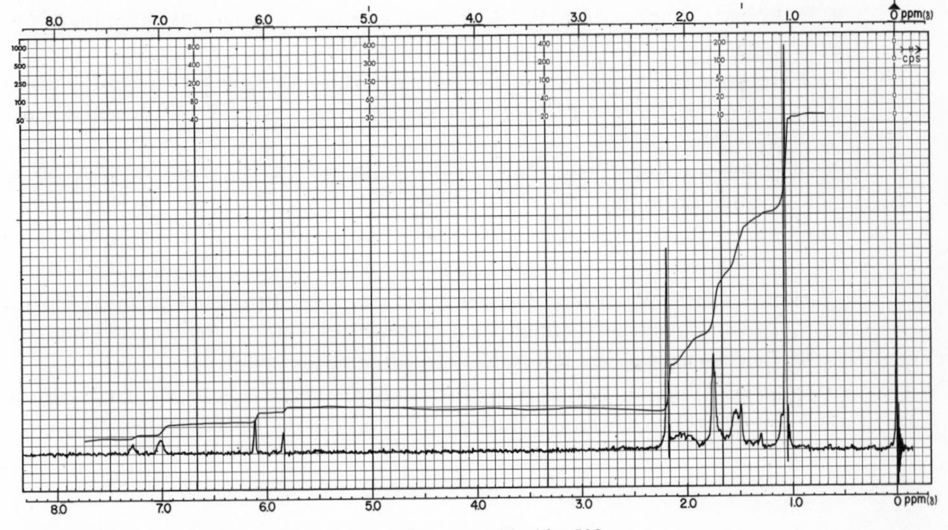

Fig. 4-60 Compound **10a,** 20% (w/v) in carbon tetrachloride, 500 cps sweep width.

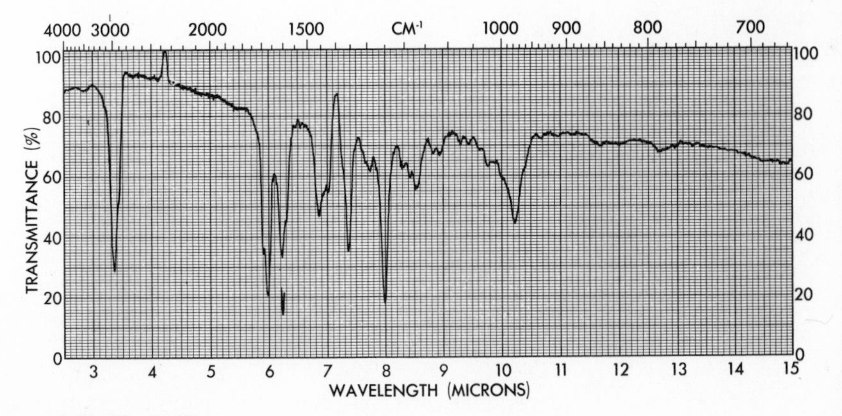

Fig. 4-61 Compound **10a,** liquid film.

converted to compound **10e,** $C_{10}H_{18}O_4$. Compound **10e,** when allowed to stand with excess deuteriomethanol and sodium deuteroxide, incorporated nearly two deuterium atoms per molecule. Give structural formulas for compounds **10a** through **10e** that are consistent with the data given.

SELECTED REFERENCES

J. A. Pople, W. G. Schneider, and H. J. Bernstein, *High Resolution Nuclear Magnetic Resonance*. New York: McGraw-Hill Book Company, 1959.

L. M. Jackman, *Applications of Nuclear Magnetic Resonance Spectroscopy in Organic Chemistry*. New York: Pergamon Press, 1959.

J. D. Roberts, *Nuclear Magnetic Resonance. Applications to Organic Chemistry*. New York: McGraw-Hill Book Company, 1959.

J. D. Roberts, *An Introduction to the Analysis of Spin-Spin Splitting in High-Resolution Nuclear Magnetic Resonance Spectra*. New York: W. A. Benjamin, Inc., 1962.

K. B. Wiberg and B. J. Nist, *The Interpretation of NMR Spectra*. New York: W. A. Benjamin, Inc., 1962.

Varian Associates, *High Resolution NMR Spectra Catalogue,* Vol. 1 (1962) and Vol. 2 (1963).

Nuclear Magnetic Resonance Spectral Data. American Petroleum Institute, Project 44, Chemical Thermodynamic Properties Center, Agricultural and Mechanical College of Texas, College Station, Texas.

A Catalogue of the Nuclear Magnetic Resonance Spectra of Hydrogen in Hydrocarbons and their Derivatives. Humble Oil and Refining Co., Baytown, Texas.

Supplemental Problems

Derive structural formulas that are consistent with the data given for the following compounds. The molecular weights, such as might be determined from the mass spectrum of the substance, are given; the ultraviolet spectra are given for ethanol solutions except where noted otherwise; the infrared spectra are given for liquid film or potassium bromide pellet determinations, and only those prominent absorptions in the region 2.5–7.0 μ (4000–1429 cm^{-1}) are given; the nuclear magnetic resonance spectra are given for deuteriochloroform solutions. In addition to carbon, hydrogen, and oxygen, the compounds may contain nitrogen and/or halogen.

1. Molecular Weight: 58.
UV: no λ_{max} above 210 mμ.
IR: λ_{max} 3.40–3.50 (m) and 6.86 μ (m) [2941–2857 (m) and 1458 cm^{-1} (m)].
NMR: 5.25 (triplet, J = 7.1 cps, 29.4 squares) and 7.25 τ (quintet, J = 7.1 cps, 14.6 squares).

2. Molecular Weight: 69.
UV: no λ_{max} above 200 mμ.
IR: λ_{max} 3.40 (m), 4.40 (m), and 6.85 μ (m) [2941 (m), 2273 (m), and 1460 cm^{-1} (m)].
NMR: 7.28 (septet, J = 6.7 cps, 4.2 squares) and 8.67 τ (doublet, J = 6.7 cps, 25.8 squares).

3. Molecular Weight: 71.
UV: no λ_{max} above 210 mμ.
IR: λ_{max} 3.40–3.50 (m), 4.45 (m), and 6.85 μ (m) [2941–2857 (m), 2247 (m), and 1460 cm^{-1} (m)].
NMR: 5.78 (singlet, 16.8 squares) and 6.51 τ (singlet, 23.9 squares).

4. Molecular Weight: 72.
UV: λ_{max} 274 mμ, ε 17.
IR: λ_{max} 3.40–3.50 (m), 5.83 (s), and 6.85 μ (m) [2941–2857 (m) 1715 (s), and 1460 cm^{-1} (m)].
NMR: 7.52 (quartet, J = 7.3 cps, 12.0 squares), 7.88 (singlet, 17.6 squares), and 8.93 τ (triplet, J = 7.3 cps, 18.2 squares).

5. Molecular Weight: 73.
UV: λ_{max} 219 mμ, ε 60 (water).
IR: λ_{max} 2.93 (m), 3.09 (m), 3.30–3.45 (m), 6.00 (s), 6.12 (s), and 6.85 μ (m) [3413 (m), 3236 (m), 3030–2899 (m), 1667 (s), 1634 (s), and 1460 cm^{-1} (m)].
NMR: 3.50 (very broad singlet, 13.0 squares), 7.75 (quartet, J = 7.5 cps, 12.8 squares), and 8.90 τ (triplet, J = 7.5 cps, 19.7 squares).

6. Molecular Weight: 88.
UV: λ_{max} 206 mμ, ε 50.
IR: λ_{max} 3.28–3.42 (m), 5.76 (s), and 6.92 μ (m) [3049–2924 (m), 1736 (s), and 1445 cm^{-1} (m)].
NMR: 1.93 (singlet, 5.9 squares), 5.88 (triplet, J = 7.0 cps, 12.2 squares), 8.33 (sextet, J = 7.0 cps, 11.6 squares), and 9.05 τ (triplet, J = 7.0 cps, 18.6 squares).

7. Molecular Weight: 89.
UV: λ_{max} 204 and 276 mu, ε 4,800 and 20.
IR: λ_{max} 3.30–3.42 (m), 6.43 (m), and 6.82 μ (m) [3030–2924 (m), 1555 (m), and 1466 cm^{-1} (m)].
NMR: 5.30 (septet, J = 6.7 cps, 6.2 squares), and 8.47 τ (doublet, J = 6.7 cps, 37.8 squares).

8. Molecular Weight: 104.
UV: λ_{max} 203 mμ, ε 40 (water).
IR: λ_{max} 3.20–3.50 (m), 3.71 (w), 3.81 (w), 5.82 (s), and 6.90 μ (m) [3125–2857 (m), 2695 (w), 2625 (w), 1718 (s), and 1449 cm^{-1} (m)].
NMR: −0.95 (singlet, 5.4 squares), 5.87 (singlet, 11.0 squares), 6.34 (quartet, J = 7.1 cps, 10.6 squares), and 8.73 τ (triplet, J = 7.1 cps, 16.2 squares).

9. Molecular Weight: 108.
UV: λ_{max} 255 mμ, ε 200 (water).
IR: λ_{max} 2.94 (s, b), 3.25 (w), 3.45 (m), 6.67 (w, sh), and 6.87 μ (m, sh) [3401 (s, b), 3077 (w), 2899 (m), 1499 (w, sh), and 1456 cm^{-1} (m, sh)].
NMR: 2.74 (singlet, 24.7 squares), 5.40 (singlet, 9.8 squares), and 6.14 τ (singlet, 5.2 squares).

10. Molecular Weight: 110.
UV: λ_{max} 239 mμ, ε 21,400.
IR: λ_{max} 3.25–3.50 (m), 6.02 (w), 6.22 (w), and 6.90 μ (m) [3077–2857 (m), 1661 (w), 1608 (w), and 1449 cm^{-1} (m)].
NMR: 4.00 (singlet, 6.4 squares), 8.10 (singlet, 17.9 squares), and 8.17 τ (singlet, 18.6 squares).

11. Molecular Weight: 112.
UV: no λ_{max} above 200 mμ.
IR: λ_{max} 3.40 (m) and 6.83 μ (m) [2941 (m) and 1464 cm^{-1} (m)].
NMR: 8.48 τ (singlet).

12. Molecular Weight: 116.
UV: λ_{max} 205 mμ, ε 50 (water).
IR: λ_{max} 3.42 (m), 5.73 (s), and 6.87 μ (m) [2924 (m), 1745 (s), and 1456 cm^{-1} (m)].
NMR: 8.03 (singlet, 11.3 squares) and 8.55 τ (singlet, 32.9 squares).

13. Molecular Weight: 116.
UV: λ_{max} 270 mμ, ε 25 (water).
IR: λ_{max} 3.20–3.50 (m), 3.69 (w), 3.81 (w), 5.84 (s), and 6.95 μ (m) [3125–2857 (m), 2710 (w), 2625 (w), 1712 (s), and 1439 cm^{-1} (m)].
NMR: −0.98 (singlet, 5.0 squares), 7.08–7.68 (complex symmetrical pattern, 20.8 squares), and 7.88 τ (singlet, 14.8 squares).

14. Molecular Weight: 120.
UV: λ_{max} 268 mμ, ε 480.
IR: λ_{max} 3.26–3.44 (m), 6.22 (m, sh), and 6.79 μ (m) [3067–2907 (m), 1608 (m, sh), and 1473 cm^{-1} (m)].
NMR: 3.21 (singlet, 10.4 squares) and 7.74 τ (singlet, 31.0 squares).

15. Molecular Weight: 134.
UV: λ_{max} 215 mμ, ε 70 (methanol).
IR: λ_{max} 3.40–3.50 (m), 5.60 (s), and 6.85 μ (m) [2941–2857 (m), 1786 (s), and 1460 cm^{-1} (m)].
NMR: 5.20 (singlet, 4.3 squares), 6.20 (singlet, 13.2 squares), and 6.52 τ (singlet, 25.8 squares).

16. Molecular Weight: 135.
UV: no λ_{max} above 200 mμ.
IR: λ_{max} 3.28 (m) and 6.45 μ (m) [3049 (m) and 1550 cm^{-1} (m)].
NMR: 5.98 τ (triplet, J = 10.8 cps).

17. Molecular Weight: 138.
UV: λ_{max} 225 and 311 mμ, ε 9,200 and 40.
IR: λ_{max} 3.25–3.50 (m), 5.95 (s), 6.02 (m), and 6.88 μ (m) [3077–2857 (m), 1681 (s), 1661 (m), and 1453 cm^{-1} (m)].
NMR: 3.24 (doublet of doublets, J = 7.9 and 16.2 cps, 3.2 squares), 3.92 (doublet, J = 16.2 cps, 3.4 squares), 7.20–7.65 (complicated, 3.5 squares), 7.76 (singlet, 10.1 squares), and 8.10–8.70 τ (complicated, 26.4 squares).

18. Molecular Weight: 152.
UV: λ_{max} 230, 280, and 310 mμ, ε 16,000, 10,700, and 10,700.
IR: λ_{max} 2.86 (m, b), 3.40–3.50 (w), 3.52 (w), 3.63 (w), 5.93 (s), 6.23 (m), 6.35 (m), 6.63 (m), and 6.85 μ (w) [3497 (m, b), 2941–2857 (w), 2841 (w), 2755 (w), 1686 (s), 1605 (m), 1575 (m), 1508 (m), and 1460 cm^{-1} (w)].
NMR: 0.20 (singlet, 5.1 squares), 2.50–3.10 (complex asymmetric pattern, 15.5 squares), 3.50 (broad singlet, 4.9 squares), and 6.10 τ (singlet, 15.8 squares).

19. Molecular Weight: 153.
UV: λ_{max} 223 mμ, ε 100.
IR: λ_{max} 3.20–3.45 (m), 3.72 (w), 3.84 (w), 5.83 (s), and 6.95 μ (m) [3125–2899 (m), 2688 (w), 2604 (w), 1715 (s), and 1439 cm^{-1} (m)].
NMR: −1.93 (singlet, 7.8 squares), 5.48 (quartet, J = 7.2 cps, 7.4 squares), 8.17 τ (doublet, J = 7.2 cps, 22.4 squares).

20. Molecular Weight: 157.
UV: λ_{max} 214 mμ, ε 60.
IR: λ_{max} 3.43 (m), 5.70 (s), and 6.88 μ (m) [2915 (m), 1754 (s), and 1453 cm^{-1} (m)].
NMR: 4.07 (singlet, 7.2 squares), 5.65 (quartet, J = 7.0 cps, 13.9 squares), and 8.62 τ (triplet, J = 7.0 cps, 22.0 squares).

21. Molecular Weight: 158.
UV: λ_{max} 225 mμ, ε 50 (hexane).
IR: λ_{max} 3.25–3.50 (m), 5.47 (s), 5.69 (m), and 6.87 μ (m) [3077–2857 (m), 1828 (s), 1757 (m), and 1456 cm^{-1} (m)].
NMR: 7.30 (septet, J = 6.7 cps, 6.4 squares) and 8.80 τ (doublet, J = 6.7 cps, 37.2 squares).

22. Molecular Weight: 164.
UV: λ_{max} 220 mμ, ε 1,800.
IR: λ_{max} 3.25 (w), 3.36 (w), 5.73 (s), 6.22 (m), 6.68 (m), and 6.87 μ (m) [3077 (w), 2976 (w), 1745 (s), 1608 (m), 1497 (m), and 1456 cm^{-1} (m)].
NMR: 2.71 (singlet, 16.5 squares), 5.70 (triplet, J = 7.3 cps, 6.2 squares), 7.07 (triplet, J = 7.3 cps, 6.7 squares), and 7.98 τ (singlet, 10.2 squares).

23. Molecular Weight: 170.
UV: λ_{max} 216 mμ, ε 80.
IR: λ_{max} 2.83 (m), 3.40–3.50 (m), 4.45 (m), 5.73 (s), 5.95 (s), 6.12 (s), and 6.85 μ (m) [3534 (m), 2941–2857 (m), 2247 (m), 1745 (s), 1681 (s), 1634 (s), and 1460 cm^{-1} (m)].
NMR: 3.23 (broad singlet, 4.7 squares), 4.47 (doublet, J = 6.7 cps, 4.4 squares), 5.61 (quartet, J = 7.2 cps, 9.0 squares), 7.90 (singlet, 14.8 squares), and 8.62 τ (triplet, J = 7.2 cps, 15.1 squares).

24. Molecular Weight: 174.
UV: λ_{max} 213 mμ, ε 60.
IR: λ_{max} 3.40–3.50 (m), 5.73 (s), and 6.86 μ (m) [2941–2857 (m), 1745 (s), and 1458 cm^{-1} (m)].
NMR: 5.86 (quartet, J = 7.2 cps, 10.4 squares), 7.40 (singlet, 10.8 squares), and 8.73 τ (triplet, J = 7.2 cps, 16.0 squares).

25. Molecular Weight: 188.
UV: no λ_{max} above 210 mμ.
IR: λ_{max} 3.27 (m) and 6.90 μ (w) [3058 (m) and 1449 cm^{-1} (m)].
NMR: 4.11 (quartet, J = 6.0 cps, 9.8 squares) and 7.50 τ (doublet, J = 6.0 cps, 30.3 squares).

Appendix

WAVELENGTH—Wave Number Conversion Table

	Wave number (cm^{-1})									
	0	1	2	3	4	5	6	7	8	9
2.0	5000	4975	4950	4926	4902	4878	4854	4831	4308	4785
2.1	4762	4739	4717	4695	4673	4651	4630	4608	4587	4566
2.2	4545	4525	4505	4484	4464	4444	4425	4405	4386	4367
2.3	4348	4329	4310	4292	4274	4255	4237	4219	4202	4184
2.4	4167	4149	4132	4115	4098	4082	4065	4049	4032	4016
2.5	4000	3984	3968	3953	3937	3922	3906	3891	3876	3861
2.6	3846	3831	3817	3802	3788	3774	3759	3745	3731	3717
2.7	3704	3690	3676	3663	3650	3636	3623	3610	3597	3584
2.8	3571	3559	3546	3534	3521	3509	3497	3484	3472	3460
2.9	3448	3436	3425	3413	3401	3390	3378	3367	3356	3344
3.0	3333	3322	3311	3300	3289	3279	3268	3257	3247	3236
3.1	3226	3215	3205	3195	3185	3175	3165	3155	3145	3135
3.2	3125	3115	3106	3096	3086	3077	3067	3058	3049	3040
3.3	3030	3021	3012	3003	2994	2985	2976	2967	2959	2950
3.4	2941	2933	2924	2915	2907	2899	2890	2882	2874	2865
3.5	2857	2849	2841	2833	2825	2817	2809	2801	2793	2786
3.6	2778	2770	2762	2755	2747	2740	2732	2725	2717	2710
3.7	2703	2695	2688	2681	2674	2667	2660	2653	2646	2639
3.8	2632	2625	2618	2611	2604	2597	2591	2584	2577	2571
3.9	2564	2558	2551	2545	2538	2532	2525	2519	2513	2506
4.0	2500	2494	2488	2481	2475	2469	2463	2457	2451	2445
4.1	2439	2433	2427	2421	2415	2410	2404	2398	2392	2387
4.2	2381	2375	2370	2364	2358	2353	2347	2342	2336	2331
4.3	2326	2320	2315	2309	2304	2299	2294	2288	2283	2278
4.4	2273	2268	2262	2257	2252	2247	2242	2237	2232	2227
4.5	2222	2217	2212	2208	2203	2198	2193	2188	2183	2179
4.6	2174	2169	2165	2160	2155	2151	2146	2141	2137	2132
4.7	2128	2123	2119	2114	2110	2105	2101	2096	2092	2088
4.8	2083	2079	2075	2070	2066	2062	2058	2053	2049	2045
4.9	2041	2037	2033	2028	2024	2020	2016	2012	2008	2004
5.0	2000	1996	1992	1988	1984	1980	1976	1972	1969	1965
5.1	1961	1957	1953	1949	1946	1942	1938	1934	1931	1927
5.2	1923	1919	1916	1912	1908	1905	1901	1898	1894	1890
5.3	1887	1883	1880	1876	1873	1869	1866	1862	1859	1855
5.4	1852	1848	1845	1842	1838	1835	1832	1828	1825	1821
5.5	1818	1815	1812	1808	1805	1802	1799	1795	1792	1788
5.6	1786	1783	1779	1776	1773	1770	1767	1764	1761	1757
5.7	1754	1751	1748	1745	1742	1739	1736	1733	1730	1727
5.8	1724	1721	1718	1715	1712	1709	1706	1704	1701	1698
5.9	1695	1692	1689	1686	1684	1681	1678	1675	1672	1669
6.0	1667	1664	1661	1658	1656	1653	1650	1647	1645	1642
6.1	1639	1637	1634	1631	1629	1626	1623	1621	1618	1616
6.2	1613	1610	1608	1605	1603	1600	1597	1595	1592	1590
6.3	1587	1585	1582	1580	1577	1575	1572	1570	1567	1565
6.4	1563	1560	1558	1555	1553	1550	1548	1546	1543	1541
6.5	1538	1536	1534	1531	1529	1527	1524	1522	1520	1517
6.6	1515	1513	1511	1508	1506	1504	1502	1499	1497	1495
6.7	1493	1490	1488	1486	1484	1481	1479	1477	1475	1473
6.8	1471	1468	1466	1464	1462	1460	1458	1456	1453	1451
6.9	1449	1447	1445	1443	1441	1439	1437	1435	1433	1431
	0	1	2	3	4	5	6	7	8	9

WAVELENGTH—Wave Number Conversion Table (cont.)

	Wave number (cm^{-1})									
	0	1	2	3	4	5	6	7	8	9
7.0	1429	1427	1425	1422	1420	1418	1416	1414	1412	1410
7.1	1408	1406	1404	1403	1401	1399	1397	1395	1393	1391
7.2	1389	1387	1385	1383	1381	1379	1377	1376	1374	1372
7.3	1370	1368	1366	1364	1362	1361	1359	1357	1355	1353
7.4	1351	1350	1348	1346	1344	1342	1340	1339	1337	1335
7.5	1333	1332	1330	1328	1326	1325	1323	1321	1319	1318
7.6	1316	1314	1312	1311	1309	1307	1305	1304	1302	1300
7.7	1299	1297	1295	1294	1292	1290	1289	1287	1285	1284
7.8	1282	1280	1279	1277	1276	1274	1272	1271	1269	1267
7.9	1266	1264	1263	1261	1259	1258	1256	1255	1253	1252
8.0	1250	1248	1247	1245	1244	1242	1241	1239	1238	1236
8.1	1235	1233	1232	1230	1229	1227	1225	1224	1222	1221
8.2	1220	1218	1217	1215	1214	1212	1211	1209	1208	1206
8.3	1205	1203	1202	1200	1199	1198	1196	1195	1193	1192
8.4	1190	1189	1188	1186	1185	1183	1182	1181	1179	1178
8.5	1176	1175	1174	1172	1171	1170	1168	1167	1166	1164
8.6	1163	1161	1160	1159	1157	1156	1155	1153	1152	1151
8.7	1149	1148	1147	1145	1144	1143	1142	1140	1139	1138
8.8	1136	1135	1134	1133	1131	1130	1129	1127	1126	1125
8.9	1124	1122	1121	1120	1119	1117	1116	1115	1114	1112
9.0	1111	1110	1109	1107	1106	1105	1104	1103	1101	1100
9.1	1099	1098	1096	1095	1094	1093	1092	1091	1089	1088
9.2	1087	1086	1085	1083	1082	1081	1080	1079	1078	1076
9.3	1075	1074	1073	1072	1071	1070	1068	1067	1066	1065
9.4	1064	1063	1062	1060	1059	1058	1057	1056	1055	1054
9.5	1053	1052	1050	1049	1048	1047	1046	1045	1044	1043
9.6	1042	1041	1040	1038	1037	1036	1035	1034	1033	1032
9.7	1031	1030	1029	1028	1027	1026	1025	1024	1022	1021
9.8	1020	1019	1018	1017	1016	1015	1014	1013	1012	1011
9.9	1010	1009	1008	1007	1006	1005	1004	1003	1002	1001
10.0	1000	999	998	997	996	995	994	993	992	991
10.1	990	989	988	987	986	985	984	983	982	981
10.2	980	979	978	978	977	976	975	974	973	972
10.3	971	970	969	968	967	966	965	964	963	962
10.4	962	961	960	959	958	957	956	955	954	953
10.5	952	951	951	950	949	948	947	946	945	944
10.6	943	943	942	941	940	939	938	937	936	935
10.7	935	934	933	932	931	930	929	929	928	927
10.8	926	925	924	923	923	922	921	920	919	918
10.9	917	917	916	915	914	913	912	912	911	910
11.0	909	908	907	907	906	905	904	903	903	902
11.1	901	900	899	898	898	897	896	895	894	894
11.2	893	892	891	890	890	889	888	887	887	886
11.3	885	884	883	883	882	881	880	880	879	878
11.4	877	876	876	875	874	873	873	872	871	870
11.5	870	869	868	867	867	866	865	864	864	863
11.6	862	861	861	860	859	858	858	857	856	855
11.7	855	854	853	853	852	851	850	850	849	848
11.8	847	847	846	845	845	844	843	842	842	841
11.9	840	840	839	838	838	837	836	835	835	834
	0	1	2	3	4	5	6	7	8	9

WAVELENGTH—Wave Number Conversion Table (cont.)

	Wave number (cm^{-1})									
	0	1	2	3	4	5	6	7	8	9
12.0	833	833	832	831	831	830	829	829	828	827
12.1	826	826	825	824	824	823	822	822	821	820
12.2	820	819	818	818	817	816	816	815	814	814
12.3	813	812	812	811	810	810	809	808	808	807
12.4	806	806	805	805	804	803	803	802	801	801
12.5	800	799	799	798	797	797	796	796	795	794
12.6	794	793	792	792	791	791	790	789	789	788
12.7	787	787	786	786	785	784	784	783	782	782
12.8	781	781	780	779	779	778	778	777	776	776
12.9	775	775	774	773	773	772	772	771	770	770
13.0	769	769	768	767	767	766	766	765	765	764
13.1	763	763	762	762	761	760	760	759	759	758
13.2	758	757	756	756	755	755	754	754	753	752
13.3	752	751	751	750	750	749	749	748	747	747
13.4	746	746	745	745	744	743	743	742	742	741
13.5	741	740	740	739	739	738	737	737	736	736
13.6	735	735	734	734	733	733	732	732	731	730
13.7	730	729	729	728	728	727	727	726	726	725
13.8	725	724	724	723	723	722	722	721	720	720
13.9	719	719	718	718	717	717	716	716	715	715
14.0	714	714	713	713	712	712	711	711	710	710
14.1	709	709	708	708	707	707	706	706	705	705
14.2	704	704	703	703	702	702	701	701	700	700
14.3	699	699	698	698	697	697	696	696	695	695
14.4	694	694	693	693	693	692	692	691	691	690
14.5	690	689	689	688	688	687	687	686	686	685
14.6	685	684	684	684	683	683	682	682	681	681
14.7	680	680	679	679	678	678	678	677	677	676
14.8	676	675	675	674	674	673	673	672	672	672
14.9	671	671	670	670	669	669	668	668	668	667
	0	1	2	3	4	5	6	7	8	9

Compound Index

This index is an alphabetical list of compounds for which *specific* spectral data are given in the text. The page numbers on which ultraviolet, infrared, and nuclear magnetic resonance spectral data are given are preceded by UV, IR, and NMR, respectively. Numbers of pages on which the spectra of particular compounds are given are enclosed in parentheses.

Acetaldehyde, UV, 9; NMR, (73), 86
Acetamide, UV, 9
Acetanilide, UV, 18
Acetic acid, UV, 9; IR, 28; NMR, 125
Acetic anhydride, IR, 46, (47)
Acetone, UV, 9, (13); NMR, 86
Acetonitrile, UV, 9
Acetophenone, UV, 18; IR, 41, (42)
Acetoxime, UV, 9
Acetylacetone, NMR, 91, (92)
Acetyl chloride, UV, 9
1-Acetylcyclohexene, UV, 12, 54; IR, 54
Acetylene, NMR, 76, 99
β-Alanine, NMR, (109)
Ammonia, NMR, 96
Aniline, UV, 11, 18; NMR, 88
Anilinium cation, UV, 11, 18
Anisole, UV, 18
L-Aspartic acid, IR, (46), 49
Azidoacetic ester, UV, 9
Azomethane, UV, 9

Benzaldehyde, UV, 18; IR, (42), 43; NMR, (79)
Benzene, UV, 11, (17), 18; NMR, 88, 99
Benzenesulfonamide, UV, 18
Benzhydrol, IR, (55)
Benzoate anion, UV, 18
Benzoic acid, UV, 18; IR, 44, (45)
Benzonitrile, UV, 18; IR, 50, (51)
Benzophenone, IR, (55)
Biphenyl, UV, 19; IR, (51)
Bromobenzene, UV, 18
1-Bromo-2-chloroethane, NMR, 108, (109)
2-Bromothiophene, NMR, (130)
Butadiene, UV, 12
2-Butenal, UV, 16
N-*n*-Butylcrotonaldimine, UV, 12
t-Butylethylene, NMR, 115
Butyl nitrate, UV, 9
Butyl nitrite, UV, 9
n-Butylpropiolic acid, UV, 12
Butyrolactone, IR, 43, (44)

Carbon disulfide, IR, (27)
Carbon tetrachloride, IR, (27)
3-Carboxy-2,4-pentadienal lactol, UV, 56; IR, 56
3-Carboxy-2,4-pentadienal lactol, barium salt, UV, 56; IR, 56
trans-β-Carotene, UV, 16
Carveol, IR, 56
Carvone, UV, 56; IR, 56
Catechol, NMR, (111)
Chlorine trifluoride, NMR, 125
o-Chloroaniline, NMR, (93)
p-Chloroanisole, NMR, (110)
Chlorobenzene, UV, 18
p-Chlorobenzonitrile, IR, (53)
Chloroform, IR, (28)
cis-Cinnamic acid, UV, 20
trans-Cinnamic acid, UV, 20
Citric acid, NMR, 122
Crotonaldehyde, UV, 12, (13)
cis-Crotonic acid, UV, 12
Cyclobutane, NMR, 86
1,3-Cyclodecadiene, UV, 14
1,3-Cyclododecadiene, UV, 14

1,3-Cycloheptadiene, UV, 14
Cycloheptane, NMR, 86
1,3-Cyclohexadiene, UV, 14
Cyclohexane, NMR, 86, 113
Cyclohexanone, IR, (41)
2-Cyclohexenone, UV, 12
1-(1-Cyclohexenyl)cyclohexene, UV, 20
2-Cyclohexylidenecycloheptanone, UV, 54; IR, 54
2-Cyclohexylidenecyclohexanone, UV, 12
1,3-Cyclononadiene, UV, 14
1,3-Cyclooctadiene, UV, 14
Cyclooctane, NMR, 86
Cyclopentadiene, UV, 14
Cyclopentane, NMR, 86
Cyclopentanone, IR, (41)
2-Cyclopentenone, UV, 12
2-Cyclopentylidenecyclopentanone, UV, 20
Cyclopropane, UV, 6; NMR, 86
1,3-Cycloundecadiene, UV, 14

2,4,6,8-Decatetraenal, UV, 16
2,4,6,8-Decatetrayne, UV, 16
Diazoacetic ester, UV, 9
Diazomethane, UV, 9
Di-*n*-butyl ether, IR, (39)
Diethyl ethylmalonate, NMR, (127)
15,16-Dihydro-15,16-dimethylpyrene, NMR, 82
Dimesityl, UV, 19
2,6-Dimethylaniline, NMR, (130)
1,4-Dimethylbicyclo[2.2.1]-7-heptanone, IR, 54
1,4-Dimethyl-1,3-cyclohexadiene, UV, 20
3,4-Dimethyl-2-cyclopentenone, UV, 54; IR, 54
1,1-Dimethylcyclopropane, NMR, 113
Dimethyl ether, NMR, 86
N,N-Dimethylformamide, NMR, (114), (115)
2,3-Dimethyl-2-penten-4-one, UV, 12
4,8-Dimethylperhydroazulene-2,6-dione, IR, 56
2,2-Dimethyl-2-silapentane-5-sulfonate, NMR, 65
Diphenylmethane, NMR, 76
Diphenylmethyl cation, NMR, 76
Dipotassium malate, NMR, 120, (121)
2,4,6,8,10-Dodecapentaenal, UV, 16

Ethane, NMR, 76
Ethanol, NMR, (66), (67), 69, (70), 89, 101, 123
Ethyl acetate, UV, 9
Ethyl acetoacetate, IR, 44, (45); NMR, (127)
Ethyl acrylate, NMR, (107)
Ethyl benzoate, IR, 43, (44)
Ethyl cyanoacetate, IR, (53)
Ethylene, UV, 9; NMR, 76
2-Ethyl-4-hydroxybutyrolactone, IR, 56
Ethyl 2-(4-methyl-3-pentenyl)-*cis*-2-butenoate, NMR, 78
Ethyl 2-(4-methyl-3-pentenyl)-*trans*-2-butenoate, NMR, 78

Formaldehyde 2,4-dinitrophenylhydrazone, UV, 10
Furan, NMR, 89, 99

Glyoxal, UV, 12

Hexachlorobutadiene, IR, (26)
2,4,6,8,10,12,14-Hexadecaheptaenal, UV, 16
2,4-Hexadienal, UV, 16
2-Hexen-4-one, UV, 54; IR, 54
1-Hexyn-3-one, UV, 12
Hydrogen, NMR, 96, 99
Hydrogen bromide, NMR, 96
Hydrogen chloride, NMR, 96
Hydrogen deuteride, NMR, 96
Hydrogen fluoride, NMR, 96
Hydrogen iodide, NMR, 96
Hydrogen sulfide, NMR, 96
o-Hydroxyacetophenone, NMR, (91)
2-Hydroxy-5-chloroacetophenone, NMR, (128)
5-Hydroxy-2-hexenoic acid lactone, IR, 54
2-Hydroxy-2-methyl-4-pentanone, NMR, (126)

Indene, NMR, (128)
Iodobenzene, UV, 18
β-Ionone, UV, 131; IR, (131); NMR, (131)
Isoborneol, IR, (40)
Isophorone, UV, 129; IR, (129); NMR, (129)
Isopropylbenzene, NMR, (126)
Isopropyl ether, NMR, (97)
1,2-*O*-Isopropylidene-3-*O*-benzoyl-5-deoxy-*β*-*L*-arabinose, NMR, (118), 119
2-Isopropylidene-4-methylcyclopentanone, UV, 20

Lauryl alcohol, IR, (39)
Lead (II) chloride, NMR, 125
Limonene, IR, (49), 50; NMR, (87)

Malic acid, NMR, 120, (121)
Mesitylene, UV, 19
Mesityl oxide, UV, 8, 12, (13)
Methacrylonitrile, UV, 12
Methane, NMR, 76
Methanol, UV, 6; NMR, (72)
o-Methoxyacetanilide, IR, 47, (48)
o-Methoxyaniline, IR, (48)
p-Methoxytoluene, NMR, 87
N-Methylacetamide, UV, 47; NMR, (95)
Methylammonium cation, NMR, 93, (94), 95
Methyl bromide, NMR, 75, 86
2-Methyl-1-buten-3-one, UV, 12
Methyl chloride, UV, 6; NMR, 75, 86
3-Methylene-6-isopropylcyclohexene, UV, 20
Methyl fluoride, NMR, 75, 86
2-Methyl-3-hydroxymethylfuran, NMR, (103)
Methyl iodide, UV, 6; NMR, 75, 86
3-Methyl-3-penten-2-one, UV, 12
4-Methyl-3-penten-2-one, UV, 8
3-Methyl-1-pentyn-3-ol, IR, (54)
Methyl phenylacetate, IR, (43)
Methyl salicylate, NMR, 91
Methyl *p*-toluate, NMR, (80), 81
Methyl vinyl ketone, UV, 12

Naphthacene, UV, 18
Neopentane, NMR, 86
Nicotinamide, NMR, (112)
Nitrobenzene, UV, 18, 19; NMR, 88
o-Nitro-*t*-butylbenzene, UV, 19
o-Nitrocumene, UV, 19
Nitromethane, UV, 9
1-Nitro-1-propene, UV, 12
Nitrosobutane, UV, 9
o-Nitrotoluene, UV, 19
p-Nitrotoluene, NMR, 87
Nonanoic acid, IR, 44, (45)
Nujol, IR, 25, (26), 38, 39

3-Octanone, IR, 41
2,4,6-Octatrienal, UV, 16
1-Octene, UV, 9
2-Octyne, UV, 9
Oxalic acid, UV, 12

[1.8]Paracyclophane, NMR, 82
Pentacene, UV, 18
3-Penten-2-one, UV, 12
Phenol, UV, 18; NMR, (90)
Phenoxide anion, UV, 18
Phenylacetic acid, NMR, (92)
Phenylacetylene, IR, (50)
Phosphine, NMR, 96, 125
Phosphorus trifluoride, NMR, 125
Pinane, NMR, 80
α-Pinene, NMR, 80, (81)
β-Pinene, NMR, 80
Polystyrene, IR, 24, (25)
Potassium hydrogen malate, NMR, 120, (121)
Propane, UV, 6
n-Propyl iodide, NMR, 98, 99, (100)
Pulegone, UV, 54; IR, 55
Pyridine, NMR, 89, 99
Pyrogallol, NMR, (105)
Pyrrole, NMR, 89, 99
Pyrrole-2-carboxylic acid, NMR, (104)

Salicylaldehyde, NMR, 91
Silane, NMR, 96
Sodium borohydride, NMR, 125
cis-Stilbene, UV, 20
trans-Stilbene, UV, 20
Styrene, NMR, (106), 115

2,4,6,8,10,12-Tetradecahexenal, UV, 16
Tetramethylsilane, NMR, 65
Thiophene, NMR, 89, 99
Toluene, UV, 18; NMR, 76
1,2,4,-Trichlorobenzene, NMR, (106)
Trifluoroacetic acid, NMR, 95
1,3,5-Trimethoxybenzene, NMR, 88
Trimethylamine, UV, 6; NMR, 86
1,3,5-Trinitrobenzene, NMR, 88
Triphenylmethane, NMR, 76

Valine, NMR, 122
β-Vetivone, UV, 56; IR, 56
Vinylacetylene, UV, 12

Water, IR, 25; NMR, 93, 96

Subject Index

The reader is referred to the correlation tables and charts in the text (UV, pp. 9, 12, and 18; IR, pp. 33–38; NMR, pp. 84–85) for absorption characteristics to be anticipated for various functional groups. Additional references are listed in this index.

Absorbance, 5
Acetylenes (*see* Alkynes)
Acids, carboxylic:
  anhydride, IR, 46
  salts, IR, 46
  saturated, IR, 44, 46; NMR, 91
  α,β-unsaturated, rules for estimating UV absorption of, 15
Acetyl groups, NMR, 86
Alcohols, UV, 8; IR, 39–40; NMR, 87, 89–90
Aldehydes:
  saturated, UV, 10; IR, 42–43; NMR, 86–88:
    2,4-dinitrophenylhydrazones, UV, 10
  α,β-unsaturated:
    2,4-dinitrophenylhydrazones, UV, 14
    rules for estimating UV absorption of, 11, 13
Alkanes, UV, 8; IR, 38–39; NMR, 86–88
Alkenes, UV, 10; IR, 49–50; NMR, 88
  diamagnetic anisotropic deshielding effects of, 77–78
Alkynes, UV, 16; IR, 50; NMR, 88:
  diamagnetic anisotropy of, 77–78
  paramagnetic shielding by, 76
Amides, IR, 46–47; NMR, 95–96:
  hindered rotation, 113–114
Amines, IR, 47–48; NMR, 91, 93–95:
  effect of *p*H on proton exchange rate of, 93–95
Analysis of NMR spectra (*see* Spin-spin coupling)
Angular momentum of nucleus, 58
Anisotropic effects (*see* Shielding, diamagnetic)
Aromatic hydrocarbons, UV, 17; IR, 51; NMR, 88
Aromatic hydrocarbons:
  benzenoid, substitution type, IR, 52
  heterocyclic, UV, 19; NMR, 89
  nonbenzenoid, UV, 18–19
  polynuclear, UV, 18
  shielding by (*see* Benzene ring)
Auxochrome, 10–11
Azobenzene, UV, 11
Azulene, UV, 18–19

Beer's law, 5
Benzene ring, NMR shielding and deshielding by, 81–82
Biphenyls, hindered rotation in, UV, 19
Boron (B^{11}) spectra, NMR, 125

Carbohydrate conformation, 119
Carbon-13 (C^{13}) spectra, 125
Charge-transfer spectra, 8, 19
Chemical exchange, 69–71:
  effect of temperature on, 71
  intermolecular exchange of amines, 93
  residence time of protons at coalescence, 71
  and spin coupling, 71
  and spin decoupling, 70
Chemical shift:
  definition, 64
  measurement, 64
  and shielding, 63
Chromophore, 9
Coalescence (*see* Chemical exchange)
Combination bands, 23
Coupling (*see* Spin-spin coupling)
Cross-conjugated systems, 15

Delta (δ), definition, 65
Deshielding, 77–78
Deuterium exchange, 89, 96
Diamagnetic anisotropy, 77–81
Diamagnetic shielding, 75–76
Diamagnetism, atomic, 75
Dienes, conjugated, rules for estimating UV absorption of, 14
Dienones, conjugated, rules for estimating UV absorption of, 16
Difference bands, 23
Dipole moment, 23–24
Double irradiation (*see* Double resonance)
Double resonance, 122–123

Electric quadrupole moment, 62, 124–125
Electronegativity, NMR relationship, 83
End absorption, 6
Energy:
  absorption of, UV, 2, 5–8; IR, 2, 22–24; NMR, 2, 60–62
  fate of absorbed, UV, 1; IR, 1, 22; NMR, 61
  numerical interconversions, 2
Electromagnetic spectrum, *chart,* 3
Enols, NMR, 91
$E^{1\%}_{1\,\mathrm{cm}}$, 5
Epoxides, NMR, 86
Equivalent nuclei, 98, 108
Esters:
  β-keto, IR, 43–44
  saturated, IR, 43
  α,β-unsaturated, rules for estimating UV absorption of, 15
Ethers, IR, 39
p-Ethoxyazobenzene, UV, 11
Experimental techniques (*see* Spectral measurement)
Extinction coefficient, molar, 5, 24

Far infrared, 22
Fingerprint region, 29
Fluorine (F^{19}) spectra, NMR, 125

Heteroannular dienes, 14
Hindered rotation:
  in amides, NMR, 113–114
  in biphenyls, UV, 19
  in nitrobenzene derivatives, UV, 19
Homoannular dienes, 14
Hydrogen bonding, 89, 91

Integration, NMR spectral, 67
Isomerism, geometric, UV, 19–20; IR, 50; NMR, 115–116

Kaysers, 2
Ketones:
  saturated:
    2,4-dinitrophenylhydrazones, UV, 10
    α-halogen effect, IR, 41–42
    UV, 10
  α,β-unsaturated:
    2,4-dinitrophenylhydrazones, UV, 14
    IR, 41
    rules for estimating UV absorption of, 11, 13

Lactones, IR, 43
Lambert's law, 5
Lattice, 61
Lead (Pb^{207}) spectra, NMR, 125
Line shape, 2, 61–62:
  and chemical exchange, 71
  electric quadrupole broadening of, 62
  paramagnetic broadening of, 62
Longitudinal relaxation, 61

Magnetic moment, μ, 59
Magnetic properties of nuclei, *table,* 124
Methylene protons, nonequivalence of, 119–122

Near infrared, 22
Nitriles, IR, 50
Nitrobenzenes, hindered rotation in, 19
Nuclear spin:
  number, 58
  table, 124

Olefins (*see* Alkenes)
Optical density, 5
Orbitals:
  antibonding, 5–6
  bonding, 5–6
  n, 5
  pi (π), 5
  sigma (σ), 5
Overtones (harmonics), 23

Paramagnetic broadening of spectral line, 62
Paramagnetic shielding, 81–83
Paramagnetism, 76–77
Phenols, NMR, 90–91
Phosphorescence, 1
Polyacetylenes, 16
Polyene aldehydes, 16
Polyenes, 16
Precession, 59–60

Rate studies of proton exchange, 71
Reference signals, NMR, 64–65
Relaxation processes, 61
Relaxation wiggles (*see* Ringing)
Resonance, 60
Ring current (*see* Shielding)
Ringing, 73
Ring strain, IR:
  in cyclic ketones, 41
  in lactones, 43

Sample spinning, 72–73
Saturation, 61
Shape of absorption peak, 2, 61–62, 69–70 (*see also* Line shape)
Shielding, 74–83:
  conformational effects, 83, 86
  dependence on electron density, 75
  diamagnetic, 75–76
  diamagnetic anisotropic effects, 77–78
  by double and triple bonds, 77–79
  paramagnetic, 76
  ring current:
    in aromatic systems, 81–82
    in cyclic alkanes, 82–83
Solvent effects (*see* Spectral measurement)
Solvents (*see* Spectral measurement)
Spectra:
  absorption, 1
  emission, 1
Spectral measurement:
  calibration, IR, 24; NMR, 64
  energy source, UV, 4; IR, 24; NMR, 63
  solvent effects, UV, 14; IR, 28, 47; NMR, 74
  solvents for, UV, 4; IR, 27–28; NMR, 74
  spectrometers, UV, 4; IR, 24; NMR, 63
  units, UV, 1, 4; IR, 1, 22; NMR, 65
Spectrum, electromagnetic, *chart,* 3
Spin decoupling (*see also* Double resonance):
  through chemical exchange, 70
Spin-lattice relaxation, 61–62
Spin number I, 58 (*see also* Nuclear spin)
Spin-spin coupling:
  in complex systems, 97–113:
    labeling of nuclei, 98
    two nuclei, 102
    three nuclei, 102–107
    four nuclei, 107–111
    five nuclei, 111
    summary, 111–113
  of equivalent nuclei, 108
  influence of electric quadrupole relaxation on, 124–125
  mechanism of, 67–68
  of nuclei other than hydrogen, 96, 125
  in simple systems, 69:
    asymmetry of multiplets, 98
    intensities of multiplets, 69
Spin-spin coupling constant J, 68:
  carbon^{13}-hydrogen, 125:
    correlation with bond hybridization, 97
    satellite peaks, 96–97
  conformational effects on, 117–118
  deuterium-hydrogen, 96
  electronegativity effects on, 118
  fluorine-hydrogen, 96
  geminal, 113, 116:
    bond angle dependence, 116
  independence of field, 68
  magnitude of, 114–117
  nitrogen-hydrogen, 93
  phosphorus-hydrogen, 96
  sign of, 112–113
  stereochemical effects on, 114–115
  table, 99
  vicinal, 113:
    bond angle dependence, 116–117
Spin-spin multiplets, 66 (*see also* Spin-spin coupling)
Spin-spin relaxation, 61
Sweep offset, 68–69
Sweep width, 65–66, 69

Tau (τ), definition, 65
Transitions, electronic:
  $n \rightarrow \sigma^*$, 6–8
  $n \rightarrow \pi^*$, 6–8
  $\pi \rightarrow \pi^*$, 6–8
  $\sigma \rightarrow \sigma^*$, 6–7
Transmittance, 27
Transverse relaxation, 61
Triple resonance, 123
Tropolone, UV, 18–19

Vacuum ultraviolet region, 5
Vibration, molecular:
  bending, 22–23
  stretching, 22–23
Vibrational modes, fundamental, 22–23

Wavelength:
  micron (μ), 1, 22
  millimicron (mμ), 1
Wave number (cm^{-1}), 1, 22 (*see also* Kaysers)